Michael Timmons

706 Alexander

or

8715 Green Pastures Dr.

Towson 4, Maryland

9H Powell Dr.

Raleigh N.C. 27606   851-5548

508 Currituck Dr.

Raleigh NC 27609

782-5030

Textbook of Inorganic Chemistry

THE MACMILLAN COMPANY
NEW YORK · CHICAGO
DALLAS · ATLANTA · SAN FRANCISCO
LONDON · MANILA

IN CANADA
BRETT-MACMILLAN LTD.
GALT, ONTARIO

TEXTBOOK OF INORGANIC CHEMISTRY

by

S. Young Tyree, Jr.
University of North Carolina

and

Kerro Knox
Bell Telephone Laboratories

THE MACMILLAN COMPANY   NEW YORK

First Printing

The Macmillan Company, New York
Brett-Macmillan Ltd., Galt, Ontario

Printed in the United States of America

Library of Congress catalog card number: 61-5008

Preface

The trend in American universities during the past few decades in the first course in chemistry has been to place more and more emphasis on theories and concepts and to devote less and less time to the variegated behavior of the elements, which cannot be fitted into a rationale encompassing nuclear physics and biochemistry. Subsequent courses expose the student to the aqueous chemistry of sulfides and some other compounds in qualitative analysis, to a few special stoichiometric reactions in quantitative analysis, to a few very special equilibria and reactions in physical chemistry, and to the reactions of some inorganic reagents with organic compounds in organic chemistry. Seldom is inorganic chemistry treated apart and in its own right. The present book is the outgrowth of twelve years experience in teaching a course suitable for students whose background in inorganic chemistry as such goes little beyond the inorganic content of courses in freshman general chemistry.

The general approach has been to treat the chemistry of *all* of the elements, insofar as it is known, at the same level. In this way it is hoped that the student will get an over-all view of the variety of chemical behavior to which he can relate further study and research. The treatment relies upon the principles and some of the facts learned in freshman chemistry; further courses will certainly enhance the student's appreciation of the material presented. Along with the descriptive chemistry of the elements, some of the generalizations and theories that make it coherent and that have contributed to the latter-day renaissance of inorganic chemistry have been brought in throughout the discussion.

Somewhat more than one half of the text provides the basis for a one-semester course at Chapel Hill; the material used in its entirety is probably sufficient for a full year's course, especially if supplemented by further theoretical aspects in an advanced course. In the laboratory part of our course, representative inorganic preparations are carried out, each exercise chosen to illustrate one or more specific techniques and to enlarge the student's store of descriptive knowledge.

Many professional friends have been generous with suggestions during the years of development of this text, and their help is gratefully acknowledged. Particular thanks are due to Dr. S. B. Knight and Dr. D. L. Venezky of this department for their kindly criticisms during the revisions of the manuscript.

Chapel Hill, N.C.
Summit, N.J.

S. Young Tyree, Jr.
Kerro Knox

Contents

Textbook of Inorganic Chemistry

Chapter 1   Periodicity

The subject of inorganic chemistry deals with all of the chemical elements, of which there are 102 at this writing. The task of memorizing the properties of so many distinct species is enormous; it is therefore advantageous to learn the behavior patterns that are exhibited by the elements. Insofar as these patterns are well-defined, the mass of information may be correlated and more easily learned. The object of this chapter is to point out regular gradations of chemical and physical properties among the elements. The correlations are not always applicable to all cases, but learning general rules and then exceptions to them will provide a method for understanding the astonishing variety of matter. Chemistry is, however, too complex for all of it to be reduced to general rules, and so there is still no substitute for a good memory.

ATOMIC WEIGHTS AND ISOTOPES

Reference to the table of atomic weights shows that chlorine has an atomic weight of 35.457. This does not mean that every atom of chlorine weighs 35.457/16.000 times as much as every atom of oxygen.* In 1913 J. J. Thomson showed that the element neon contains two kinds of atoms, both with atomic numbers of 10, but with masses of 20 and 22. Subsequently, F. W. Aston and many others have shown by means of mass spectrometers that most of the

* At the 1959 meeting of the International Union of Pure and Applied Chemistry the Council of the same organization tentatively adopted a new scale of atomic weights based on the whole number 12 as the atomic weight of the dominant natural isotope of carbon, carbon-12. Final adoption of the new scale will be considered at the 1961 meeting of the IUPAC after the International Union of Pure and Applied Physics meets in 1960 to consider the same proposal. Should the new scale be adopted the new values of atomic weights would be changed by -0.0042% of the current chemical scale values.

elements contain atoms of different masses, which are called isotopes. A few elements are monoisotopic, such as sodium and fluorine. Tin has the greatest number of stable isotopes, ten. The standard element for atomic weight scales, oxygen, has three natural isotopes of mass numbers* 16, 17, and 18. They are symbolized ^{16}O, ^{17}O, ^{18}O and occur in the ratio 99.757:0.039:0.204. Thus, there are two scales of atomic weights: the physical, which defines ^{16}O alone as the standard weight of 16.0000, and the chemical, which defines the natural mixture of oxygen isotopes as having the standard weight of 16.0000. Since the unit weight on the chemical scale is heavier, chemical atomic weights are smaller. By knowing the actual masses of the oxygen isotopes and their relative abundance, as determined by the mass spectrometer, the ratio of weights on the two scales can be calculated; it is 1.000275. Chlorine has two isotopes of mass numbers 35 and 37. Their relative abundance in nature is such that the average atomic weight on the chemical scale is 35.457. It is very difficult to separate the isotopes of an element; the average mixture goes through all ordinary chemical and physical processes without perceptible change in ratio. Thus, the chemist can use his scale of atomic weights with confidence in stoichiometric calculations.

ABUNDANCE OF THE ELEMENTS

The abundance of the elements on the surface of the earth is a subject of great economic as well as scientific interest. Geologists, particularly the great geochemist V. M. Goldschmidt, have done most of the work on this subject. Table 1.1 gives the abundance in the earth's crust, including the sea and atmosphere, of the elements from atomic numbers 1 to 92. The unit used is grams per metric ton, which is equivalent to parts per million. These figures are only estimates, and they are, of course, subject to constant revision as man explores his planet more fully. The table shows that an element whose atomic number is even is generally more abundant than the adjacent elements of odd atomic numbers. This generalization does not hold true for elements of widely different numbers: e.g., vana-

---

* The mass number of an isotope is the whole number nearest to its actual mass. It is also the number of protons and neutrons in the nucleus. It is approximately, but not exactly, equal to the actual mass.

TABLE 1.1
Abundance and Physical Properties of the Elements*

Atomic No.	Element	Abundance g/ton	Density of Solid g/cc	m.p. °C	b.p. °C
1	H	1400	0.0808	−259.14	−252.7
2	He	10^{-3}	0.18	−272.0	−268.9
				(25 atm)	
3	Li	65	0.53	186	1336
4	Be	6	1.8	1278	2970
5	B	3	2.5	2300	2550
6	C	320	2.26	3600	4200
7	N	46	1.026	−209.86	−195.8
8	O	466,000	1.426	−218.4	−183.0
9	F	300	1.3	−223	−187
10	Ne	5×10^{-3}	1.4	−248.67	−245.99
11	Na	28,300	0.97	97.5	880
12	Mg	20,900	1.74	651	1110
13	Al	81,300	2.702	660	1800
14	Si	277,200	2.4	1420	2600
15	P	1,180	1.83	44.1	280.5
16	S	520	2.06	118.95	444.60
17	Cl	314	2.1	−101.6	−34.6
18	Ar	4×10^{-2}	1.65	−189.2	−185.7
19	K	25,900	0.86	62.3	760
20	Ca	36,300	1.55	810	1200
21	Sc	5	2.5	1200	2400
22	Ti	4,400	4.5	1725	>3000
23	V	150	5.96	1710	
24	Cr	200	7.1	1615	2200
25	Mn	1,000	7.2	1260	1900
26	Fe	50,000	7.86	1535	
27	Co	23	8.9	1480	2900
28	Ni	80	8.9	1425	2900
29	Cu	70	8.92	1083	2310
30	Zn	132	7.14	419.43	907
31	Ga	15	5.91	29.75	2030
32	Ge	7	5.36	937	2700
33	As	5	5.73	814	615
34	Se	9×10^{-2}	4.82	220.2	685
35	Br	1.6	4.05	−7.2	58.78
36	Kr	2×10^{-4}	3.13	−169	−151.8
37	Rb	310	1.53	38.5	700
38	Sr	300	2.6	800	1150
39	Y	28	4.34	1490	2500
40	Zr	220	6.49	1845	
41	Nb	24	8.4	1950	
42	Mo	15	10.2	2625	3700
43	Tc	?	11.50	2140	
44	Ru	10^{-5}	12.2	2450	
45	Rh	10^{-5}	12.5	1955	
46	Pd	10^{-2}	12	1555	2200
47	Ag	10^{-1}	10.5	960.5	1950

TABLE 1.1 (Continued)

Atomic No.	Element	Abundance g/ton	Density of Solid g/cc	m.p. °C	b.p. °C
48	Cd	1.5×10^{-1}	8.6	320.9	767
49	In	10^{-1}	7.3	156.2	2100
50	Sn	40	7.285	231.8	2362
51	Sb	1	6.684	630.5	1380
52	Te	2×10^{-3}	6.24	452	1390
53	I	3×10^{-1}	4.93	113.5	184.35
54	Xe	3×10^{-5}	4.32	-140	-109.1
55	Cs	7	1.90	26	670
56	Ba	250	3.5	850	1140
57	La	18	6.2	826	1800
58	Ce	46	6.8	770	
59	Pr	5.5	6.8	940	
60	Nd	24	7.004	840	
61	Pm	?			
62	Sm	6.5	6.93	1350	
63	Eu	1.1	5.244	1100	
64	Gd	6.4	7.948		
65	Tb	9×10^{-1}	8.332		
66	Dy	4.5	8.562		
67	Ho	1.2	8.764		
68	Er	2.5	9.164	1250	
69	Tm	2×10^{-1}	9.346		
70	Yb	2.7	7.010	1800	
71	Lu	8×10^{-1}	9.740		
72	Hf	4.5	13.09	1975	
73	Ta	2.1	16.6	2800	
74	W	69	19.3	3370	5900
75	Re	10^{-3}	21.40	3137	
76	Os	10^{-3}	22.48	2700	
77	Ir	10^{-3}	22.4	2450	
78	Pt	5×10^{-3}	21.45	1755	4300
79	Au	5×10^{-3}	19.3	1063	2600
80	Hg	5×10^{-1}	14.2	-38.87	356.90
81	Tl	6×10^{-1}	11.85	303.5	1650
82	Pb	16	11.34	327.5	1620
83	Bi	2×10^{-1}	9.8	271	1450
84	Po	10^{-10}			
85	At	?			
86	Rn	10^{-11}	5.7	-71	-61.8
87	Fr	?			
88	Ra	10^{-6}	5	960	1140
89	Ac	10^{-10}			
90	Th	12	11.2	1845	
91	Pa	10^{-7}			
92	U	4	18.7	1150	

*The tabulated values of course are subject to change.

dium is much more abundant than platinum. There are also some exceptions, particularly among the lighter elements. One very good example of where it does hold true is in the rare-earth series, 57 to 71 (see Chapter 9).

Furthermore, it will be noticed that elements in the third and fourth periods, 11 to 18 and 19 to 36, appear to be the most abundant. Generally, the abundance of elements in a group decreases with increase in atomic weight, except in period 2. For example, Na is about as abundant as K, which is more abundant than Rb, etc. Exceptions are apparent in the second and sixth groups, where Ca and O respectively are the most abundant.

SOME PHYSICAL PROPERTIES OF THE ELEMENTS

Figure 1.1 shows the variation in density of the solid elements as a function of atomic number. Notice that the curve is a periodic one, with the alkali metals in the valleys and the group VIII elements at the peaks. These peaks become higher with increasing atomic number. On the same graph is plotted the atomic volume, which is the density divided by the atomic weight. The density of the solid is used for all the elements, so that atomic volume is roughly proportional to the size of the atom. This curve is essentially the complement of the density curve, since the greater the density, the more atoms there are in unit space, and the less the volume taken up by one atom.

The variation of the melting points of the elements as a function of atomic number is shown in Figure 1.2. Again the plot is periodic. The periodicity of these properties is typical of the curves obtained when most physical properties of the elements are plotted against atomic number; it was first pointed out by Lothar Meyer in 1870.

Correlations between the periodicity of different properties can be drawn also. Thus, it is seen that within a period, the reactive elements, such as K, Ca, and Br have large atomic volumes, while unreactive elements, such as Co, Ni, and Cu have small atomic volumes.

ELECTRONIC CONFIGURATION OF ATOMS

The chemical properties of the elements also obey the Periodic Law: indeed, the periodic table was constructed from the known

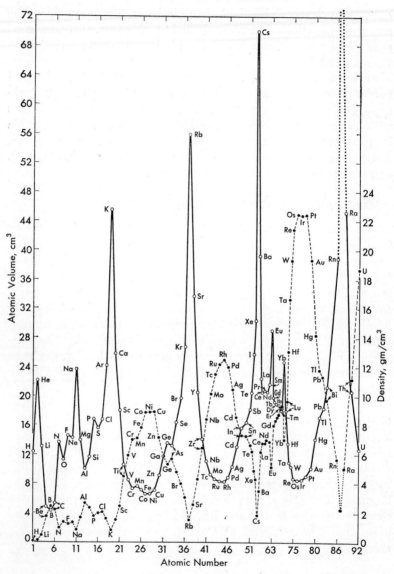

Fig. 1.1   Atomic volumes and densities of the elements vs. atomic number.

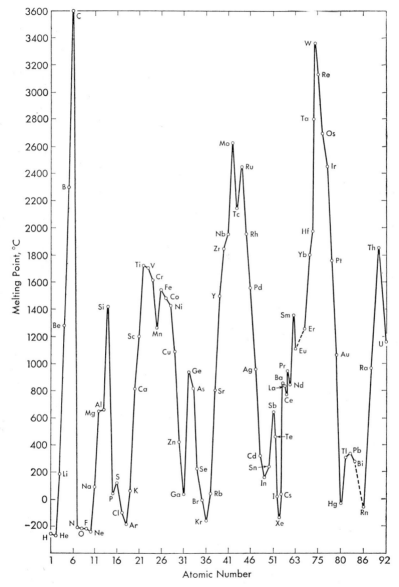

Fig. 1.2 Melting points of the elements vs. atomic number.

chemical and physical properties of the elements. The concept of periodicity has, however, been given a fundamental basis by modern theories of electron structure, and we shall deal first with the results of these basic concepts.

In 1911 E. Rutherford showed that atoms consist of small, heavy nuclei, positively charged, surrounded by a much larger cloud of negative electrons. A few years later N. Bohr arranged the electrons into orbits about the nucleus. Today we know that the positions of these orbits are not nearly so definite as was once thought. The distance between the electron and the nucleus can vary within wide limits—much wider than, say, the relative variation in distance between the earth and the sun—and the position of the electron is best described by means of a distribution function. One thing is still fixed about the electron, however—its energy. Since it is by the energetics of electron movement that physical and chemical properties are determined, the indefinite position of the electron does not matter. The positions of the atoms, and hence the sizes and shapes of molecules, can still be delineated by the average size of the electron cloud.

The energy which an electron in an atom can have is not continuous, as is that of an object on a smooth inclined plane, which can have any potential energy between the values at the top and the bottom, rather, the electron energy can have only discrete values, like an object on a flight of stairs. Furthermore, there are limits to the number of electrons that may occupy the same energy level, the number increasing with the value of the energy. The energy values and the number of electrons in a level have been worked out mostly through the aid of spectroscopy, and spectroscopic notation is still used to a large extent. The energy levels that electrons may assume about a nucleus are also called quantum levels and are numbered 1, 2, 3, 4, . . . , beginning with the lowest energy. In spectroscopy these are called the K, L, M, N, . . . shells, the word now meaning energy shell and not position shell. The maximum number of electrons that may occupy these levels are 2 for the first, 8 for the second, 18 for the third, and 32 for the fourth. This sequence of numbers may be easily memorized by noting that the number of electrons is equal to twice the square of the number of the level.

Both of the electrons in the first energy level have the same energy, but the higher levels are further divided into sublevels. The number of sublevels in a principal level is equal to the number of the principal level; thus, there are one in the first, two in the second, three in the third, etc. Spectroscopic notation is used exclusively for the sublevels. Spectral lines arising from the electronic transitions involving these sublevels are called sharp, principal, diffuse, and fundamental, and the sublevels are designated s, p, d, and f, in order of increasing energy. The number of electrons which can be accommodated in a sublevel is limited, and this number is independent of the number of the principal level, depending only on the designation of the sublevel. Each sublevel is made up of orbitals, each of which can hold a pair of electrons. An s-sublevel has one orbital, and so can hold at most two electrons. There are 3 orbitals all of the same energy in a p-sublevel, 5 in a d, and 7 in an f. Thus these sublevels can have at most 6, 10, and 14 electrons, respectively.

An atom left to itself will acquire the structure of lowest energy: viz., the ground state. In order then to write down the electronic structures of atoms, we need to know the sequence of the energies of the sublevels. In some of the heavier elements the sequence cannot be decided with certainty. When there is uncertainty, however, the possible structures are all of approximately the same energy, and the difference is not significant chemically. In the lower principal levels with few sublevels the sequence is normal. As the number of sublevels increases, overlap of the higher sublevels of one principal level with the lower sublevels of the following principal level occurs. Nevertheless, the order can be found: it is given in Figure 1.3 for a light atom.*

Given this sequence, the electron structures of the elements can be built up by adding electrons one at a time, filling up the lowest available sublevel to its maximum before going on to the next. The first element, hydrogen, has one electron, which goes into the orbital designated 1s. The two electrons of helium both occupy the 1s orbital, so its electron structure is written $1s^2$. In lithium the third electron must go into the 2s orbital because the 1s is full, giving $1s^2 2s$. Then beryllium is $1s^2 2s^2$. With boron the fifth electron occupies

* For a simple mnemonic for the order of filling of the orbitals, see p. 97 of the third reference in the list at the end of this chapter.

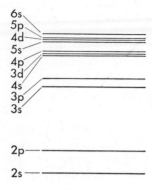

Energy

1s

Fig. 1.3 Sequence of sub-level energies in a light atom.

a 2p orbital, giving $1s^2 2s^2 2p$. Note that if there is only one electron in a sublevel, no superscript is put after the designation. From boron to neon the 2p fills up to its maximum of 6. Then sodium has the structure $1s^2 2s^2 2p^6 3s$, magnesium $1s^2 2s^2 2p^6 3s^2$, aluminum $1s^2 2s^2 2p^6 3s^2 3p$, silicon $1s^2 2s^2 2p^6 3s^2 3p^2$, . . . , and argon $1s^2 2s^2 2p^6 3s^2 3p^6$, when the 3p sublevel is filled. In potassium the nineteenth electron goes into the 4s orbital, not a 3d, because, as is shown in Figure 1.3, the 4s lies lower in energy. Thus, potassium and calcium have the structures $1s^2 2s^2 2p^6 3s^2 3p^6 4s$ and $1s^2 2s^2 2p^6 3s^2 3p^6 4s^2$, respectively. Only with scandium does the 3d begin to fill. Even though the 4s has a lower energy than the 3d in this region of atomic numbers, the designation for the 3d electrons is still put before the 4s in order to preserve the numerical order of the principal levels. Thus, scandium is written $1s^2 2s^2 2p^6 3s^2$-$3p^6 3d 4s^2$. The 3d orbitals then fill up to their maximum of 10. Because the energy levels are lying so close together here, there is some irregularity in this region. Nevertheless, the regularity is restored at zinc, which is $1s^2 2s^2 2p^6 3s^2$-$3p^6 3d^{10} 4s^2$. Then the 4p sublevel fills up to 6 from gallium to krypton. Table 1.2 shows the electronic structures of the first 102 elements.

PERIODIC TABLES

The periodic table proposed by Mendelejeff in 1872 is shown in Figure 1.4. It is a slight modification of his 1869

TABLE 1.2
The Electronic Configuration of the Elements

		NUMBER OF ELECTRONS IN EACH QUANTUM GROUP																		
Atomic Number	Element	1s	2s	2p	3s	3p	3d	4s	4p	4d	4f	5s	5p	5d	5f	5g	6s	6p	6d	7s	7p
1	H	1																			
2	He	2																			
3	Li	2	1																		
4	Be	2	2																		
5	B	2	2	1																	
6	C	2	2	2																	
7	N	2	2	3																	
8	O	2	2	4																	
9	F	2	2	5																	
10	Ne	2	2	6																	
11	Na	2	2	6	1																
12	Mg	2	2	6	2																
13	Al	2	2	6	2	1															
14	Si	2	2	6	2	2															
15	P	2	2	6	2	3															
16	S	2	2	6	2	4															
17	Cl	2	2	6	2	5															
18	Ar	2	2	6	2	6															
19	K	2	2	6	2	6		1													
20	Ca	2	2	6	2	6		2													
21	Sc	2	2	6	2	6	1	2													
22	Ti	2	2	6	2	6	2	2													
23	V	2	2	6	2	6	3	2													
24	Cr	2	2	6	2	6	5	1													
25	Mn	2	2	6	2	6	5	2													
26	Fe	2	2	6	2	6	6	2													
27	Co	2	2	6	2	6	7	2													
28	Ni	2	2	6	2	6	8	2													
29	Cu	2	2	6	2	6	10	1													
30	Zn	2	2	6	2	6	10	2													
31	Ga	2	2	6	2	6	10	2	1												
32	Ge	2	2	6	2	6	10	2	2												
33	As	2	2	6	2	6	10	2	3												
34	Se	2	2	6	2	6	10	2	4												
35	Br	2	2	6	2	6	10	2	5												
36	Kr	2	2	6	2	6	10	2	6												
37	Rb	2	2	6	2	6	10	2	6			1									
38	Sr	2	2	6	2	6	10	2	6			2									
39	Y	2	2	6	2	6	10	2	6	1		2									

TABLE 1.2 (Continued)

		NUMBER OF ELECTRONS IN EACH QUANTUM GROUP																			
Atomic Number	Element	1s	2s	2p	3s	3p	3d	4s	4p	4d	4f	5s	5p	5d	5f	5g	6s	6p	6d	7s	7p
40	Zr	2	2	6	2	6	10	2	6	2		2									
41	Nb	2	2	6	2	6	10	2	6	4		1									
42	Mo	2	2	6	2	6	10	2	6	5		1									
43	Tc	2	2	6	2	6	10	2	6	6		1									
44	Ru	2	2	6	2	6	10	2	6	7		1									
45	Rh	2	2	6	2	6	10	2	6	8		1									
46	Pd	2	2	6	2	6	10	2	6	10											
47	Ag	2	2	6	2	6	10	2	6	10		1									
48	Cd	2	2	6	2	6	10	2	6	10		2									
49	In	2	2	6	2	6	10	2	6	10		2	1								
50	Sn	2	2	6	2	6	10	2	6	10		2	2								
51	Sb	2	2	6	2	6	10	2	6	10		2	3								
52	Te	2	2	6	2	6	10	2	6	10		2	4								
53	I	2	2	6	2	6	10	2	6	10		2	5								
54	Xe	2	2	6	2	6	10	2	6	10		2	6								
55	Cs	2	2	6	2	6	10	2	6	10		2	6				1				
56	Ba	2	2	6	2	6	10	2	6	10		2	6				2				
57	La	2	2	6	2	6	10	2	6	10		2	6	1			2				
58	Ce	2	2	6	2	6	10	2	6	10	2	2	6				2				
59	Pr	2	2	6	2	6	10	2	6	10	3	2	6				2				
60	Nd	2	2	6	2	6	10	2	6	10	4	2	6				2				
61	Pm	2	2	6	2	6	10	2	6	10	5	2	6				2				
62	Sm	2	2	6	2	6	10	2	6	10	6	2	6				2				
63	Eu	2	2	6	2	6	10	2	6	10	7	2	6				2				
* 64	Gd	2	2	6	2	6	10	2	6	10	7	2	6	1			2				
65	Tb	2	2	6	2	6	10	2	6	10	8	2	6	1			2				
66	Dy	2	2	6	2	6	10	2	6	10	10	2	6				2				
67	Ho	2	2	6	2	6	10	2	6	10	11	2	6				2				
68	Er	2	2	6	2	6	10	2	6	10	12	2	6				2				
69	Tm	2	2	6	2	6	10	2	6	10	13	2	6				2				
70	Yb	2	2	6	2	6	10	2	6	10	14	2	6				2				
71	Lu	2	2	6	2	6	10	2	6	10	14	2	6	1			2				
72	Hf	2	2	6	2	6	10	2	6	10	14	2	6	2			2				
73	Ta	2	2	6	2	6	10	2	6	10	14	2	6	3			2				
74	W	2	2	6	2	6	10	2	6	10	14	2	6	4			2				
75	Re	2	2	6	2	6	10	2	6	10	14	2	6	5			2				
76	Os	2	2	6	2	6	10	2	6	10	14	2	6	6			2				
77	Ir	2	2	6	2	6	10	2	6	10	14	2	6	7			2				
78	Pt	2	2	6	2	6	10	2	6	10	14	2	6	9			1				
79	Au	2	2	6	2	6	10	2	6	10	14	2	6	10			1				
80	Hg	2	2	6	2	6	10	2	6	10	14	2	6	10			2				

TABLE 1.2 (Continued)

Atomic Number	Element	1s	2s	2p	3s	3p	3d	4s	4p	4d	4f	5s	5p	5d	5f	5g	6s	6p	6d	7s	7p
81	Tl	2	2	6	2	6	10	2	6	10	14	2	6	10			2	1			
82	Pb	2	2	6	2	6	10	2	6	10	14	2	6	10			2	2			
83	Bi	2	2	6	2	6	10	2	6	10	14	2	6	10			2	3			
84	Po	2	2	6	2	6	10	2	6	10	14	2	6	10			2	4			
85	At	2	2	6	2	6	10	2	6	10	14	2	6	10			2	5			
86	Rn	2	2	6	2	6	10	2	6	10	14	2	6	10			2	6			
87	Fr	2	2	6	2	6	10	2	6	10	14	2	6	10			2	6		1	
88	Ra	2	2	6	2	6	10	2	6	10	14	2	6	10			2	6		2	
89	Ac	2	2	6	2	6	10	2	6	10	14	2	6	10			2	6	1	2	
90	Th	2	2	6	2	6	10	2	6	10	14	2	6	10			2	6	2	2	
91	Pa	2	2	6	2	6	10	2	6	10	14	2	6	10	2		2	6	1	2	
92	U	2	2	6	2	6	10	2	6	10	14	2	6	10	3		2	6	1	2	
93	Np	2	2	6	2	6	10	2	6	10	14	2	6	10	5		2	6		2	
94	Pu	2	2	6	2	6	10	2	6	10	14	2	6	10	6		2	6		2	
95	Am	2	2	6	2	6	10	2	6	10	14	2	6	10	7		2	6		2	
96	Cm	2	2	6	2	6	10	2	6	10	14	2	6	10	7		2	6	1	2	
97	Bk	2	2	6	2	6	10	2	6	10	14	2	6	10	9		2	6		2	
98	Cf	2	2	6	2	6	10	2	6	10	14	2	6	10	10		2	6		2	
99	Es	2	2	6	2	6	10	2	6	10	14	2	6	10	11		2	6		2	
100	Fm	2	2	6	2	6	10	2	6	10	14	2	6	10	12		2	6		2	
101	Md	2	2	6	2	6	10	2	6	10	14	2	6	10	13		2	6		2	
102	—	2	2	6	2	6	10	2	6	10	14	2	6	10	14		2	6		2	

NUMBER OF ELECTRONS IN EACH QUANTUM GROUP

* Some doubt still exists as to the configuration of some of the lanthanide and actinide elements. The configurations shown are generally considered the most likely for the ground state.

original. In this table the elements are arranged in columns according to similarities in chemical properties. For example, elements exhibiting a primary valence of 2 are placed in the same column, which is numbered II. Mendelejeff recognized that calcium, strontium, and barium are very similar to each other and somewhat similar to zinc, cadmium, and mercury. In order to delineate the two groups, column II was subdivided as shown. This subdividing is done in all groups numbered I to VII, and it is retained in modern tables. Thus, in both the old and the new tables vanadium, niobium, and tantalum are members of group Va, and arsenic, antimony, and bismuth of Vb.

Group / Series	I R_2O	II RO	III R_2O_3	IV RH_4 RO_2	V RH_3 R_2O_5	VI RH_2 RO_3	VII RH R_2O_7	VIII RO_4
1	H							
2	Li	Be	B	C	N	O	F	
3	Na	Mg	Al	Si	P	S	Cl	
4	K	Ca	...	Ti	V	Cr	Mn	Fe Co Ni Cu
5	(Cu)	Zn	...	...	As	Se	Br	
6	Rb	Sr	Y	Zr	Nb	Mo	...	Ru Rh Pd Ag
7	(Ag)	Cd	In	Sn	Sb	Te	I	
8	Cs	Ba	Di	Ce	...	...	...	...
9	...	...	...	...	...	...	...	... ...
10	...	...	Er	La	Ta	W	...	Os Ir Pt Au
11	(Au)	Hg	Tl	Pb	Bi	...	...	
12	...	...	...	Th	...	U	...	...

Fig. 1.4 Mendelejeff's periodic table of 1872.

The correlation between the electron structure and the position of an element in the periodic table is now apparent. The positive valence of an atom arises from the electrons that it loses or shares; it loses or shares electrons from its outer orbitals, which contain the most loosely bound electrons. Thus, calcium of structure $1s^22s^22p^63s^23p^64s^2$, strontium of structure $1s^22s^22p^63s^23p^63d^{10}4s^24p^65s^2$, and zinc with $1s^22s^22p^63s^23p^63d^{10}4s^2$, all have two electrons in their outermost orbitals which they can lose to form dipositive ions. The greater similarity of calcium and strontium to each other than to zinc may also be shown by noticing that when the ion is formed from both calcium and strontium, the remaining outer electrons are arranged

p^6, while in zinc they are d^{10}. The situation is more complicated when the d orbitals are filling up. This case is discussed below under transition elements.

The discovery of the inert gases and a more complete knowledge of the rare earths brought Mendelejeff's table into sharper focus, but it still suffers from the fundamental difficulty of inadequate emphasis on the horizontal periods. From Lothar Meyer's atomic volume curve and, more clearly, from electronic configurations it is evident that the elements are divided into seven periods; the first has only two members, and it is followed by two short periods of eight members each, two of eighteen each, and finally two longer periods, the last of which is incomplete. Thus, the elements in periods 4 and 5 of Figure 1.4 belong together in one period. The same is true of periods 6 and 7. The limitations have been overcome by the development of the modern long forms. The classification chosen as the most suitable for inorganic chemistry is the form devised by Carnelley, popularized by von Antropoff, and given in Figure 1.5.

The von Antropoff table offers many advantages in the classification of chemical properties. For example, group I is subdivided into the "typical elements" Li and Na, and two subgroups: Ia, containing K, Rb, Cs, and Fr in it; and Ib, including Cu, Ag, and Au. No longer are all of these elements put into one vertical column. The broad band connecting Li and Na with Ia shows that they are quite similar to K, Rb, Cs, and Fr. The narrow band connecting them to Ib indicates the lesser similarity between these elements. In fact, in all respects except the formation of the $+1$ oxidation state, the chemistry of Cu is more like that of Ni and Zn than of the Ia elements.

Hydrogen is not assigned to any group, since it is a unique element.

C and Si, members of group IV, are in this classification likened about as much to subgroup IVa as they are to subgroup IVb. This connection between the typical elements and the subgroups is the most reasonable simple arrangement consistent with the chemical properties of the elements.

The elements in which the inner orbitals are filling are arranged together in groups IIIa to Ib. They are called the transition elements or transition metals because they make a transition from the metallic

I
H
1.0080

0	Ia	IIa	IIIa	IVa	Va	VIa	VIIa	VIII	VIII	VIII	Ib	IIb	IIIb	IVb	Vb	VIb	VIIb	0
2 He 4.003																		10 Ne 20.183
10 Ne 20.183	3 Li 6.940	4 Be 9.013		5 B 10.82	6 C 12.011	7 N 14.008	8 O 16.000	9 F 19.00										18 Ar 39.944
18 Ar 39.944	11 Na 22.991	12 Mg 24.32		13 Al 26.98	14 Si 28.09	15 P 30.975	16 S 32.066	17 Cl 35.457										36 Kr 83.80
36 Kr 83.80	19 K 39.100	20 Ca 40.08	21 Sc 44.96	22 Ti 47.90	23 V 50.95	24 Cr 52.01	25 Mn 54.94	26 Fe 55.85	27 Co 58.94	28 Ni 58.71	29 Cu 63.54	30 Zn 65.38	31 Ga 69.72	32 Ge 72.60	33 As 74.91	34 Se 78.96	35 Br 79.916	54 Xe 131.30
54 Xe 131.30	37 Rb 85.48	38 Sr 87.63	39 Y 88.92	40 Zr 91.22	41 Nb 92.91	42 Mo 95.95	43 Tc ---	44 Ru 101.1	45 Rh 102.91	46 Pd 106.4	47 Ag 107.88	48 Cd 112.41	49 In 114.82	50 Sn 118.70	51 Sb 121.76	52 Te 127.61	53 I 126.91	86 Rn ---
86 Rn ---	55 Cs 132.91	56 Ba 137.36	57-71	72 Hf 178.50	73 Ta 180.95	74 W 183.86	75 Re 186.22	76 Os 190.2	77 Ir 192.2	78 Pt 195.09	79 Au 197.0	80 Hg 200.61	81 Tl 204.39	82 Pb 207.21	83 Bi 209.00	84 Po ---	85 At ---	
	87 Fr ---	88 Ra 226.05	89-103															

LANTHANIDE SERIES RARE EARTHS	57 La 138.92	58 Ce 140.13	59 Pr 140.92	60 Nd 144.27	61 Pm ---	62 Sm 150.35	63 Eu 152.0	64 Gd 157.26	65 Tb 158.93	66 Dy 162.51	67 Ho 164.94	68 Er 167.27	69 Tm 168.94	70 Yb 173.04	71 Lu 174.99
ACTINIDE SERIES	89 Ac ---	90 Th 232.05	91 Pa ---	92 U 238.07	93 Np ---	94 Pu ---	95 Am ---	96 Cm ---	97 Bk ---	98 Cf ---	99 Es ---	100 Fm ---	101 Mv ---	102	

Fig. 1.5 Von Antropoff's periodic table.

subgroup Ia to the metallic subgroup Ib without the appearance of nonmetals. There are two types of transition series: the outer transition elements, where the next to last, or penultimate, sublevel is filling, and the inner transition elements, where the second inner, or antepenultimate, sublevel is filling. The elements scandium to copper are representative of the outer series; lanthanum to lutetium, called the rare earths, represent the inner. As might be expected, the chemistry of transition elements is more complex than that of nontransition elements. They exhibit more variable valence and form colored, paramagnetic ions.

Since the Mendelejeff group numbers are retained in the von Antropoff table, the rule still holds that the maximum positive oxidation number possible for an element is equal to its group number. There are only two exceptions to this rule. The most familiar occurs in subgroup Ib, where copper and silver have a valence of $+2$ and gold exhibits $+3$, and all having the group valence of $+1$ as well. The second exception occurs in the rare-earth series of group IIIa, where some of the elements have valences of $+4$ and $+5$. In view of the great use of the periodic table in systematizing the chemistry of the elements, the student is advised to memorize it as early as possible in his study of inorganic chemistry. It is not perfect—if it were, chemistry could be learned in a few months—but it is an excellent starting point.

It is profitable to compare the von Antropoff periodic table with Figures 1.1 and 1.2. Elements in the middle of the table occupy the peaks in the density-atomic number plot and the valleys in the complementary plot of atomic volume. These middle elements are also high-melting, and the melting point drops off toward both sides of the table. They are also on the ascending portions of the ionization potential curve shown below, Figure 1.7.

THE SIZES OF ATOMS AND IONS

The sizes of atoms and ions are useful in explaining many of the properties of the elements. In view of what has been said about the positions of electrons, it is apparent that the very concept of the size of an atom cannot be too definite. We know that atoms and ions approach each other to close distances in forming compounds. By measuring the interatomic distances in many compounds, using such techniques as X-ray diffraction, numbers can be assigned to atoms and ions representing the average space taken up by them. Goldschmidt, L. Pauling, and others have done this for many elements, and the results of the calculations are given in Figure 1.6. These values are not extremely accurate, and many other sets of numbers can be found in the literature. For many of the ions of higher charge—e.g., Si^{+4}—the radii are hypothetical, since the species do not exist as such in compounds. Their ratios are much more accurate than the absolute values of the numbers themselves.

Periodic variations are noticed for these radii. In going across a period—e.g., from Na to Cl—the atomic radius decreases. This decrease can be rationalized in terms of electron structure. The addition of electrons into the same quantum level puts them, on the average, no farther from the nucleus. But for each electron added, the nuclear charge increases by one, thereby attracting the electrons more strongly and resulting in a net decrease in size. In a long period the radius decreases at first and then remains almost constant for the later transition elements. In going down a group—e.g., from K to Cs—the radius increases. In this case, the added electrons go to higher quantum levels which are, on the average, farther from the nucleus. Even the increased nuclear charge cannot then attract the electrons to a shorter distance than in the atom above it. An exception is found in the ions of the third long period, where the effect of the "lanthanide contraction" is felt. (See Chapters 9, 13, ff.)

Regular variations occur for the ions also. The largest cations are about the same size as the smallest anions. When an atom loses electrons to form a cation, the remaining electrons are pulled closer to the nucleus because it has fewer electrons to hold. If two cations of different charge are formed by the same element, the ion with the larger charge will be smaller for the same reason: e.g., Fe^{+++}, $0.60Å$; Fe^{++}, $0.75Å$. If an atom gains an electron to become an anion, on the other hand, the resulting ion is bigger than the original atom. Thus, the larger the charge on an anion, the larger the size of the anion.

H
0.53
H$^+$
~10^{-5}
H$^-$
2.08

Li 1.26 Li$^+$ 0.60	Be 0.89 Be^{++} 0.31			B 0.80 B^{+++} 0.20	C 0.77	N 0.74 N^{---} 1.71	O 0.74 O^{--} 1.40	F 0.72 F$^-$ 1.36
Na 1.57 Na$^+$ 0.95	Mg 1.36 Mg^{++} 0.65			Al 1.25 Al^{+++} 0.50	Si 1.17 Si^{++++} 0.41	P 1.10 P^{---} 2.12	S 1.04 S^{--} 1.84	Cl 0.99 Cl$^-$ 1.81

K 2.03 K$^+$ 1.33 | Ca 1.74 Ca^{++} 0.99 | Sc 1.44 Sc^{+++} 0.81 | Ti 1.32 Ti^{+++} 0.69 Ti^{++++} 0.68 | V 1.22 V^{+++} 0.66 V^{+++++} 0.59 | Cr 1.17 Cr^{+++} 0.64 | Mn 1.17 Mn^{++} 0.80 Mn^{+++} 0.62 | Fe 1.17 Fe^{++} 0.75 Fe^{+++} 0.60 | Co 1.16 Co^{++} 0.72 | Ni 1.15 Ni^{++} 0.69 | Cu 1.17 Cu$^+$ 0.96 | Zn 1.25 Zn^{++} 0.74 | Ga 1.25 Ga^{+++} 0.62 | Ge 1.22 Ge^{++++} 0.53 | As 1.21 As^{+++++} 0.47 As^{---} 2.22 | Se 1.17 Se^{--} 1.98 | Br 1.14 Br$^-$ 1.95

Rb 2.16 Rb$^+$ 1.48 | Sr 1.91 Sr^{++} 1.13 | Y 1.62 Y^{+++} 0.93 | Zr 1.45 Zr^{++++} 0.87 | Nb 1.34 Nb^{+++++} 0.69 | Mo 1.29 Mo^{++++++} 0.62 | Te | Ru 1.24 | Rh 1.25 | Pd 1.28 | Ag 1.34 Ag$^+$ 1.26 | Cd 1.41 Cd^{++} 0.97 | In 1.50 In^{+++} 0.81 | Sn 1.41 Sn^{++++} 0.71 | Sb 1.41 Sb^{+++++} 0.62 Sb^{---} 2.45 | Te 1.37 Te^{--} 2.21 | I 1.35 I$^-$ 2.16

Cs 2.35 Cs$^+$ 1.69 | Ba 1.98 Ba^{++} 1.35 | La 1.69 Lu 1.56 La^{+++} 1.04 Lu^{+++} 0.99 | Hf 1.44 Hf^{++++} 0.84 | Ta 1.34 Ta^{+++++} 0.68 | W 1.30 | Re 1.28 | Os 1.26 | Ir 1.26 | Pt 1.29 | Au 1.34 Au$^+$ 1.37 | Hg 1.44 Hg^{++} 1.10 | Tl 1.55 Tl$^+$ 1.44 Tl^{+++} 0.95 | Pb 1.54 Pb^{++} 1.21 Pb^{++++} 0.84 | Bi 1.52 Bi^{+++} 0.74 | Po 1.53 | At

Th
1.65
Th^{++++}
0.95

Fig.1.6 Atomic and ionic radii in Angstrom units (1Å = 10^{-8} cm).

19

IONIZATION POTENTIAL AND ELECTRON AFFINITY

The forces which hold elements together in compounds are electrical. Electrons can be transferred completely from one atom to another to form an ionic bond, or two atoms may share a pair of electrons to form a covalent bond. Thus, the relative ease with which atoms gain, lose, or share electrons is fundamental in compound formation.

The energy required to remove an electron from an isolated atom in its ground state is called the first ionization potential or ionization energy. The second ionization potential is the energy necessary to remove a second electron after the first is gone. Figure 1.7 is a plot of the first ionization potential of the elements against atomic number. The curve is periodic and can be correlated with the electron structure. The peaks are occupied by the inert gases, which have eight electrons in the outer shell. In view of the great chemical inertness of these elements, the configuration must be a particularly stable one. The alkali metals have one more electron than the inert gases, and this is lost very easily. Note that Figure 1.7 indicates that the energy required to remove an electron increases in going across a period. This is true for the same reason that the atoms become smaller as the nuclear charge increases: viz., the electrons are held more tightly. When an electron goes into a higher principal level (as in the transition from Ne to Na), however, two other effects combine to overcome increasing nuclear charge, and the result is the abrupt drop in ionization potential. The first effect is the increased distance which lowers the coulombic attraction. The second is the presence of completed sublevels between the outside electron and the nucleus, the so-called "shielding effect," which also lowers the attraction. For these same reasons the ionization potential decreases with increasing atomic number in a group, as is evident from the height of the peaks for the inert gases.

After sodium has lost one electron, the ion has the stable structure of neon. So sodium forms +1 ions only. When Mg has lost one electron, it still has one more left in its outer shell which it can lose fairly readily. The second ionization potential of Mg is higher than the first, but it is not nearly so large as the second ionization potential of sodium. Therefore, Mg forms +2 ions. The successive ionization potentials of the elements are given in Table 1.3.

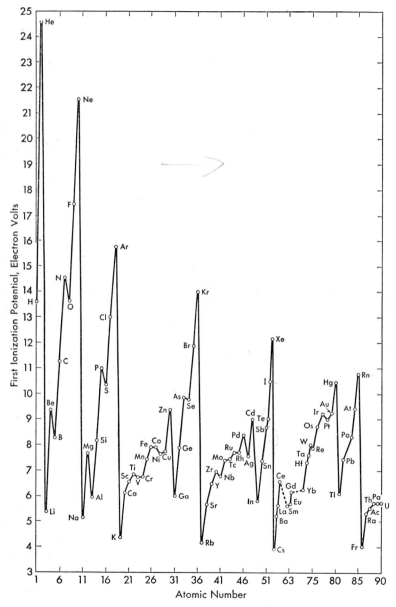

Fig. 1.7 First ionization potentials of the elements vs. atomic number.

TABLE 1.3

Some Ionization Potentials of the Elements

No.	Symbol	\multicolumn{8}{c}{Ionization Potential (electron volts)}							
		I	II	III	IV	V	VI	VII	VIII
1	H	13.595							
1	D	13.598							
2	He	24.580	54.40						
3	Li	5.390	75.619	122.42					
4	Be	9.320	18.206	153.85	217.657				
5	B	8.296	25.149	37.920	259.30	340.127			
6	C	11.264	24.376	47.864	64.476	391.99	489.84		
7	N	14.54	29.605	47.426	77.450	97.863	551.93	666.83	
8	O	13.614	35.146	54.934	77.394	113.873	138.080	739.11	871.12
9	F	17.42	34.98	62.646	87.23	114.214	157.117	185.139	953.6
10	Ne	21.559	41.07	64		97.16	126.4	157.9	
11	Na	5.138	47.29	71.65	98.88	138.60	172.36	208.444	264.155
12	Mg	7.644	15.03	80.12	109.29	141.23	186.86	225.31	265.957
13	Al	5.984	18.823	28.44	119.96	153.77	190.42	241.93	285.13
14	Si	8.149	16.34	33.46	45.13	166.73	205.11	246.41	303.87
15	P	11.0	19.65	30.156	51.35	65.007	220.414	263.31	309.26
16	S	10.357	23.4	35.0	47.29	72.5	88.029	280.99	328.80
17	Cl	13.01	23.80	39.90	53.5	67.80	96.7	114.27	348.3
18	Ar	15.755	27.62	40.90	59.79	75.0	91.3	124.0	143.46
19	K	4.339	31.81	46	60.90		99.7	118	155
20	Ca	6.111	11.87	51.21	67	84.39		128	147
21	Sc	6.56	12.89	24.75	73.9	92	111.1		159
22	Ti	6.83	13.63	28.14	43.24	99.8	120	140.8	
23	V	6.74	14.2	29.7	48	65.2	128.9	151	173.7
24	Cr	6.763	16.49	30.95	49.6	73	90.6	161.1	185
25	Mn	7.432	15.64	33.69		76		119.24	196
26	Fe	7.90	16.18	30.64					151
27	Co	7.86	17.05	33.49					
28	Ni	7.633	18.15	36.16					
29	Cu	7.724	20.29	36.83					
30	Zn	9.391	17.96	39.70					
31	Ga	6.00	20.51	30.70	64.2				
32	Ge	7.88	15.93	34.21	45.7	93.4			
33	As	9.81	20.2	28.3	50.1	62.6	127.5		
34	Se	9.75	21.5	32.0	42.9	73.1	81.7	155	
35	Br	11.84	21.6	35.9					193
36	Kr	13.996	24.56	36.9					
37	Rb	4.176	27.5	40					
38	Sr	5.692	11.027		57				
39	Y	6.5	12.4	20.5		77			
40	Zr	6.95	14.03	24.8	33.97		99		
41	Nb	6.77	14	28.1	38.3	50	103	125	
42	Mo	7.383							
43	Tc	7.45							
44	Ru	7.7							
45	Rh	7.7							
46	Pd	8.334	19.9						

TABLE 1.3 (Continued)

Element		Ionization Potential (electron volts)						
No.	Sym-bol	I	II	III	IV	V	V	VII	VIII
47	Ag	7.574	21.960	36.10					
48	Cd	8.991	16.904	38.217					
49	In	5.785	18.867	28.030	58.037				
50	Sn	7.332	14.629	30.654	40.740	81.13			
51	Sb	8.64	18.6	24.825	44.147	55.69			
52	Te	9.007	21.543	30.611	37.817	60.27			
53	I	10.44	19.010						
54	Xe	12.127	21.204	32.115	46	76			
55	Cs	3.893	32.458	35	51	58			
56	Ba	5.2097	10.001						
57	La	5.614	11.43	19.17					
58	Ce	6.57		19.70	36.715				
62	Sm	5.6	11.4						
63	Eu	5.67	11.24						
64	Gd	6.16							
70	Yb	6.25	12.11						
72	Hf	7.3							
73	Ta	7.6							
74	W	7.98							
75	Re	7.85							
76	Os	8.7							
77	Ir	9.2							
78	Pt	9.0	19.3						
79	Au	9.223	20.1						
80	Hg	10.434	18.752	34.5	72	82			
81	Tl	6.106	20.423	29.8	50.8				
82	Pb	7.415	15.04	32.1	38.97	69.7			
83	Bï		16.7	25.56	45.3	56.0			
84	Po	8.3							
85	At	9.4							
86	Rn	10.746							
87	Fr	4.0							
88	Ra	5.278	10.145						
89	Ac	5.5							
90	Th	5.7							
91	Pa	5.7							
92	U	5.7							

Sources:
Elements Nos. 1–41 taken from U.S. Bureau of Standards Circular #467
Tc value from W. F. Meggers, Journal of Research, National Bureau of Standards 47, 7 (1951)
Re value from W. F. Meggers, ibid. 6, 1050 (1931)
Ru value from L. A. Summer, Zeitschrift für Physik 45, 181 (1927)
Values for Hf, Ta, Po, Fr, Ac, Th, Pa, and U calculated and reported by W. Finkelnburg, Zeitschrift für Naturforschung 2a, 16–20 (1947)
All other values from Atomic Spectra and Atomic Structure by G. Herzberg. Dover Publications, 1944.

When one atom loses electrons, another must gain them. The energy involved when an electron is added to an isolated atom in the ground state is called the electron affinity of the element. This is a negative quantity when energy is given off, and a positive quantity when energy is absorbed. The experimental determination of electron affinities is much more difficult than that of ionization potentials, for which emission spectra can be used. For electron affinities an indirect determination is usually employed. A few representative values are given in Table 1.4.

TABLE 1.4
Electron Affinities of Some Atoms*
(kcal/mole)

Atom	Ion Formed	Electron Affinity
H	H^-	-17.2
F	F^-	-83.5
Cl	Cl^-	-88.2
Br	Br^-	-81.6
I	I^-	-74.6
O	O^{--}	$+156$
S	S^{--}	$+80$
Se	Se^{--}	$+97$
N	N^{---}	$+547$
C	C^{----}	$+708$

* From H. O. Pritchard, *Chemical Reviews*, Vol. 52, p. 529 (1953).

INTERATOMIC FORCES AND THE CHEMICAL BOND

The division of bonds between atoms into two distinct types, ionic and covalent, is an oversimplification. The pair of electrons which is shared by two atoms joined by a covalent bond will not be shared equally by different atoms. One certainly will attract the pair more than the other—not enough to gain both completely, but enough to get more than half-share in them. Likewise, in ionic bonds the positive ion must exert some influence over the electrons of the near negative ions. Thus, all real bonds have some ionic and some covalent character. A bond is called ionic when the ionic character predominates and covalent when the covalent character predominates.

If an ion has a high positive charge and a small radius, it will have a high charge density near it and will be able to exert appreciable influence on the electrons of nearby negative ions. It is said to have great polarizing power. The greater the polarizing power of a cation, the less ionic the bond will be between it and an anion. On the other hand, a large, highly charged negative ion will hold its outer electrons only weakly and can be easily distorted by a positive ion. It is said to have a large polarizability. The greater the polarizability of an anion, the less ionic the bond will be between it and a cation. The factors which favor the formation of covalent over ionic bonds have been summarized by K. Fajans. They are:

(1) a large charge on both ions
(2) a small cation
(3) a large anion
(4) the possession by the cation of an electron configuration which is not that of an inert gas

The fourth condition will be discussed in Chapter 5.

INTERIONIC AND INTERMOLECULAR FORCES

The electrical field surrounding an ion extends equally in all directions. In the solid phase, the result of the nondirectional character of this force is a crystal lattice of alternate positive and negative ions. For example, in sodium chloride, which is an ionic compound, there is one Na^+ ion for each Cl^- ion, but these ions are not associated in pairs in the crystal. Rather, the structure is that shown in Figure 1.8, in which each sodium ion is surrounded at equal distances by six chloride ions, and each chloride equally by six sodium ions. The forces holding the lattice together are electrostatic, or coulombic, in nature, and there are no sodium chloride molecules. Most salts and many oxides are of this ionic type.

In silicon tetrachloride, on the other hand, the bond is essentially covalent, owing to the small size and high charge of the silicon. Covalent bonds are directional in nature and hold the atoms together as groups. $SiCl_4$ consists of discrete molecules containing one silicon and four chlorine atoms bound together as a unit. It is called a molecular compound. The intermolecular forces which hold the molecules together in the solid phase of a molecular compound are much weaker than either covalent bonds or ionic bonds.

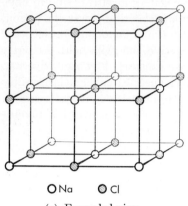

○ Na   ◎ Cl

(a) Expanded view.

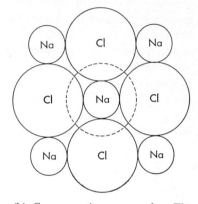

(b) Cross section to scale. The dotted circle represents the two Cl⁻ above and below the plane of the paper.

Fig. 1.8 Crystal structure of NaCl.

These van der Waal's forces can be classified as of three types: hydrogen bonding, permanent dipole interactions, and induced dipole interactions. The first is discussed below under the properties of various hydrogen compounds. It accounts for water's being a liquid and not a gas at room temperature. The second arises when the distribution of electrical charge in a molecule is not symmetrical, with the result that one end of the molecule has a slight excess positive charge and the other a negative. The third, which is more difficult to visualize, results when molecules approach each other closely and distort each other, inducing dipoles which are not present in the isolated molecules. The more polarizable the atoms in a molecule are, the more easily these induced dipoles are formed, and the greater the attraction. The second and third forces account for the eventual liquefaction and solidification at low temperature of polar compounds such as PCl_3 and H_2Se. The third alone causes condensation in the symmetrical molecules N_2, CCl_4, He, etc.

Many compounds contain ions which are aggregates of atoms held together by covalent bonds, the whole bearing a charge. These aggregates are called radicals or complex ions: the sulfate ion and the ammonium ion are examples. When a radical forms a compound by joining an oppositely charged ion in a lattice, as in Na_2SO_4, the compound is identified as an ionic compound, because the forces holding the lattice together are ionic bonds.

It is interesting to compare the properties of ionic and molecular compounds in the terms of the above structures. When an ionic compound is scratched or melted, the ions must be moved relative to one another against the coulombic attraction. Thus, these substances are hard and have high melting points with high heats of fusion. When a molecular compound is scratched or melted, the molecules move as units against the van der Waal's forces, the covalent bonds remaining unbroken. Thus, molecular compounds are soft and have low melting points with low heats of fusion. For the two examples above, the melting points are: NaCl, 800°C; $SiCl_4$, −70°C. There are many gradations between these two extremes.

STRUCTURAL CONSIDERATIONS

The size of an atom has been shown to be important in determining the nature of the bond it will form with another atom. Relative sizes are also important in determining the structures of crystals, molecules, and radicals. They even have a bearing on the existence of compounds. Suppose that a compound composed of elements A and B is predicted to have the formula AB_n from valence considerations. In order for this formula to be realized, the B atoms must all be near enough to A for it to exert a sufficient influence to hold them, yet the B atoms cannot overlap. If, in order to get nB atoms just touching each other and equidistant from A, the A-B distance is too great, then, since A cannot sufficiently influence B, the compound will not exist. The ratio of the sizes of the two atoms will determine the number of B atoms that can be associated with A at the requisite distance. This number is called the coordination number of A. The term "coordination number" is used in two related, but different, senses. The crystallographer uses coordination number to mean the number of particles of one kind that are arranged equidistantly about another particle in the solid state, regardless of the type of particles or the type of bonding. The chemist uses the term to mean the number of atoms of one kind that are covalently bound to another atom, regardless of the physical state; the word "covalency" is used as a synonym for the term in this sense. In this book, we shall call the first the crystal C.N. and the second the covalent C.N. or the covalency. A few examples will make the distinction clear.

Consider the uniform packing of two types of spheres of different radii into a given space. Let one be a cation of radius r_c, and the other an anion of radius r_a. Geometry will tell us what kind of structure to expect in the resulting crystal. For stability, all of the anions must touch the cation. Closest packing is obtained when the anions just touch each other. The limiting case for the triangular arrangement of C.N. 3 is shown in Figure 1.9(a), with the cation at the center of three anions. In the right triangle 123, the angle 312 is 60°, side $12 = r_c + r_a$, and side $23 = r_a$. Thus,

$$\frac{\text{side } 12}{\text{side } 23} = \frac{r_c + r_a}{r_a} = \frac{r_c}{r_a} + 1 = \frac{2}{\sqrt{3}}, \text{ and } \frac{r_c}{r_a} = 0.155$$

The quantity r_c/r_a is the minimum radius ratio for triangular coordination. As the radius ratio increases, the anions no longer touch. When it becomes large enough, four anions can be brought into contact with the cation and a different arrangement results, the tetrahedral. The tetrahedron is best visualized as the part of a cube made by joining alternate corners. The cation is located at the center of the cube, point 1, and the anions at the alternate corners, numbered 2, 3, 4, 5 in Figure 1.9(b). In the triangle 123 redrawn in Figure 1.9(c), side 12 $(= r_c + r_a)$ is one-half of the diagonal of the unit cube: $\frac{1}{2}\sqrt{3}$. Side 23 $(= 2r_a)$ is the diagonal of one face: $\sqrt{2}$. Thus, for tetrahedral C.N. 4,

$$\frac{r_c + r_a}{2r_a} = \frac{\frac{1}{2}\sqrt{3}}{\sqrt{2}}, \text{ and } \frac{r_c}{r_a} = 0.225$$

C.N. 5 is rare. As the radius ratio increases, the next stable arrangement is with C.N. 6, obtained by placing the cations and anions alternately at the corners of a cube as has already been shown in Figure 1.8. This arrangement is called octrahedral because the polyhedron made by joining the six anions has eight faces, this designation being standard mathematical nomenclature. C.N. 7 is also rare.

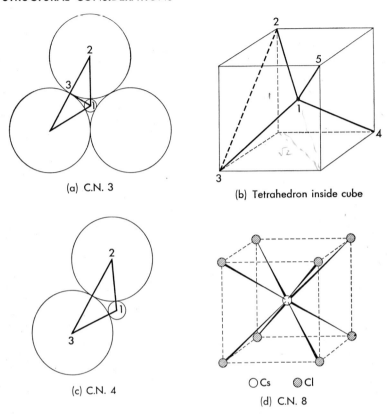

(a) C.N. 3

(b) Tetrahedron inside cube

(c) C.N. 4

(d) C.N. 8

○ Cs   ◎ Cl

Fig. 1.9 Geometry of crystals.

The next stable arrangement occurs when the cation occupies the center of a cube and eight anions the corners as shown in expanded form in Figure 1.9(d). This C.N. is called cubic. The calculation of the minimum radius ratio for C.N. 6 and 8 is left as an exercise for the student. The results are summarized below.

Geometry	C.N.	Radius Ratio Limits
Linear	2	0
Triangular	3	0.115
		0.225
Tetrahedral	4	0.414
Octahedral	6	0.732
Cubic	8	

The radius ratio of NaCl, calculated using the numbers in Figure 1.6, is 0.52, and so this salt crystallizes in the face-centered cubic or rock-salt structure shown in Figure 1.8. In CsCl, the radius ratio is 0.93, giving the cesium-chloride structure shown in Figure 1.9(d). RbCl is an interesting example of an intermediate compound. At room temperature and atmospheric pressure, it assumes the NaCl structure with C.N. 6. At low temperature or high pressure, however, the ions will pack more closely into the CsCl structure with C.N. 8.

In compounds where there are more ions of one kind than another, different coordination numbers will be observed for the two different types. For example, in rutile, TiO_2, each titanium ion is surrounded octahedrally by six oxygen ions, while each oxygen ion is surrounded by three titanium ions in a triangle. Since silicon is smaller than titanium, in SiO_2 the coordination numbers are $4:2$. In ThO_2, on the other hand, they are $8:4$.

It must be noted that in the above geometrical considerations, spherical ions are assumed. Real ions are polarizable, and consequently structures are occasionally observed that do not obey the radius ratio rules. For example, $r_{Si}/r_F = 0.301$, yet SiF_6^{-2} exists.

In the second sense of coordination number, sulfur has a C.N. of 2 in SO_2, 3 in SO_3, 4 in SO_4^{-2}, and 6 in SF_6. N.V. Sidgwick has given empirical rules limiting the covalent C.N. of an atom according to its position in the periodic table. Hydrogen has a maximum covalency of 2. The elements in the second period are limited to 4. The third and fourth periods have a maximum of 6, and the remaining periods a limit of 8. Not all elements in a period reach the maximum, but none can go above it. The tremendous difference in reactivity between CF_4 and SiF_4 can be explained, for example, by these limits. In CF_4 carbon has its maximum allowed covalency of 4 and thus is very unreactive. Silicon can have a covalent C.N. of 6, and so SiF_4 will react with NaF to give Na_2SiF_6, expanding the covalency of Si to 6.

ELECTROMOTIVE FORCE SERIES OF THE ELEMENTS

Many chemical reactions are carried out in solution, and, at least in inorganic chemistry, water is the chief solvent used. An important class of reactions is that involving oxidation-reduction, the "redox" reactions. The E.M.F. Series refers to redox reactions taking place in water. Since redox reactions involve the transfer of electrons from one species to another, the strengths of oxidizing and reducing agents are best understood in electrical terms. If a piece of zinc metal is placed in a solution of a copper(II) salt, it is observed that the zinc dissolves and the copper is deposited as the metal. The reaction, broken up into two half reactions, is

$$Zn \rightarrow Zn^{++} + 2e^-$$
$$\underline{Cu^{++} + 2e^- \rightarrow Cu}$$
$$Zn + Cu^{++} \rightarrow Zn^{++} + Cu$$

If a piece of copper is placed in a solution of a zinc salt, no observable reaction occurs. Thus, we see that Zn is a stronger reducing agent than Cu, or that the Cu^{++} ion in water is a better oxidizing agent than the Zn^{++} ion. In general, an active metal will replace a less

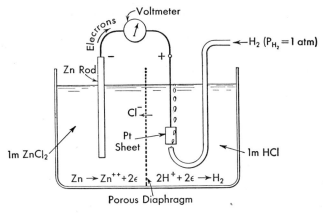

Fig. 1.10   The $Zn-H_2$ electrical cell.

electropositive metal from a solution of a salt of the latter, unless the metals are both active enough to release hydrogen from the water.

In order to measure quantitatively the relative tendencies of metals to lose electrons in solution, a cell of the type shown in Figure 1.10 is set up. Two half-cells are separated by some device, such as the porous diaphragm shown in the figure or a salt-bridge, which permits the passage of ions to carry the electric current but prevents the macroscopic mixing of the solutions. Since we are interested in aqueous solutions, the hydrogen electrode is chosen as the reference electrode. Since hydrogen is a gas, an electrode cannot be made of it directly, but, by bubbling hydrogen gas over an inert metal, the reaction $H_2 \rightleftharpoons 2H^+ + 2e^-$ takes place reversibly. The electromotive force of the hydrogen half-cell is defined as 0.000 volts. The emf of the above cell is found to be 0.763 volts, with the zinc electrode negative, showing that the zinc has a greater tendency to lose electrons than hydrogen. There are two conventions regarding the sign assigned to the emf of a half-cell. In this book the thermodynamic one will be used, by which the zinc potential is called positive, because zinc is more electropositive than hydrogen. Thus, the reaction $Zn \rightleftharpoons Zn^{++} + 2e^-$, tends to go as written from left to right, while the reaction $H_2 \rightleftharpoons 2H^+ + 2e^-$, when opposed by zinc, tends to go in the reverse direction, from right to left. The over-all cell reaction will then be

$$Zn + 2H^+ \rightarrow Zn^{++} + H_2, \qquad E^0 = +0.763v$$

both expressing the fact, which we already know, that zinc will release hydrogen from acid solutions and giving it in addition a quantitative measure for comparison with other redox reactions. By measuring the emf's of many cells of this and other types under standard conditions of 25°C with all gases at 1 atm and all ions at 1 molal,* the Electromotive Force Series of the elements is derived. W. M. Latimer has collected and evaluated all of these measurements into a comprehensive table of Standard Oxidation-Reduction Potentials, E^0. (See the second reference at the end of Chapter 5.) A part of it is given in Table 1.5.

The higher up an element is in the E.M.F. Series, the stronger its reducing properties are. The order of elements in Table 1.5 corresponds to the generalizations made above about the activities of the elements. The elements to the left of the periodic table, which lose electrons easily, are high up in the series. In going from left to right— say, from Cs to Ba to La to Hf—the activity of the metals decreases.

---

* Unit molality is only the first approximation. Actually, all substances are at unit activity, not unit molality. The difference can be significant, but its explanation is beyond the scope of this text. It is discussed in any text on physical chemistry.

TABLE 1.5

The E.M.F. Series of the Elements

Couple	E^0	Couple	E^0
$Li \rightleftharpoons Li^+ + e^-$	3.045	$Ga \rightleftharpoons Ga^{+++} + 3e^-$	0.53
$K \rightleftharpoons K^+ + e^-$	2.925	$Fe \rightleftharpoons Fe^{++} + 2e^-$	0.440
$Rb \rightleftharpoons Rb^+ + e^-$	2.925	$Cd \rightleftharpoons Cd^{++} + 2e^-$	0.403
$Cs \rightleftharpoons Cs^+ + e^-$	2.923	$In \rightleftharpoons In^{+++} + 3e^-$	0.342
$Ra \rightleftharpoons Ra^{++} + 2e^-$	2.92	$Co \rightleftharpoons Co^{++} + 2e^-$	0.277
$Ba \rightleftharpoons Ba^{++} + 2e^-$	2.90	$Ni \rightleftharpoons Ni^{++} + 2e^-$	0.250
$Sr \rightleftharpoons Sr^{++} + 2e^-$	2.89	$Pb \rightleftharpoons Pb^{++} + 2e^-$	0.126
$Ca \rightleftharpoons Ca^{++} + 2e^-$	2.87	$H_2 \rightleftharpoons 2H^+ + 2e^-$	0.0000
$Na \rightleftharpoons Na^+ + e^-$	2.714	$Cu \rightleftharpoons Cu^{++} + 2e^-$	-0.337
$La \rightleftharpoons La^{+++} + 3e^-$	2.52	$2I^- \rightleftharpoons I_2 + 2e^-$	-0.5355
$Mg \rightleftharpoons Mg^{++} + 2e^-$	2.37	$Ag \rightleftharpoons Ag^+ + e^-$	-0.7991
$Th \rightleftharpoons Th^{++++} + 4e^-$	1.90	$2Br^- \rightleftharpoons Br_2(l) + 2e^-$	-1.0652
$Be \rightleftharpoons Be^{++} + 2e^-$	1.85	$2H_2O \rightleftharpoons O_2 + 4H^+ + 4e^-$	-1.229
$Hf \rightleftharpoons Hf^{++++} + 4e^-$	1.70	$2Cl^- \rightleftharpoons Cl_2 + 2e^-$	-1.3595
$Al \rightleftharpoons Al^{+++} + 3e^-$	1.66	$Au \rightleftharpoons Au^{+++} + 3e^-$	-1.50
$Zr \rightleftharpoons Zr^{++++} + 4e^-$	1.53	$2F^- \rightleftharpoons F_2 + 2e^-$	-2.8
$Zn \rightleftharpoons Zn^{++} + 2e^-$	0.763		

The correlation between the ionization potentials of the elements and their Standard E.M.F.'s is not exact, however. The ionization potential is a measure of the energy absorbed when an isolated atom loses electrons to form an isolated ion, whereas the Standard E.M.F. is a measure of a composite process in which an element in molecular or metallic form breaks up into atoms, loses electrons, and becomes a *hydrated* ion. Thus, lithium is above potassium in the series because its ions are smaller, and consequently more strongly hydrated, than those of potassium. The alkaline earths are above sodium for the same reason. The order of the elements in the series follows their positions in the periodic table in a general way, but not exactly.

Oxidation potentials are used in inorganic chemistry to compare the stability of the various oxidation states of the elements. One needs a knowledge of thermodynamics in order to use them quantitatively, but much can be done qualitatively to predict what substances will oxidize what others to what oxidation state. The values in the table should, nevertheless, be used with caution, because, as will be seen later, the oxidation potential is also a function of the concentration of the substances present. Reactions are seldom carried out in exactly 1 molal solution. In addition, a change in pH or the presence of a complexing agent can sometimes drastically change the concentration of a species, and hence its oxidation potential.

PERIODICITY AS AN AID TO STUDY

The following chapters of this book present many factual details. These facts should be examined with a view to establishing a connection between them and the periodicity of the properties of the elements. For example, the von Antropoff periodic table shows that the chemistry of rubidium, cesium, and francium will be very similar to that of potassium. Likewise, calcium chemistry will resemble potassium chemistry. Along with similarities, however, go gradations in properties, and an over-all picture of these gradations should be fitted to the periodic table, enabling the student of inorganic chemistry to predict further facts from his necessarily small store of known facts. There follow several examples of the kinds of generalizations which can be made about the properties of the elements and their compounds.

Basicity of Oxides

Within a subgroup, oxides with the elements in the same oxidation state increase in basicity as the atomic weight increases. For example, CaO is less basic than SrO, which is less basic than BaO. The trioxides of arsenic, antimony, and bismuth increase in basicity in the order given.

In the second and third periods the oxides of the elements decrease in basicity from left to right. Thus, BeO is more basic than B_2O_3, Al_2O_3 is more basic than SiO_2, etc. In the long periods the gradation is more complex. From group Ia to VIIa there is a decrease in basicity. Thus,

$$K_2O > CaO > Sc_2O_3 > TiO_2 > V_2O_5 > CrO_3 > Mn_2O_7$$

Then follows an increase, so that ZnO, an amphoteric oxide, lies somewhere between Sc_2O_3 and TiO_2. After group IIb there is again a decrease to group VIIb. Thus,

$$ZnO > Ga_2O_3 > GeO_2 > As_2O_5 > SeO_3$$

In the comparisons above, only the highest oxides of the elements have been considered. Many of these elements form several oxides. For most elements, the lower the oxide, the greater the basicity. So,

$$MnO > Mn_2O_3 > MnO_2 > Mn_2O_7, \text{ and } CrO > Cr_2O_3 > CrO_3.$$

Melting Points of Alkali Metal Halides

Figure 1.10 shows the gradations in melting points for the alkali metal halides. Notice that for each alkali metal the melting points of its halides gradually decrease from the fluoride to the iodide. Note also that NaF melts higher than KF, which melts higher than RbF, etc. The lithium curve is the outstanding exception, being far out of place. Such exceptions are often noted in generalizations of this kind. Sometimes they can be rationalized, sometimes not. For an explanation of this one, see pages 72–75 of the sixth reference listed at the end of the chapter.

Heats of Formation

Figure 1.11 shows the variation in heats of formation for several series of hydrogen compounds. The heat of formation of a compound is the heat change when a mole of the compound is produced from the elements. If heat is given off in producing the compound, the heat of formation is negative and the compound is called exothermic; if heat is absorbed, it is positive and the compound is endothermic.

It can be seen that the negative heats of formation of the hydrides decrease with atomic number in a group. This is expected, since the atomic size of, say, bromine is greater than that of chlorine, and bromine will therefore exert relatively less influence than chlorine over the hydrogen's electron, forming a weaker chemical bond. The weaker the bond, the less the energy required to break it, or the less the energy released in forming it.

Boiling Points of Halides

Another way in which the properties of compounds may be compared is shown in Figure 1.12. Here boiling points in °K. are plotted against the boiling points of the corresponding rare gases. By "corresponding" is meant the rare gas nearest in atomic number to the variable element in a series. In these series the halogens are the vari-

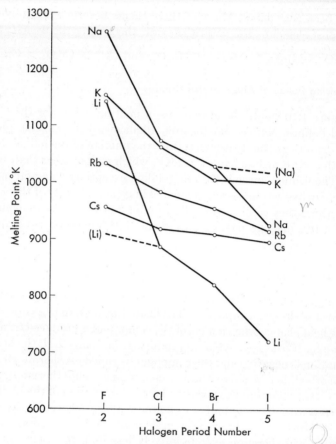

Fig. 1.11   Melting points of alkali halides.

able elements. It can be seen that $AlCl_3$ is more volatile than $AlBr_3$, which is more volatile than AlI_3—the increase in boiling point is almost linear on this kind of plot.

Again, exceptions to the linear relationships are apparent in, for instance, the titanium series. The chloride, bromide, and iodide behave regularly, but the fluoride shows a distinct anomaly. Also, with aluminum, the fluoride is a high melting solid whose boiling point is so high that it does not appear on the plot. Two explanations may be offered for this exceptional behavior. First the titanium-fluorine bond is considerably more ionic than the bonds between

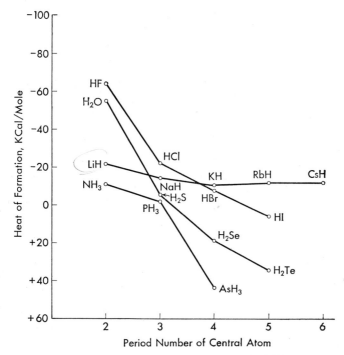

Fig. 1.12　Heats of formation of some hydrides.

titanium and the other halogens. In order for the regular increase in boiling points to be realized in a series, all of the members must be of nearly the same bond type. Secondly, differences in structure may account for divergences from expected properties. In the AlF_3 structure, each Al is surrounded by six fluorine atoms, giving rise to a salt-like structure. In the other halides of aluminum, however, the smaller coordination number of four is reached. This smaller C.N. and the less ionic bonds result in discrete molecules of Al_2X_6:

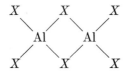

where X is Cl, Br, or I.*

　　*The structure of *solid* $AlCl_3$ is actually somewhat more complicated. See the sixth reference at end of the chapter.

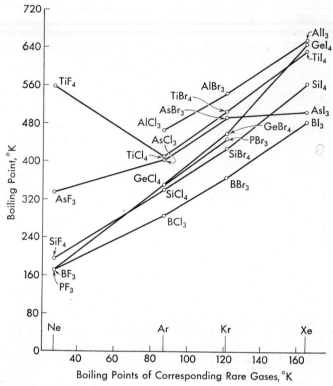

Fig. 1.13   Boiling points of various halides.

Hydrogen Bonding

Further examples of regular gradations in physical properties are seen in Figures 1.13 and 1.14. Note that the abcissae may be period numbers as well as the same property of the corresponding rare gas. Again, exceptions to the regular gradations appear. In the series H_2O, H_2S, H_2Se, H_2Te, H_2Po, water is out of line. This exception and the ones apparent for HF and NH_3 are explained by what is known as hydrogen bonding. To visualize hydrogen bonding, consider adjacent water molecules in the liquid phase:

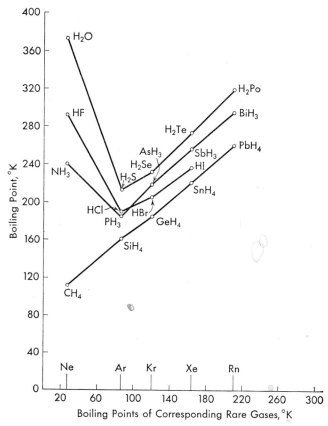

Fig. 1.14 Boiling points of various hydrides.

The hydrogen atom of the water molecule on the left, which is sharing its single electron with the oxygen atom of its water molecule (on the left), represents a center of positive charge. If another oxygen atom approaches it with the correct orientation, as the oxygen atom on the right in the diagram has done, there will be an attraction between the positive hydrogen and the unshared negative electrons of the oxygen. This electrostatic attraction, called hydrogen bonding, is represented by the dotted line in the diagram. It is much stronger than ordinary van der Waals forces, but still weaker than ionic or covalent bonds. It is enough to account for the abnormally high boiling points and heats of vaporizations of HF, H_2O, and NH_3.

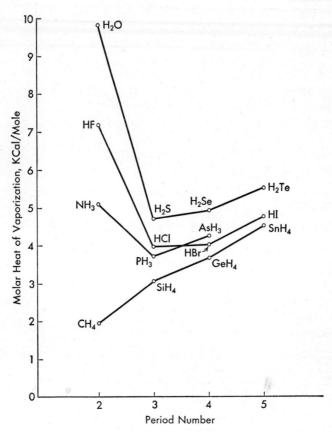

Fig. 1.15 Molar heats of vaporization of various hydrides.

If the water molecules were held together by van der Waals forces only, water would boil below $-100°C$ with a heat of vaporization nearer $+4$ than $+10$ kcal/mole. Since, however, hydrogen bonding results in greater forces between adjacent molecules, the expected properties of water are not realized.

Two questions come to mind immediately. Why is hydrogen necessary for this type of bonding? Why does hydrogen bonding not occur in H_2S, H_2Se, . . . , HCl, etc.? The answers to both lie in the electron structure of the atoms involved. First, hydrogen, alone among the elements, shares all of its electrons—one—in forming a covalent bond, and thereby leaves its positive nucleus much more exposed than any other element does. Second, oxygen, nitrogen, and fluorine have fewer completed inner shells than the elements below them, and so they are smaller and have a higher concentration of residual negative charge with which to attract the hydrogen.

One last question needs answering: why, then, is CH_4 "normal"? Two reasons can be given. In CH_4 the carbon atom is surrounded tetrahedrally by four hydrogen atoms, and there is little space left for a fifth to approach it close enough to form a hydrogen bond. Moreover, in CH_4 carbon has reached the maximum covalency of four allowable for the second period, and so cannot form any more bonds.

Thus, the criteria for hydrogen bonding are covalently bound hydrogen and a small, and hence very electronegative, exposed other atom.

Prediction of Properties of Unfamiliar Elements

The concept of periodicity allows one to predict the properties of unfamiliar elements. Consider rhenium:

(1) With respect to valency, rhenium will resemble manganese. Furthermore, these two elements will show gradations similar to those found between chromium and tungsten, their immediate neighbors. Chromium exhibits oxidation states of 6, 3, and 2, all moderately stable. Tungsten exhibits a stable oxidation number of 6 and several lower, much less stable states. Since, then, manganese has valence states of 7, 6, 4, and 2, rhenium would be expected and proves to be most stable in the +7 condition, although capable of forming less stable compounds in which it exhibits lower oxidation states.

K_2CrO_4 is a good oxidizing agent, while K_2WO_4 is a poor oxidizing agent. $KMnO_4$ is a good oxidizing agent, so $KReO_4$ should be a poor one. It is.

(2) Recollection of the melting point curve of the elements, which is rising to its highest peak in the region of rhenium, permits a good estimate of the melting point of rhenium. The same type of reasoning can be applied profitably to any physical property of the metal.

(3) In similar fashion, the physical properties of compounds can be predicted. WO_3 is appreciably volatile above 900°C. OsO_4 boils at 140°C. It is reasonable to expect Re_2O_7 to have a vapor pressure of 1 atm at about 400°C. Actually, it boils at 360°C.

The outstanding example of the use of periodicity in prediction is found in the work of D. I. Mendelejeff, one of the early proponents of the periodic law. In 1871, before elements 21, 31, and 32 had been discovered, Mendelejeff left positions for them in his table, calling them ekaboron, ekaaluminum, and ekasilicon (Sanskrit, *eka*, next in order). Furthermore, he described several properties expected of these elements. Scandium, gallium, and germanium were discovered during his lifetime, and the observed properties of the elements were found to correspond closely to Mendelejeff's predictions. The comparisons are tabulated in Chapter XXII of the fifth reference in the suggestions for further reading.

Throughout the detailed chemistry of the elements that follows, it will be profitable to refer constantly to the periodic relationships pointed out in this chapter.

SUGGESTIONS FOR FURTHER READING

R. M. Caven and G. D. Lander, *Systematic Inorganic Chemistry*, 6th ed., revised by A. B. Crawford, van Nostrand, New York, 1939, pp. 23–43.

T. M. Lowry, *Historical Introduction to Chemistry*, Macmillan, London, 1936, Chapter XVIII.

T. Moeller, *Inorganic Chemistry*, Wiley, New York, 1952, Chapters 3–6.

A. E. van Arkle, *Molecules and Crystals*, translated by J. C. Swallow, Butterworths, London, 1949, pp. 1–86.

M. E. Weeks, *Discovery of the Elements*, 6th ed., Journal of Chemical Education, Easton, Pa., 1956, Chapters XXI and XXII.

A. F. Wells, *Structural Inorganic Chemistry*, 2nd ed., Oxford, London, 1950, Chapters I–III.

STUDY QUESTIONS

1. The two natural isotopes of chlorine have masses of 34.979 and 36.978 on the physical scale, and they occur in the percentages 75.59% and 24.41%, respectively. Calculate the atomic weight of chlorine on the chemical scale.

2. Where do the best conductors of heat and electricity lie in the periodic table?

3. Calculate the minimum radius ratio for coordination numbers 6 and 8, in octahedral and cubic structures respectively.

4. The density of cesium is 1.90 gms/cc at 20°C. Calculate the atomic volume in cc/mole.

5. Enumerate the discontinuities in the melting point vs. atomic number curve.

6. Account for the following facts:

(a) The first ionization potential of boron is less than that of beryllium.

(b) The first ionization potential of oxygen is less than that of nitrogen.

7. In the series $AsCl_3$, $SbCl_3$, $BiCl_3$ a trend to more ionic bonding is observed. Is this to be expected? Explain.

8. Which is more ionic, $SbCl_3$ or $SbCl_5$? Why?

9. Compare several physical properties of H_2O, H_2S, H_2Se, and H_2Te. Predict those properties of H_2Po.

10. (a) Which is more abundant, Ga or Ge?

(b) Which has the higher ionization potential, K or Rb?

(c) Which has the higher ionization potential, Al or Si?

(d) Which is the larger in atomic volume, Ti or Zr?

(e) Which is larger in atomic volume, Sc or Ni?

(f) Which has the greater electron affinity, H or He?

(g) Which has the greater electron affinity, Ge or Pb?

(h) Which is more volatile, SnH_4 or SiH_4?

(i) Which is smaller, Fe^{++} or Fe^{+++}?

(j) Which is larger, S^{--} or Cl^-?

(k) Which is more basic, FeO or Fe_2O_3?

(l) Which is more basic, Ga_2O_3 or In_2O_3?

(m) What is the electron configuration of niobium?

11. Predict the properties of technetium.

12. Inscribe a regular octahedron in a cube.

13. List the first twenty-five elements in order of abundance by weight.

14. List the first fifteen elements in order of abundance by number of atoms.

15. List the first five elements in order of abundance by volume. Use the ionic radii in Figure 1.6.

16. Follow the passage of electricity around a complete circuit in the cell in Figure 1.10, and show what is carrying the current in every different part of the cell.

Chapter 2

The Rare Gases

OCCURRENCE AND HISTORY

Table 2.1 shows that all of the elements of group 0 except radon occur in the earth's atmosphere.

TABLE 2.1

Composition of Dry Air

Substance	Per Cent by Volume
N_2	78
O_2	21
Ar	0.93
CO_2	varies–average 0.03
H_2	0.01
Ne	0.0018
He	0.0005
Kr	0.0001
Xe	0.00001

Air is the only source of neon, argon, krypton, and xenon, but helium occurs in natural gases and trapped in certain minerals. The helium in these sources arises from radioactive processes in which alpha particles are emitted. It does not occur to a larger extent in the atmosphere because the very light molecule has a great enough velocity to escape the gravitational pull of the earth. Radon occurs in some radioactive minerals.

In view of the relatively great abundance of argon, it is surprising that it eluded discovery for so long. The reason for this is, of course, its chemical inertness. In 1785 Cavendish actually isolated argon when, after he removed all of the components of air that he could by chemical means, he had a small residue left. He did not, however, realize that he had a new element. A spectral line from the sun that did not correspond with any line from any element known on earth at the time was observed in 1868. It was thought that this new element occurred on the sun, but not the earth; hence the name, helium. It remained for Ramsay and coworkers to isolate all of the rare gases except radon in the short period of 1894 to 1898. Radon was isolated two years later by Dorn as a product of radium radioactivity. It is radioactive itself, decaying with a half-life of 3.8 days.*

PREPARATION OF THE ELEMENTS

Helium is produced in large quantity in the United States by fractional liquefaction of certain natural gases. Prior to the development of this source, it was obtained by heating minerals in which alpha decay had been going on for a long time. Neon, argon, krypton, and xenon result from the liquefaction and fractional distillation of air.

PHYSICAL PROPERTIES OF THE ELEMENTS

All of these elements are very low melting and boiling, and are colorless, odorless, and tasteless. Helium is unique in many of its properties in the liquid state. For instance, under its own vapor pressure it remains a liquid at the lowest temperature to which it has been cooled, and theory shows that it will be liquid even at the absolute zero of temperature. The attractive forces between its molecules are so low that they cannot overcome the small vibrational energy that molecules possess at $0°K$—that is, the zero-point energy. Only by the application of an external pressure of 25 atm or more can it be solidified.

Electrical discharges through these gases at low pressure produce brilliant colors: yellow for helium, orange-red for neon, red for argon, yellow-green for krypton, blue for xenon. The best way to identify these elements is by their characteristic emission spectra.

* Incidentally, the last element in the periodic table which has a *stable* isotope is bismuth.

CHEMICAL PROPERTIES AND COMPOUNDS

The inert gases form no ordinary chemical compounds, and so their group valency is zero. They exist as monatomic gases under ordinary conditions. Some compounds have been reported as existing at low temperatures, but these are now regarded as aggregates held together by van der Waals's forces rather than true compounds in which chemical bonds are formed.

THE OCTET RULE

Even though the inert gases form no chemical compounds, they are of great interest to the chemist. Their discovery clarified understanding of the periodic table by placing these completely inert elements between the most active nonmetals of group VII and the most active metals of group I. It helped lead the way to the modern conception of chemical bond formation in terms of the gain or loss of electrons. The rare gases are so unreactive chemically that their electron configuration must be particularly stable. Many elements have eight electrons in their outer shell when they exist in compounds, achieving this number by losing electrons to, gaining electrons from, or sharing electrons with other atoms. Familiar examples are:

$$\text{Na } 1s^2 2s^2 2p^6 3s \xrightarrow{-1e^-} \text{Na}^+ \quad 1s^2 2s^2 2p^6 \qquad \text{(Ne structure)}$$

$$\text{Cl } 1s^2 2s^2 2p^6 3s^2 3p^5 \xrightarrow{+1e^-} \text{Cl}^- \quad 1s^2 2s^2 2p^6 3s^2 3p^6 \text{ (Ar structure)}$$

$$\text{Cl } 1s^2 2s^2 2p^6 3s^2 3p^5 \xrightarrow{+Cl} \text{Cl}_2 \quad 1s^2 2s^2 2p^6 3s^2 3p^6 \text{ (Ar structure)}$$

$$\text{S } \quad 1s^2 2s^2 2p^6 3s^2 3p^4 \xrightarrow{+2e^-} \text{S}^{--} \quad 1s^2 2s^2 2p^6 3s^2 3p^6 \text{ (Ar structure)}$$

$$\text{S } \quad 1s^2 2s^2 2p^6 3s^2 3p^4 \xrightarrow[+2e^-]{+4O} \text{SO}_4{}^{--} \; 1s^2 2s^2 2p^6 3s^2 3p^6 \text{ (Ar structure)}$$

Representing the valence electrons by dots, the formation of these products can be visualized as follows:

$$\text{Na} \cdot \qquad \xrightarrow{-1e^-} \text{Na}^+$$

$$: \overset{..}{\underset{..}{\text{Cl}}} \cdot \qquad \xrightarrow{+1e} \; : \overset{..}{\underset{..}{\text{Cl}}} : \; -$$

$$: \overset{..}{\underset{..}{\text{Cl}}} \cdot + : \overset{..}{\underset{..}{\text{Cl}}} \cdot \longrightarrow \; : \overset{..}{\underset{..}{\text{Cl}}} : \overset{..}{\underset{..}{\text{Cl}}} :$$

$$\ddot{\text{S}} : \quad\quad \xrightarrow{+2e^-}\quad : \ddot{\text{S}} : \text{--}$$

$$: \ddot{\text{S}} : + 4 : \ddot{\text{O}} : \xrightarrow{+2e^-} \begin{array}{c} : \ddot{\text{O}} : \text{--} \\ : \ddot{\text{O}} : \ddot{\text{S}} : \ddot{\text{O}} : \\ : \ddot{\text{O}} : \end{array}$$

From these and many other examples arose the Octet Rule stating that atoms tend to have eight electrons in their outer shell when in compounds.

The octet of electrons is not the only configuration possible in compounds, however. Exceptions to the Octet Rule are so numerous that it cannot conceivably be said to apply to all elements. For example, silicon has eight electrons in its outer shell in SiF_4, but it has twelve in SiF_6^{--}; phosphorus has ten in PCl_5; boron has six in BF_3; sulfur has twelve in SF_6; iodine has fourteen in IF_7. It is the availability of the d orbitals as well as the s and p orbitals to hold electrons which allows the octet to be expanded.

USES

A large use of helium is in the lifting apparatus of lighter-than-air craft. It also finds commercial application as a diluent for oxygen when fresh gas under pressure must be supplied to human beings, as in deep-sea diving and in caissons. If compressed air is used, the nitrogen dissolves to a greater extent than at atmospheric pressure. Upon decompression, the nitrogen forms bubbles of gas in the blood vessels and causes the illness known as "bends." Helium is much less soluble in blood and therefore does not cause this trouble to such an extent. Liquid helium finds important application in low-temperature research. More recently it has been used to provide an inert atmosphere for the welding of active metals.

Argon is relatively cheap and is used in the gas filling of incandescent light bulbs. It has been found that the metal filaments can be run at a higher temperature in the presence of argon-nitrogen mixtures than with nitrogen alone. The reason is that nitrogen is a reactive gas at high temperatures. When the nitrogen is diluted with argon, the filament is attacked more slowly. The use of some of the rare gases in "neon" signs is familiar.

Radon is used as a source in radiotherapy. To make a source, radium is sealed inside a needle and the sample is aged. After some time, the amount of radon and other radioactive decomposition products of the radium has built up, and the source is much more active. With the large scale production of other radioactive sources developed in recent years, the use of radium and radon in therapy has diminished.

SUGGESTIONS FOR FURTHER READING

N. V. Sidgwick, *The Chemical Elements and Their Compounds*, Oxford, London, 1950, pp. 1–10.

M. E. Weeks, *Discovery of The Elements*, 6th ed., Journal of Chemical Education, Easton, Pa., 1956, Chapter XXV.

STUDY QUESTIONS

1. Given 1 cc of radon at NTP, how many cc will be left after 3.8 days; 7.6 days; 1.9 days?

2. Helium has what percentage of the lifting power of hydrogen, with reference to a balloon operating at sea level?

3. List a dozen exceptions to the Octet Rule.

4. Give six ions which have a rare gas electron configuration; give six ions which do not.

5. Describe the preparation of pure krypton from the atmosphere.

Chapter 3 Hydrogen

OCCURRENCE AND HISTORY

Very little hydrogen occurs in the uncombined state, because the molecule is light enough to escape the earth's gravitational pull, but the amount of water on earth manifests the great abundance of combined hydrogen. By weight, hydrogen makes up about 1 per cent of the earth's crust, but in percentage of atoms it is almost as abundant as silicon. Some of this hydrogen exists in compounds other than water, such as petroleum, natural gases, and other organic matter.

While hydrogen was certainly observed several centuries earlier, the work of Cavendish in the latter half of the eighteenth century established the elementary nature of gaseous hydrogen. Our real knowledge of the properties of hydrogen dates from his thorough work.

PREPARATION OF THE ELEMENT

By the Reaction of Elements with Water

Practically all methods of preparing this element use water as the source of hydrogen. Some hydrogen is also produced as a by-product of various industrial cracking processes on organic compounds.

The displacement of hydrogen from water by other elements is a familiar reaction. The ease with which this reaction proceeds varies greatly, depending upon the elements involved and the experimental conditions of temperature and of the states of the reactants and products. Lithium, sodium, and the metals of groups Ia and IIa react vigorously with water at room temperature to give hydrogen

49

and the hydroxide of the metal:

$$2Me + 2H_2O \rightarrow 2MeOH + H_2\uparrow$$
$$Me + 2H_2O \rightarrow Me(OH)_2 + H_2\uparrow$$

Most other metals, such as magnesium, aluminum, zinc, iron, etc., will react with gaseous water if the temperature is high enough:

$$Me + H_2O \overset{\Delta}{\rightarrow} MeO + H_2$$

Such reactions are rarely used to produce hydrogen on a large scale, however, owing to the high cost of producing the free metals.

A few metals will not react with water even at very high temperature—for example, gold, silver, mercury, and platinum.

Many nonmetals react with water, but carbon is the only one which reacts to give significant amounts of hydrogen, and then only with steam at very high temperature:

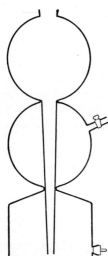

$$C + H_2O \overset{\Delta}{\rightarrow} CO + H_2$$

Since both of the products are combustible gases and both of the reactants, water and carbon in the form of coke, are readily available, this reaction is widely used for the production of fuel gas. It is also a major source of hydrogen for industrial consumption.

When water is acidified with a strong, non-oxidizing acid, many more metals react at room temperature to liberate hydrogen. Thus, magnesium, zinc, and iron liberate hydrogen from dilute solutions of sulfuric acid in water. Aluminum reacts very slowly at first because of its protective oxide coating. The most practical method of preparing hydrogen in the laboratory has long been the reaction between

Fig. 3.1 Kipp generator.

zinc and hydrochloric acid in the Kipp generator, shown in Figure 3.1. Of course, some metals react with acid solutions more readily than others. The familiar activity series of the elements gives essentially the order of the rate of evolution of hydrogen from dilute acids by the elements, although the activity series is set up from equilibrium measurements and cannot be expected to hold rigidly as a measure of rate phenomena. For instance, potassium reacts much more violently with water or dilute acids than lithium does, even though it is below lithium in the series.

Certain elements react with solutions of strong bases in water to liberate hydrogen:

$$Si + 2NaOH + H_2O \rightarrow Na_2SiO_3 + 2H_2\uparrow$$
$$2Al + 2NaOH + 2H_2O \rightarrow 2NaAlO_2 + 3H_2\uparrow$$
$$Zn + 2NaOH \rightarrow Na_2ZnO_2 + H_2\uparrow$$

In these cases, the elements form salts in which the elements themselves are in the acid radicals. Only elements capable of forming such salts will liberate hydrogen from basic solution, unless of course they will liberate hydrogen from water itself. Silicon forms salts of this type only, while aluminum and zinc form both salts in which the elements are in the anions and salts in which they are the cations. Thus, silicon reacts with basic solutions only, while aluminum and zinc are amphoteric.

Magnesium is not amphoteric, only basic. Thus, it will not dissolve in sodium hydroxide solution. These facts illustrate one way in which aluminum and magnesium can be separated chemically.

By Reaction of Compounds with Water

Some compounds liberate hydrogen from water, particularly the hydrides of the more electropositive elements. In these compounds hydrogen has an oxidation number of -1. They react vigorously with water at room temperature:

$$LiH + H_2O \rightarrow LiOH + H_2\uparrow$$
$$CaH_2 + 2H_2O \rightarrow Ca(OH)_2 + 2H_2\uparrow$$

These compounds are used to make hydrogen in portable generators where the weight is of primary importance.

It has been seen that many elements and compounds react with water. Therefore such substances should be protected from the action of water or moist air if it is desired to keep them in a state of purity. For example, iron must be kept away from water if it is to remain clean and free from corrosion (see Chapter 24).

By Electrolysis

It is possible to decompose water electrically. Pure water electrolyzes at essentially zero rate because of its very low conductivity. If the water is made conducting by adding an electrolyte, however, current flows and a reaction takes place. Figure 3.2 shows a eudiometer, which is used to decompose water by electrolysis and measure the volumes of gases given off at the electrodes. If the ions of the added electrolyte are more difficult to oxidize at the anode and reduce at the cathode than the water molecule, then the water alone is decomposed:

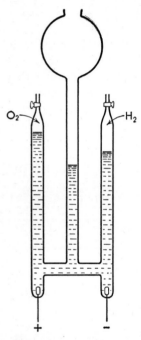

Fig. 3.2 Eudiometer.

anode: $2H_2O \rightarrow O_2\uparrow + 4H^+ + 4e^-$
cathode: $2H_2O + 2e^- \rightarrow H_2\uparrow + 2OH^-$

Doubling the second half-reaction, adding and cancelling the excess water molecules, gives the over-all reaction:

$$2H_2O \xrightarrow{\text{electrolysis}} 2H_2\uparrow + O_2\uparrow$$

Such is the reaction when sodium sulfate, sulfuric acid, etc., are added to the water. If copper sulfate is used, then the anode reaction is as above, but copper is deposited at the cathode. If sodium chloride makes the water conducting, hydrogen is released at the cathode, but chlorine, not oxygen, comes off at the anode:

anode: $2Cl^- \rightarrow Cl_2\uparrow + 2e^-$
cathode: $2H_2O + 2e^- \rightarrow H_2\uparrow + 2OH^-$

Adding up the two half-reactions and putting in the unreacting ions, the over-all reaction is seen to be:

$$2H_2O + 2NaCl \xrightarrow{\text{electrolysis}} H_2\uparrow + Cl_2\uparrow + 2NaOH$$

This important industrial reaction produces three valuable products: hydrogen, chlorine, and sodium hydroxide. The process is a source of industrial hydrogen.

By Pyrolysis

Natural gas, which is a mixture of binary compounds of hydrogen and carbon, is heated to high temperatures in an industrial process for the production of amorphous carbon (see Chapter 11). The compounds, chiefly methane, undergo pyrolysis:

$$CH_4 \xrightarrow{\Delta} C + 2H_2$$

giving by-product hydrogen, which is, of course, used and not thrown away.

PHYSICAL PROPERTIES

Hydrogen is the lightest known gas, its molecular weight of 2 being half that of helium. Its boiling point is but 20° above absolute zero. It is colorless, odorless, and tasteless, although a breath of hydrogen produces a remarkable effect on the voice, raising the pitch by its very low density.

CHEMICAL PROPERTIES AND COMPOUNDS

The hydrogen atom has one electron, and one might think that it could either lose this electron to form a positive ion or gain a second electron to form a negative ion. In fact, it does form the hydride ion, H^-, when combined with very electropositive elements, but the bare proton, H^+, is unknown under ordinary conditions. The size of the proton, which was facetiously included with other ions in Figure 1.6, is so small that the electrical field near it is tremendous. Then, according to Fajans' second rule it will form covalent compounds in which its oxidation number is $+1$. As mentioned above (pages 15 and 40) hydrogen is a unique element in that the electron shell involved in compound formation is right next to the nucleus; to place hydrogen in any group of the periodic table deceptively implies a similarity which does not exist.

Molecular and Atomic Hydrogen

The element exists as diatomic molecules in which two hydrogen atoms share the pair of electrons in a covalent bond. Molecular hydrogen can be thermally dissociated into atomic hydrogen, but the degree of dissociation is slight below 2000°C at atmospheric pressure. An electric arc, by means of which great concentration of energy is realized, dissociates hydrogen to a larger extent. Atomic hydrogen also occurs as a very short-lived intermediate in many chemical reactions. It is very reactive and will reduce many substances which molecular-hydrogen will not touch at ordinary temperatures. Atomic hydrogen can also be generated in solution by electrolysis or chemical action, when it is called "nascent hydrogen." Here it has much greater reducing power than molecular hydrogen bubbled into the solution. Numerous catalysts increase the rate of dissociation of hydrogen into atoms; catalytic hydrogenation is an important reaction in organic chemistry.

If hydrogen is dissociated and nothing is present with which the atoms may react, they quickly recombine, especially in the presence of catalysts, with the liberation of great energy. This phenomenon is used in the atomic hydrogen torch, in which hydrogen dissociated by an electric arc is passed over a metal which acts as a catalyst for the recombination. This torch is capable of reaching temperatures higher than those of the oxy-hydrogen flame. It has the additional advantage of heating the metal in a reducing atmosphere and thereby preventing corrosion.

Volatile Hydrides

Hydrogen forms covalent compounds with the elements to the right in the periodic table; that is, with boron and the typical elements and the b subgroups of groups IV, V, VI, and VII. These compounds are volatile, all except water and a few others being gases under ordinary conditions.

Hydrogen will combine directly with some elements to form volatile hydrides, although the reaction is so violent in most of these cases that it is seldom, if ever, used as a preparative method. Mixtures of oxygen or chlorine with hydrogen will not spontaneously combine, but the smallest flame or spark, or a catalyst or light, will start the reaction which then proceeds rapidly. Hydrogen and fluorine combine spontaneously and explosively under all ordinary laboratory conditions. It is possible, however, to mix the two without reaction if they are rigorously pure and confined in a suitable noncatalytic container. Mixtures of oxygen and hydrogen with a large excess of either react rapidly but not explosively, and can therefore be reacted in a burner which gives a hot, quiet flame. With more equal proportions of the two gases, violent explosions result upon ignition. Thus certain mixtures of air and hydrogen are dangerous, and caution should be exercised when an atmosphere is known to contain appreciable quantities of hydrogen.

Bromine, iodine, and nitrogen react slowly with hydrogen, and catalysts are employed to carry out the direct synthesis of their hydrides in good yields. The remaining elements which form volatile hydrides react so slowly with hydrogen that direct synthesis is not used. The usual preparative procedure in this case is to obtain the element in the electronegative condition in combination with a very electropositive metal, and then react the resulting compound with a reagent which introduces hydrogen onto the negative element: e.g.,

$$4Mg + SiO_2 \rightarrow 2MgO + Mg_2Si$$
then $$Mg_2Si + 4HCl \rightarrow 2MgCl_2 + SiH_4\uparrow \text{ and other silanes}$$
$$2Al + 3Se \rightarrow Al_2Se_3$$
then $$Al_2Se_3 + 6H_2O \rightarrow 2Al(OH)_3 + 3H_2Se\uparrow$$

The chemical character of the volatile hydrides is varied. In general, the acid strength in water increases with increasing atomic weight in a group and in a period. Thus, hydrogen fluoride is only about 10 per cent ionized in 0.1N solution, whereas the other hydrogen halides are essentially 100 per cent hydrolyzed:

$$HX + H_2O \rightarrow H_3O^+ + X^-$$

Water is neutral, of course, and hydrogen sulfide, selenide, and telluride are only slightly hydrolyzed:

$$H_2O + H_2O \rightleftharpoons H_3O^+ + OH^-$$
$$H_2S + H_2O \rightleftharpoons H_3O^+ + HS^-, \text{ etc.}$$

Ammonia hydrolyzes partially to give a basic solution:

$$NH_3 + H_2O \rightleftharpoons NH_4^+ + OH^-$$

while phosphine and the hydrides of Group Vb do not hydrolyze appreciably. Methane does not react with water at all. In silane the nonmetal is less electronegative than hydrogen, which then behaves as negative hydrogen, and the hydrolysis proceeds via an oxidation-reduction reaction:

$$SiH_4 + 4H_2O \rightarrow Si(OH)_4 + 4H_2\uparrow$$

The same type of reaction occurs for the lowest hydride of boron, which is dimerized and so has the formula B_2H_6 and the name diborane.

Some of the volatile hydrides, such as diborane, silane, and phosphine, are very inflammable and must be handled with extreme caution. In addition, all except water are extremely objectionable to body tissues and should not be handled outside a hood.

Ionic Hydrides

When hydrogen gains one electron to form the hydride ion, it has the helium configuration of two electrons in the first level. It will do this only when combined with very electropositive metals, however, and the hydride ion does not approach the stability of the helium atom, because the two electrons are held by two protons in helium and only one in hydrogen.

Lithium, sodium, and the elements of groups Ia and IIa react with hydrogen to form ionic hydrides; LiH, NaH, CaH₂, etc. These compounds are typically salt-like and have crystal structures like the corresponding chlorides. They are all prepared by passing hydrogen over the hot metal. That these compounds are ionic and contain hydrogen anions was proved experimentally by carrying out the electrolysis of fused lithium hydride (the only one which is stable enough to be melted without decomposition). Hydrogen gas is evolved at the *anode* in the reaction:

$$2H^- \rightarrow H_2 + 2e^-$$

It has been shown above that the "saline" hydrides react with water, giving hydrogen and the hydroxide of the metal. In addition, the finely powdered compounds are inflammable.

Other Metal Hydrides

Most of the metals will absorb hydrogen in varying amounts, depending on the temperature and the pressure. For example, sodium will absorb hydrogen readily at a temperature of 250°C, to form the stoichiometric compound NaH. Iron, too, absorbs hydrogen, but the resulting substance does not appear to be a stoichiometric compound. Rather, it appears that the hydrogen is adsorbed by the iron. Many transition metals behave in this manner toward hydrogen, giving what are called nonstoichiometric hydrides. Hot titanium and zirconium absorb hydrogen in quantities that correspond approximately to the formulae TiH_2 and ZrH_2. The resulting powders look like the metal powders. Indeed many of the nonstoichiometric hydrides have been called metallic hydrides.

Hydrogen as a Reducing Agent

Hydrogen is of some importance as a reducing agent due to the energy liberated when it unites with oxygen to form water. For example,

$$MeO + H_2 \rightarrow H_2O + Me$$

When hydrogen reduces an oxide to the metal, the reaction may be thought of as proceeding in steps:

$$(1) \quad MeO \quad \rightarrow Me + \tfrac{1}{2}O_2$$
$$(2) \quad \tfrac{1}{2}O_2 + H_2 \rightarrow H_2O$$

In most cases, energy will be absorbed by step (1), whereas step (2) will liberate energy. If the energy liberated in step (2) is not more than the energy absorbed in step (1), the process will not be spontaneous. Note that the energy changes in all such reactions vary with the temperature at which the reactions occur. The spontaneity of a process does not necessarily determine whether or not the reaction will go to completion. Using the classic example of the reaction between Fe_3O_4 and H_2, this is seen:

$$Fe_3O_4 + 4H_2 \leftrightarrows 3Fe + 4H_2O$$

This process may be made to go to completion in either direction. If a stream of hydrogen gas is passed through a heated tube containing the oxide of iron, all of the latter will eventually be reduced to iron, because the steady stream of hydrogen keeps a relatively fixed concentration of hydrogen gas in contact with the iron oxide, simultaneously sweeping out the steam as it is produced. Just the reverse is true if a stream of steam is passed through a heated tube containing iron.

If the metal tenaciously adsorbs hydrogen to form a hydride, reduction of the oxide by hydrogen would not be a good method of preparing the free metal.

PROTON ACIDS

The Bronsted-Lowry Theory of Acids and Bases

The compound hydrogen chloride is a volatile gas consisting of discrete molecules, each containing one hydrogen atom and one chlorine atom bound together by means of a single covalent bond. This compound, when liquified, does not conduct electric current. Yet, when this compound is dissolved in water, the resulting solution readily conducts electricity, showing the presence of ions. The solution is commonly called hydrochloric acid, sometimes symbolized H^+Cl^-. The symbol is better written $H_3O^+Cl^-$, because the reaction is one of transferring the proton from one species to another:

$$H : \overset{..}{\underset{..}{Cl}} : \; + \; H : \overset{..}{\underset{..}{O}} : H \rightarrow \left[H : \overset{\overset{\textstyle H}{..}}{\underset{..}{O}} : H \right]^+ + \left[: \overset{..}{\underset{..}{Cl}} : \right]^-$$

It may be thought that the proton left its electron with the chlorine atom in moving over to the oxygen atom, and therefore the proton is not donating any of the electrons that it shares with the oxygen. Nevertheless, all three protons are tied to the oxygen in the same manner, none being distinguishable from the others. They are all held to the oxygen by sharing pairs of electrons, and, once the bonds are formed, we cannot tell where the electrons came from to form any particular bond.

The transfer of a proton from one species to another species is the

essence of the Bronsted-Lowry theory of acid-base reactions, in
which an acid is defined as a substance capable of donating a proton
to another substance, a base, which is capable of receiving the
proton. Theoretically, any substance containing a proton can act
as an acid. The relative strength of the acid as measured by the
ease with which the substance parts with its proton depends on the
nature of the compound, the temperature, the base with which it
reacts, and the solvent. In the above example, when hydrogen
chloride dissolves in water it behaves as an acid.

$$HCl + HOH \rightleftharpoons H_3O^+ + Cl^-$$

Notice, however, that once the proton has been transferred to the
water molecule, forming H_3O^+, the Cl^- residue is a base, although
it is a weak one because the equilibrium is far to the right. Furthermore, the water molecule, once having accepted a proton, becomes
a hydronium ion and is an acid. Thus, in general, an acid will react
with a base to produce another acid and another base. An acid and
the base resulting from such an acid are said to be conjugate pairs.
A base and the acid resulting from the addition of a proton to the
base are also said to be conjugate pairs. A few familiar examples are:

$$Acid_1 + Base_1 \rightleftharpoons Acid_2 + Base_2$$
$$H_3O^+ + HS^- \rightleftharpoons H_2S + H_2O$$
$$H_3O^+ + NH_3 \rightleftharpoons NH_4^+ + H_2O$$
$$H_2O + NH_3 \rightleftharpoons NH_4^+ + OH^-$$
$$H_2PO_4^- + OH^- \rightleftharpoons H_2O + HPO_4^{--}$$

conjugate pairs

conjugate pairs

Many substances are capable of acting as either acids or bases. In
the water system, examine:

$$H_3O^+ = H_2O + H^+$$
$$H_2O = OH^- + H^+$$
$$OH^- = O^{--} + H^+$$

It is possible for H_3O^+, H_2O, and OH^- to act as acids: H_3O^+ is known
to be a strong acid; H_2O is known to be a weak acid; OH^- is usually

considered a base. The ammonia system is complicated by one
additional hydrogen atom:

$$NH_4^+ \leftrightharpoons NH_3 + H^+$$
$$NH_3 \leftrightharpoons NH_2^- + H^+$$
$$NH_2^- \leftrightharpoons NH^{--} + H^+$$
$$NH^{--} \leftrightharpoons N^{---} + H^+$$

It is seen that ammonium ion, ammonia, amide ion, and imide ion
are all capable of acting as acids. Obviously the strength of these
acids is in the order: $NH_4^+ > NH_3 > NH_2^- > NH^{--}$. Conversely,
N^{---}, NH^{--}, and NH_3 are all capable of acting as bases. Obviously
again the strength of these bases is in the order $N^{---} > NH^{--} >
NH_2^- > NH_3$. A rough measure of the strength of NH_2^- and OH^-
as bases may be obtained by examining the reaction of sodium
amide with water. The amide ion quantitatively reacts to form
ammonia and hydroxyl ion,

$$NH_2^- + HOH = NH_3 + OH^-$$

from which it may be concluded that NH_2^- is a stronger base than
OH^-.

The Strength of Oxy-Acids

The so-called "oxygen acids" or "oxy-acids" are common
reagents in the laboratory, and it is important to know the relative
strengths of these acids. Qualitatively the process of ionization of
the acid HA in water is visualized as a competition between the
water molecule and the anion A^- for the proton:

$$HA + H_2O \rightleftharpoons H_3O^+ + A^-$$

In order to compare the relative strengths of acids, a quantitative
measure of the relative proton affinities of H_2O and A^- is needed;
it is given by the ionization constant of the acid in water:

$$K_i = \frac{[H_3O^+][A^-]}{[HA]}$$

Certain generalizations are useful for estimating the approximate
strengths of oxy-acids in water from their formulas and structures.

The formulas are written in the general form H_nXO_m, where n and m are small integers and X is some central element such as sulfur, chlorine, etc. These empirical formulas are not structurally correct, however. The hydrogen atoms may all be attached to oxygen atoms, as in H_2SO_4, which has the structure

$$
\begin{array}{c}
\ddot{} \\
: O : \\
\overset{..}{} \quad \overset{..}{} \quad \overset{..}{} \\
H : O : S : O : H \\
\overset{..}{} \quad \overset{..}{} \quad \overset{..}{} \\
: O : \\
\ddot{}
\end{array}
$$

or they may be attached some to oxygen atoms and some to the atom of the central element, as in H_3PO_3, which has the structure

$$
\begin{array}{c}
H \\
\overset{..}{} \quad \overset{..}{} \quad \overset{..}{} \\
H : O : P : O : H \\
\overset{..}{} \quad \overset{..}{} \quad \overset{..}{} \\
: O : \\
\ddot{}
\end{array}
$$

Of course, if none of the hydrogen atoms are attached to oxygen atoms, as in formaldehyde, H_2CO, which has the structure

$$
\begin{array}{c}
H \\
\overset{..}{} \\
\overset{.}{.}C :: \overset{..}{O} \\
\overset{..}{} \\
H
\end{array}
$$

then the substance is not an oxy-acid, since it is only the hydrogen atoms attached to oxygen that ionize to any measurable extent in water. Thus, both sulfuric acid and phosphorous acid have two ionizable hydrogen atoms. It is in terms of the number of ionizable hydrogen atoms compared to the total number of oxygen atoms that the generalizations are formulated:

(1) In oxy-acids where the number of ionizable hydrogen atoms is equal to the number of oxygen atoms, the acid is very weak with an ionization constant of the order of magnitude of 10^{-7} to 10^{-10}.

For example:

Acid	K_i at room temp.
H_3BO_3	6×10^{-10}
$HClO$	10^{-8}
H_3AsO_3	6×10^{-10}

(2) For each oxygen atom in excess of the number of ionizable hydrogen atoms, the ionization constant of the acid is increased by a factor of about 10^5. Thus, the constants for the acids with one extra oxygen lie in the range 10^{-2} to 10^{-5}, indicating that they are weak acids. For example:

Acid	K_i at room temp.
H_5IO_6	10^{-2}
H_3PO_4	7.5×10^{-3}
H_3AsO_4	5×10^{-3}
H_2SO_3	1.7×10^{-2}
H_2SeO_3	3×10^{-3}
$HClO_2$	10^{-2}
HNO_2	4×10^{-4}
$HC_2H_3O_2$	1.75×10^{-5}

Acids with two extra oxygens are strong and have ionization constants that are too high to be measured accurately. Their K's are of the order of 10^2. Three extra oxygen atoms make the acids very strong with ionization constants of the order of 10^7. Examples of these two classes are: HNO_3, H_2SO_4, and $HClO_3$; $HClO_4$ and $HMnO_4$.

(3) The above two generalizations apply to the first ionization constant of oxy-acids. If more than one hydrogen atom is ionizable, the second is more difficult to remove once the first is gone, the third more difficult once the first and second are gone, etc. The ratio of the first to the second to the third ionization constants is generally of the order of $1:10^{-5}:10^{-10}$. For example:

Acid	K_1	K_2	K_3
H_2SO_4	10^2	2×10^{-2}	—
H_3PO_4	1.1×10^{-2}	2×10^{-7}	3.6×10^{-13}
H_2SeO_3	3×10^{-3}	5×10^{-8}	—

USES

Large quantities of hydrogen are used in the synthesis of ammonia (see Chapter 15). Much smaller quantities were formerly used to inflate lighter-than-air craft, but helium has replaced hydrogen for this use except in special applications, such as weather balloons, where human beings are not carried. A great deal of hydrogen is used industrially to hydrogenate organic compounds. For example, cracking and hydrogenation increase the amount of gasoline that can be obtained from crude petroleum. It is estimated that 30 billion cubic feet of hydrogen gas were produced in the United States in 1951.

SUGGESTIONS FOR FURTHER READING

D. T. Hurd, *Chemistry of The Hydrides*, Wiley, New York, 1952.
M. E. weeks, *Discovery of The Elements*, 6th ed., Journal of Chemical Education, Easton, Pa., 1956, Chapter V.

STUDY QUESTIONS

1. List those elements that will liberate hydrogen from water at room temperature.
2. List twenty elements that will liberate hydrogen from dilute acid solution.
3. Why must calcium hydride be thoroughly desiccated?
4. Show that the compound hydrogen chloride is decomposed by water just as much as is the compound calcium hydride, even though the products are dissimilar.
5. Calculate the volume of hydrogen (STP) liberated by one gram of each of the following substances on reaction with water, acid solution, or basic solution (as necessary): LiH, NaH, CaH_2, Na, Si, Zn, $LiBH_4$.
6. Describe the operation of a Kipp generator.
7. Name five metals that are made by reduction with hydrogen.
8. What happens when the following substances are mixed:
   (a) $NaH + H_2O$
   (b) $NH_4Br + KNH_2$ (in liquid NH_3)
   (c) $HCl + H_2O$
   (d) $H_2 + As$(heat)
   (e) $Mg_2Si + HCl$(aqueous).

9. By means of equations and a few words about conditions, show how to carry out the following conversions:

    (a) make GeH_4 from GeO_2

    (b) make H_2Te from Te

    (c) make LiH from H_2O

    (d) make H_2 from H_2SO_4

    (e) make ammonia from air and water.

10. (a) List the following acids in order of increasing strength: H_2SO_3, $HReO_4$, H_4SiO_4, H_2SeO_4

    (b) Estimate the second ionization constant of H_2SO_4 and H_3PO_4.

11. By means of equations, show how ZnO in water is amphoteric on the basis of the Bronsted-Lowry theory of acids and bases.

Chapter 4

Lithium,
Sodium,
Potassium,
Rubidium,
Cesium,
and Francium

OCCURRENCE AND HISTORY

This family of elements is usually referred to as the alkali metals. Sodium and potassium are very abundant on the surface of the earth, each one making up about 3 per cent of the crust. The occurrence of large deposits of almost pure rock salt, sodium chloride, results in sodium salts being more common and cheaper as chemicals than potassium salts. Potassium also occurs as the chloride, but it is usually mixed with other salts, as in carnallite, $MgCl_2 \cdot KCl \cdot 6H_2O$. There are many other compounds of sodium and potassium in nature, such as nitrates, carbonates, sulfates, and aluminum silicates, but these sources are either limited or difficult to work for the elements. In fact, one of the most abundant minerals on earth is feldspar, $KAlSi_3O_8$, but it is uneconomical to extract soluble potassium salts from it. Lithium, rubidium, and cesium are much rarer and less accessible than sodium and potassium. They occur as aluminum silicates and aluminum phosphates. Francium occurs in minute amounts in the decay series of uranium 235. The half-life of the most stable isotope is only 21 minutes; it therefore disappears almost as fast as it is formed and builds up only to a very low steady state concentration. In view of its scarcity and extreme radioactivity, the properties of francium will probably never be studied in much detail. We can, however, deduce within narrow limits its properties from the properties of the other elements in the group.

Although they were recognized as elements a century earlier, elementary sodium and potassium were first prepared in 1807 by Sir Humphrey Davy from the electrolysis of the molten hydroxides. The preparation of such active metals was a remarkable experimental feat. About fifty years later rubidium and cesium were discovered by and named after the colors that they impart to a flame. This and other spectroscopic studies by Bunsen and Kirchhoff laid the foundation of modern spectroscopy. Lithium was identified chemically and spectroscopically in this period, but it was not until 1939 that M. Perey observed francium and named it after her country.

PREPARATION OF THE ELEMENTS

Since these elements are very electropositive, vigorous reducing action is necessary to prepare them from their compounds. The usual industrial practice involves the electrolysis of a fused compound. The two most common processes for sodium use molten sodium hydroxide and molten sodium chloride as electrolytes:

$$2NaOH + \text{electric current} \rightarrow 2Na + O_2 + H_2$$
$$2NaCl + \text{electric current} \rightarrow 2Na + Cl_2$$

Since the melting point of sodium hydroxide is 318°C and that of sodium chloride is 800°C, the sodium is liberated in the liquid state, which facilitates the handling of the product. It is piped from the reaction cell into molds or into large tanks. Because of its great reactivity towards most of the constituents of air, sodium must be protected from the atmosphere. In the laboratory it is usually stored in airtight cans or under a light petroleum oil in a bottle. All of the alkali metals may be prepared by anhydrous electrolytic processes.

Other, more costly, processes may be used to prepare small quantities of the metals. It is actually possible to prepare these metals by reduction with a less electropositive metal, such as calcium, because of the relative volatility of the alkali metals:

$$2CsCl + Ca \xrightarrow{\Delta} CaCl_2 + 2Cs\uparrow$$

PHYSICAL PROPERTIES OF THE ELEMENTS

From Figures 1.1 and 1.2, it can be seen that the alkali metals are low melting elements of relatively low density. Table 4.1 lists the melting points and densities of the elements. A tube of solid

TABLE 4.1
Some Physical Properties of the Alakali Metals

Element	Melting Point °C	Density at 20°C
Lithium	186	0.53
Sodium	98	0.97
Potassium	62	0.86
Rubidium	39	1.53
Cesium	26	1.90

cesium would melt if warmed with body heat only. Francium should be a liquid at room temperature.

Notice that the densities do not increase steadily with increasing atomic number; sodium and potassium are reversed. This anomaly is another example of the difference between the elements in the second and third periods of the periodic table and those of the longer periods, a difference which is often neglected though it is pointed out in the von Antropoff table.

All of these metals are very soft and silvery when pure. They are excellent conductors of electricity and heat.

CHEMICAL PROPERTIES AND COMPOUNDS

The alkali metals have a single s electron in the highest quantum level with the remaining electrons arranged in the very stable rare-gas type configuration. Therefore, they have the lowest ionization potentials of any elements and are the most active, or electropositive, of all the metals. With a single valence electron, these elements have oxidation numbers of +1 and 0 only. The +1 state is characterized by the monatomic cations which have a negligible tendency toward covalent bond formation. The 0 oxidation state of the free metals shows a typical metallic lattice in which the valence electrons are free to move about in the lattice. These free electrons give metals their shiny appearance and high conductivities of heat and electricity. The metallic lattice is a third type of solid crystal-line lattice, in addition to the two previously mentioned, ionic and molecular lattices.

Chemical Reactions of the Metals

The alkali metals react with most of the other elements in the periodic table and with many compounds. When they react with nonmetals, ionic compounds result. The reaction with other metals, if it goes, usually results in what are called "intermetallic com-pounds," such as $NaPb$.

All of the alkali metals react spontaneously with all of the halo-gens, violently in most cases:

$$2Me + X_2 \rightarrow 2MeX$$

The elements combine spontaneously with oxygen:

$$4Li + O_2 \qquad \rightarrow 2Li_2O \qquad \text{(white)}$$
$$2Na + O_2 \qquad \rightarrow Na_2O_2 \qquad \text{(yellow)}$$
$$K(Rb, Cs) + O_2 \rightarrow KO_2(RbO_2, CsO_2) \qquad \text{(all highly colored)}$$

Lithium reacts to form the normal oxide, while sodium forms the peroxide, which may be thought of as the normal salt of hydrogen peroxide. The more active potassium, rubidium, and cesium form even higher oxides called superoxides. (The oxidation number of the alkali metals in these compounds is still unity.) The normal oxides of sodium, potassium, rubidium, and cesium are prepared with difficulty from the metal and the corresponding nitrate:

$$10Me + 2MeNO_3 \rightarrow 6Me_2O + N_2$$

Sodium peroxide reacts with water to give sodium hydroxide and hydrogen peroxide. The superoxides with water give the metal hydroxide, hydrogen peroxide, and oxygen. The normal oxides react violently with water to form the soluble hydroxides.

At 200 to 300°C the metals react with hydrogen, yielding the ionic hydrides.

Of the alkali metals, only lithium reacts with nitrogen to form a nitride, Li_3N. In this respect, lithium resembles magnesium more than it does the other alkali metals. This diagonal relationship is discussed in detail in Chapter 8.

When sodium and mercury are mixed, a vigorous reaction takes place which can result in an explosion under certain conditions. The product is a common laboratory reagent, sodium amalgam. The amount of heat liberated in its formation indicates that something more than mere physical mixing of the elements is taking place; that is, that chemical interaction is involved. This product is typical of the reaction of two elements which both have low electron affinities. We have seen that when an element of low electron affinity forms a compound with an element of high electron affinity, the compound is ionic, and that when two elements both of high electron affinity combine, the resulting compound is covalent. The intermetallic compounds resulting from the interaction of elements both of which have low electron affinities have many of the properties of metals; that is, metallic luster and high electrical conductivity in the solid state.

The stoichiometry of intermetallic compounds is not as definite as that of ionic and molecular compounds, for two reasons. First, the ratio in which the elements are combined does not obey normal valence rules, probably because the valence electrons belong to the solid lattice as a whole rather than to individual ions or molecules. Thus, sodium and lead form a series of compounds of formulas $Na_{15}Pb_4$, Na_5Pb_2, Na_2Pb, $NaPb$, $NaPb_3$, Na_4Pb_7, Na_4Pb_9, etc. In the second place, the formula of one of these compounds in many cases represents the ideal average composition, which in fact is only approximated in many preparations. The solid lattice can accommodate a moderate excess of one metal or the other while retaining the structure and properties of the compound. In many other cases the composition varies over such wide limits that it can hardly be said that a compound is formed at all. For example, silver and gold are miscible in all proportions. The latter types are called solid solutions, or more commonly alloys. The alloys and intermetallic compounds are of great commercial interest, but their fundamental nature has been less studied and is less understood than that of ionic and molecular compounds.

Solubility of Compounds

With a few exceptions, the compounds of the alkali metals are all soluble in water. Some react with the water, such as the hydrides and oxides. The others dissolve to give the hydrated ions in solution. They go into solution by virtue of the high dielectric constant of water, about 80 at room temperature, and the hydration of the ions. These ionic compounds are not soluble in nonpolar solvents of low dielectric constant, such as carbon tetrachloride and benzene.

The alkali hydroxides are very soluble in water, yielding strongly basic solutions. These hydroxides are so strong that alkali salts of even very weak acids can be formed. In Table 4.2 are given the solubilities of a few representative salts, expressed in grams of anhydrous salt per 100 grams of water. Again a faint dividing line is noticeable between the typical elements and the subgroup. For example, lithium carbonate, fluoride, and phosphate are insoluble or only slightly soluble, their solubilities resembling those of the corresponding magnesium salts rather than those of the other alkali metals. The solubilities of potassium, rubidium, and cesium alums (e.g., $K_2SO_4 \cdot Al_2(SO_4)_3 \cdot 24H_2O$), perchlorates, and hexachloroplatinates (IV) are much less than those of the same salts of lithium and sodium. These differences are used frequently to effect separations of the alkali metals. Also, many potassium salts are used as reagents in spite of the higher cost of potassium over sodium because of differences in solubility. For instance, potassium permanganate is soluble to the extent of 7 grams per 100 grams of water at 25°C, while sodium permanganate is so soluble that it is difficult to crystallize; for this reason, the potassium salt is made in preference to the sodium salt. On the other hand, since potassium carbonate is more soluble even on a molar basis than sodium carbonate, the former is used when a high concentration of carbonate is desired, as in the metathesis of barium sulfate to barium carbonate.

In general, the solubilities of ammonium salts are about the same as those of potassium salts. All alkali metal and ammonium salts are colorless, except those in which the anion is colored. For example, potassium chromate is yellow, but the color is due to the chromate ion and not the potassium ion.

TABLE 4.2

Solubilities of Some Alkali Metal Salts, Grams of Anhydrous Salt per 100 Grams Water

	Temperature	OH⁻	NO₃⁻	SO₄⁻⁻	Alum*	Cl⁻	F⁻	CO₃⁻⁻	ClO₄⁻	PtCl₆⁻⁻	PO₄⁻⁻⁻
Li⁺	25°C	12.9(30°)	81.9	34.2	no alum	84.7	0.13	1.29	60	—	0.3
	100	17.5	194(71°)	30.7	known	128	—	0.72	245(97°)	—	—
Na⁺	25	119(30°)	90.9	28	131.8	36	4.15	21.5(20°)	211	81.5	14
	100	365(110°)	180	42.5	146.3(30°)	39	5.08	45.5	330	256(98°)	55(75°)
K⁺	25	119	37.3	12.04	14	35.5	102	112	2.04	1.26	96(23°)
	100	187	246	24.1	∞	56.7	150(80°)	156	22.2	5.18	148(45°)
Rb⁺	25	173(30°)	53(20°)	48(20°)	3.12	91(20°)	300(18°)	222(20°)	1.5	0.143	—
	100	—	452	81.8	43.25(80°)	143	—	—	20	0.634	—
Cs⁺	25	300(30°)	28.5	181	0.81	191	585(18°)	262(20°)	2.0	0.095	—
	100	—	197	220	42.54	270.5	—	—	30	0.377	—

* Grams of the hydrate per 100 grams of water.

Sodium and Potassium Hydroxides

The hydroxides of sodium and potassium are compounds of great importance to the economy of the civilized world. They are used in large quantities in the manufacture of soap, the textile industry, and the paper industry. Electrolysis of concentrated brine solutions is the usual method of production:

$$2(Na^+Cl^-) + 2H_2O \xrightarrow{\text{electrolysis}} 2(Na^+OH^-) + H_2\uparrow + Cl_2\uparrow$$

Most of the electrolysis cells in the United States use graphite anodes and steel cathodes, and the solution is electrolyzed until it contains

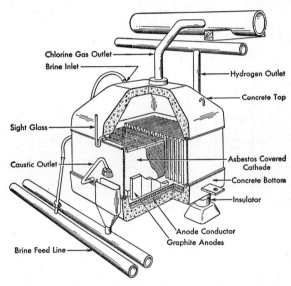

Fig. 4.1 Schematic diagram of diaphragm cell. (Courtesy Hooker Electrochemical Co.)

roughly equal quantities of dissolved sodium chloride and sodium hydroxide. The chlorine is prevented from mixing with the sodium hydroxide by diaphragms. The caustic solution is evaporated, concentrating the sodium hydroxide and salting out the sodium chloride, which is separated by settling. One type of diaphragm cell in current industrial use is illustrated by Figure 4.1. Each of these cells is rated at 7500 amperes capacity; Figure 4.2 shows how many cells are operated in parallel in a single installation. The amalgam cell, Figure 4.3, eliminates this purification procedure by using a mercury cathode in the original electrolysis:

$$2(Na^+Cl^-) + xHg + \text{electrolysis} \rightarrow 2NaHg_x + Cl_2\uparrow$$

Fig. 4.2   Cell house. (Courtesy Hooker Electrochemical Co.)

The sodium is reduced at the mercury surface in preference to the water, due to the high hydrogen overvoltage on mercury and to the lower activity of the sodium when it amalgamates with the mercury (dissolves in the mercury). The amalgam is removed periodically to a separate compartment containing graphite and pure water, where it rapidly reacts to form sodium hydroxide and hydrogen:

$$2NaHg_x + 2HOH \rightarrow 2(Na^+OH^-) + xHg + H_2\uparrow$$

The mercury is recycled to produce more amalgam. In the United States the diaphragm cell is most widely used, whereas the mercury

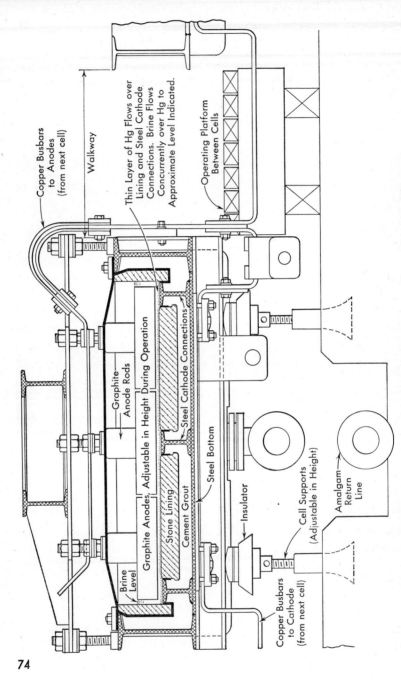

Copper Busbars to Anodes (from next cell)

Walkway

Thin Layer of Hg Flows over Lining and Steel Cathode Connections. Brine Flows Concurrently over Hg to Approximate Level Indicated.

Operating Platform Between Cells

Graphite Anode Rods

Graphite Anodes, Adjustable in Height During Operation

Steel Cathode Connections

Stone Lining

Cement Grout

Steel Bottom

Brine Level

Insulator

Cell Supports (Adjustable in Height)

Amalgam Return Line

Copper Busbars to Cathode (from next cell)

Fig. 4.3 De Nora amalgam cell cross section. (Courtesy Monsanto Chemical Co.)

74

cell is preferred in Europe. Sodium hydroxide and chlorine are coproducts of the electrolysis, and the demand for chlorine more or less controls the supply of electrolytic caustic.

Considerable quantities of "lime soda caustic" are also produced. In this process, excess slaked lime reacts with sodium carbonate,

$$Na_2CO_3 + Ca(OH)_2 \rightarrow CaCO_3\downarrow + 2NaOH$$

to precipitate calcium carbonate, leaving a solution of sodium hydroxide. Of the 3.5 million tons of sodium hydroxide produced in the United States in 1951 about 750,000 tons resulted from the lime-soda method.

Potassium hydroxide can be made by any of these processes.

Sodium Carbonate

About five million tons of sodium carbonate are produced per year in the United States. Since natural deposits of "soda ash" have long since ceased to supply the world's needs, two well-known processes have been developed to produce the substance.

In the LeBlanc process, salt is converted to sodium sulfate by heating with concentrated sulfuric acid,

$$2NaCl + H_2SO_4 \rightarrow Na_2SO_4 + 2HCl\uparrow$$

The sodium sulfate is heated with carbon and limestone in a rotating furnace, where the sulfate is reduced to the sulfide,

$$Na_2SO_4 + 2C \underset{\Delta}{\rightarrow} Na_2S + 2CO_2\uparrow$$

(Many metal sulfates can be reduced to sulfides by heating with carbon.) The sulfide then reacts with the limestone, forming sodium carbonate and calcium sulfide,

$$Na_2S + CaCO_3 \rightarrow Na_2CO_3 + CaS$$

Leaching the cooled product from the furnace with water dissolves the sodium carbonate. The slightly soluble calcium sulfide, along with impurities, is removed by filtration.

In the Solvay process, concentrated brine solutions containing dissolved ammonia are saturated with carbon dioxide under pressure. Sodium hydrogen carbonate precipitates from the solution:

$$NH_3 + CO_2 + HOH \rightleftharpoons NH_4^+HCO_3^-$$
$$NH_4^+HCO_3^- + Na^+Cl^+ \rightleftharpoons NaHCO_3\downarrow + NH_4^+Cl^-$$

Gentle heating of dry sodium hydrogen carbonate yields the normal carbonate,

$$2NaHCO_3 \rightarrow Na_2CO_3 + HOH\uparrow + CO_2\uparrow$$

The mother liquor containing ammonium chloride and unreacted salt is treated with slaked lime to recover the ammonia. Lime kilns are often associated with Solvay plants, since the thermal decomposition of limestone yields lime and carbon dioxide.

$$CaCO_3 \qquad\qquad \rightarrow CaO + CO_2\uparrow$$
$$CaO + HOH \qquad\qquad \rightarrow Ca^{++}2OH^-$$
$$Ca^{++}2OH^- + 2(NH_4^+Cl^-) \rightarrow Ca^{++}2Cl^- + 2NH_3\uparrow + 2HOH$$

The Solvay process has replaced the older LeBlanc process because it not only is more economical but also yields a much purer product. The essential feature of the Solvay process is the relatively slight solubility of sodium hydrogen carbonate in water. Its solubility here is decreased even more by the "salting-out effect" of the ammonium chloride. Potassium hydrogen carbonate is much more soluble, so the process is not at all practical for the potassium salt.

Solutions of sodium carbonate as well as those of sodium hydroxide absorb carbon dioxide readily. The product in both cases is ultimately sodium hydrogen carbonate. This is of some importance in chemical analysis. For example, strong caustic solutions are used to absorb carbon dioxide from gas samples in routine gas analysis. In volumetric analysis, dilute solutions of sodium hydroxide are used as standard solutions in titrating acids. Such solutions must be kept "carbonate free," since carbonates and "bicarbonates" result in incorrect end-points with some indicators.

The Alkali Metals in Liquid Ammonia

Molten sodium reacts rapidly with ammonia to form hydrogen and sodium amide, a reaction that resembles the reaction between sodium and water. At the boiling point of ammonia ($-33°C$), however, sodium can be dissolved in the liquid to form a fairly stable, deep blue solution. That the sodium will react with the solvent can be demonstrated by adding a catalyst, such as iron(III) oxide, whereupon hydrogen is liberated and a colorless dilute solution of sodium amide in liquid ammonia results in about an hour. In the absence of a catalyst, the reaction goes very slowly, and the color remains blue for as much as several weeks. If the solvent is evaporated off, metallic sodium is recovered as the residue. All of the alkali metals and alkaline earth metals dissolve in liquid ammonia to give solutions of the same deep blue color, which indicates that the color is due to the same species in every case. The metals behave as electrolytes in dilute solutions, and it is believed that the ionization proceeds $Na \rightarrow Na^+ + e^-$. The electrons and ions are then highly solvated, $e^- + xNH_3 \rightarrow e^-(NH_3)_x$. As the solutions are concentrated by evaporation, the conductivity approaches that of the pure metal, indicating that the electrons become free to move about without carrying along their ammonias of solvation.

Thus, metal-ammonia solutions behave as though they contained dissolved electrons. They are excellent reducing agents for many organic and inorganic substances. For example, potassium in liquid ammonia reduces $K_2Ni(CN_4)$ to $K_4Ni(CN)_4$, a compound that cannot be prepared in any other way. Liquid ammonia is very hygroscopic, and a dissolved metal reacts with absorbed water to form its hydroxide and hydrogen. In addition, solutions of metals in liquid ammonia absorb oxygen to give oxides, peroxides, and superoxides. Thus, reductions in liquid ammonia must be carried out in the absence of air and water.

Born-Haber Cycle and Lattice Energy of Ionic Crystals

When the alkali metals react with the halogens, ionic crystals are formed, with the evolution of much energy. Table 4.3 shows the measured heat evolved per mole of salt formed, assuming the reaction is carried out at ordinary temperature.

$$Me(s) + \tfrac{1}{2}X_2(g) \rightarrow MeX(s) + heat(Q)$$

TABLE 4.3

Negative* Heats of Formation of Alkali Metal Halides in Kcal per Mole

	F	Cl	Br	I
Li	145	97	87	72
Na	137	98	90	76
K	135	105	97	86
Rb	133	105	99	88
Cs	132	106	101	91

* Recall that in a process evolving heat, the sign is negative by convention.

According to Born and Haber the formation of these alkali metal halides from the elements may be analyzed in steps:

$$
\begin{array}{ccccc}
\mathrm{Na(s)} & \xrightarrow{\text{S}} & \mathrm{Na(g)} & \xrightarrow{\text{I}} & \mathrm{Na^+(g)} \\
+ & & & & + \\
\tfrac{1}{2}\mathrm{Cl_2(g)} & \xrightarrow{\text{D}} & \mathrm{Cl(g)} & \xrightarrow{\text{E}} & \mathrm{Cl^-(g)} \\
\downarrow \text{Q} & & & & \downarrow \text{U} \\
\mathrm{Na^+Cl^-(s)} & & & & \mathrm{Na^+Cl^-(s)}
\end{array}
$$

Here S is the energy needed to vaporize sodium metal, or the heat of sublimation. I is the energy needed to convert gaseous sodium atoms to gaseous ions, or the ionization potential. D is the energy needed to dissociate chlorine molecules into atoms, or the heat of dissociation. E is the energy released when a chlorine atom accepts an electron to become a gaseous chloride ion, or the electron affinity. U is the energy released when gaseous ions of sodium and chlorine condense to form crystals of salt, or the lattice energy.

For a given series of compounds—say, the alkali fluorides—D and E are the same for all five salts. Both S and I decrease from Li through Cs. However, −Q decreases also from LiF → CsF. Now Q = U + E + D + S + I from the law of conservation of energy, where Q, U, and E are negative and D, S, and I are positive. Then −U must decrease from LiF → CsF also.

It is of interest to check the values calculated for Q from the equation against the experimental values from Table 4.2. Values of S and I for all of the alkalies are known, as are values of D and E for the halogens. Then it is necessary only to obtain values of U for the individual salts. To do this, imagine a sodium ion and a chloride ion (assumed to be spheres) approaching each other until they just touch:

$$\oplus \text{-----------}\text{✳}\text{-----------} \ominus$$

The force with which they attract each other is given by Coulomb's Law, $f = \dfrac{e_1 e_2}{r^2}$, where e_1 = charge on Na^+, e_2 = charge on Cl^-, and r = distance between ions. The work done by the ions in moving towards each other from a great distance until they touch is the integral of the force times the distance from infinity to the sum of the two radii.

$$W = \int_\infty^{r_{Na^+} + r_{Cl^-}} f \, dr = \int_\infty^{r_{Na^+} + r_{Cl^-}} \frac{e_1 e_2}{r^2} \, dr = \left[-\frac{e_1 e_2}{r} \right]_\infty^{r_{Na^+} + r_{Cl^-}}$$

$$= -\frac{e_1 e_2}{r_{Na^+} + r_{Cl^-}}$$

For the formation of a mole of $Na^+Cl^-(s)$, $W = -\dfrac{N e_1 e_2}{r_{Na^+} + r_{Cl^-}}$ where $N = 6.02 \times 10^{23}$. This might be called the lattice energy, U, but it must be modified by a closer examination of the crystal. Suppose (see Figure 1.8) that we built up a huge crystal of salt by putting six chloride ions around one sodium ion first. The next step would be to bring in more sodium ions, and so on until a big crystal results. Now the first Na^+ is attracted by all six Cl^- around it, but each Cl^- repels its neighboring Cl^- ion. The new Na^+ ions are then attracted by the Cl^- ions, but repelled by the original Na^+, which modifies the calculation of the work done when they move in to build up the crystal. So, actually $U = -\dfrac{A N e_1 e_2}{r_{Na^+} + r_{Cl^-}}$, where A is Madelung's constant. The constant is a function of the geometry of the crystal lattice; for crystals of the NaCl geometry it has the value 1.75. (For a few more details, see the fourth reference at the end of the chapter, pp. 53–56.)

As an example, let us calculate Q for KCl:

D_{Cl_2} = 58 kcal/mole $D_{\frac{1}{2}Cl_2}$ = 29 kcal/mole

E_{Cl} = −87 kcal/mole

S_K = 20 kcal/mole I_K = 4.32 electron-volts = 99.6 kcal/mole

$$U_{KCl} = -\frac{A N e_1 e_2}{r_{K^+} + r_{Cl^-}} = -\frac{1.75 \times 6.02 \times 10^{23} \times (4.8 \times 10^{-10})^2}{1.33 \times 10^{-8} + 1.81 \times 10^{-8}}$$

$$= -7.7 \times 10^{12} \text{ erg/mole} = -186 \text{ kcal/mole}$$

$$Q = -186 - 87 + 29 + 20 + 100 = -124 \text{ kcal/mole}$$

Thus, it is seen that the lattice energy is the largest single term in the whole cycle and makes the alkali metal halides exothermic compounds. The very high values of U for most ionic lattice type compounds is of further interest. For example, when a mole of KCl is dissolved in water 186 kcal of energy must come from somewhere to break down the lattice and separate the ions. If a onetenth molal solution resulted, 10,000 gm of water must have yielded 186,000 calories or 18.6 cal/gm of water, or enough heat to lower the temperature about 18.6. When one mole KCl is dissolved in 10 kilograms of water, no such cooling effect is observed. It must be concluded that the solution of KCl in water involves something besides the mere physical separation of K^+ ions from Cl^- ions by the water molecules. The hydration of the ions accounts for the observation. The energy released in the hydration of the ions is approximately equal to the energy absorbed in breaking the crystal lattice. For a more detailed discussion of some of the *results* of this hydration, see Chapter 8.

INDUSTRIAL IMPORTANCE OF COMPOUNDS OF THE ALKALI METALS

The basic raw material for all sodium compounds is common salt, the bulk of which is used to produce other chemicals. Between 15 and 20 million tons of salt are processed in this country annually. About one-fifth of the caustic produced is consumed by the rayon and cellophane industry. Roughly another fifth is used to produce other chemicals. Large quantities of caustic are used in petroleum refining, textile processing, pulp and paper production, and soapmaking. Better than half of the annual output of sodium carbonate is used to make glass, sodium hydroxide, and other chemicals. Elementary sodium is used in the production of sodium cyanide and tetraethyl lead.

Agriculture claims the lion's share of potassium compounds, which are mined and processed extensively for use as fertilizers.

SUGGESTIONS FOR FURTHER READING

H. Davy, "The Decomposition of the Fixed Alkalies and Alkaline Earths," *Alembic Club Reprint No. 6*, University of Chicago Press, Chicago, 1902.

H. J. Emeleus and J. S. Anderson, *Modern Aspects of Inorganic Chemistry*, 2nd ed., Routledge and Kegan Paul, London, 1952, Chapter 15.

J. Sherman, *Chemical Reviews*, Vol. 11, p. 107 (1932).

A. E. Van Arkel, *Molecules and Crystals*, translated by J. C. Swallow, Butterworths, London, 1949.

K. A. Kobe, *Inorganic Process Industries*, Macmillan, New York, 1948.

STUDY QUESTIONS

1. Would you expect the lattice energy of barium sulfide to be greater or less than that of cesium chloride? Why?

2. Would you expect the Madelung Constant to be the same for crystals with different coordination numbers? Explain.

3. Show how the heat of formation of lithium fluoride may be calculated via a Born-Haber cycle. What values in the cycle will vary (and how) in the series LiF, LiCl, LiBr, and LiI?

4. Where does the energy come from to break down the lattice of a salt when the salt dissolves in a solvent?

5. Point out the differences between the diaphragm and the amalgam cells.

6. Who first prepared sodium? When? Where? How?

7. What happens when sodium is exposed to dry air? to moist air?

8. What specific differences may be observed between lithium and sodium on the one hand and the Ia elements on the other?

9. What is the formula of an alum?

10. What happens when the following substances are mixed?
    (a) $Cs + H_2O$
    (b) $KH + NH_3$(liquid)
    (c) $KO_2 + H_2O$
    (d) $Rb + O_2$
    (e) $Na_2CO_3 + CO_2$(aqueous)
    (f) $Na_2O_2 + H_2O$.

11. By means of equations and a few words about conditions, show how to carry out the following conversions:
    (a) Make CsOH from CsCl.
    (b) Make NaH from NaOH.
    (c) Make H_2O_2 from H_2O.
    (d) Make Na_2CO_3 from a natural sodium compound.
    (e) Make K_2CO_3 from a natural potassium compound.

Chapter 5

Copper, Silver, and Gold

OCCURRENCE AND HISTORY

Copper is present to the extent of 70 parts per million on the earth's crust, which makes it twenty-fifth in order of abundance. Silver and gold are much less abundant: 0.1 and 0.005 ppm, respectively. In spite of their relatively low abundances, all three of these metals were used at least as far back as 4000 B.C., for the reason that in nature they occur in the metallic state and in compounds which are easily reduced to the metal (usually only heat is necessary). Their long-standing use as currency has given them the name "the coinage metals." In the case of copper, the most important ores are the oxide, sulfide, and carbonate; "native" copper is found occasionally. Silver occurs as the metal about as often as it does in combined form, principally the sulfide. Gold is usually found as the metal.

PREPARATION OF THE ELEMENTS

Since all occur in nature or are easily reduced from their ores, few problems are encountered in the preparation of these metals from high-grade ores. Such problems as do arise fall into the realm of physical metallurgy and industrial chemistry. In the case of copper, increasing demands for the element have necessitated the working of very low-grade ores, where large quantities of earth have to be separated from the ore by oil flotation processes. Copper sulfide is not wet by water, so when an ore is ground with oil and water and air then blown in, it collects on the surface with the oily foam. Most ores of copper are roasted in order to remove any volatile impurities and to convert as many sulfides as possible to the corresponding oxides. The roasted ore is then mixed with coke and sand and heated strongly in a blast furnace. Most of the iron oxide present forms iron silicate and goes into the slag. The remaining iron and copper sulfides are found under the slag and are poured

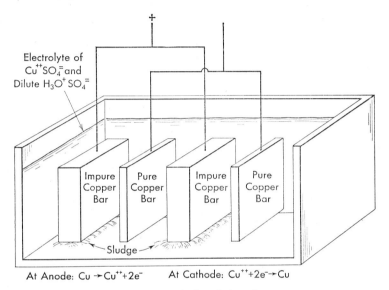

+

Electrolyte of
$Cu^{++}SO_4^=$ and
Dilute $H_3O^+ SO_4^=$

| Impure Copper Bar | Pure Copper Bar | Impure Copper Bar | Pure Copper Bar |

Sludge

At Anode: $Cu \rightarrow Cu^{++} + 2e^-$ At Cathode: $Cu^{++} + 2e^- \rightarrow Cu$

Fig. 5.1 Electrolytic refining of copper.

into a converter lined with clay, where air is blasted through the melt, converting all iron sulfide to the oxide. This oxide combines with the lining to form a slag, which can be removed. Following the removal of the iron impurity, the remaining liquid, containing copper and copper sulfide, is further blasted with air, and all copper sulfide is converted to copper and sulfur dioxide. The liquid is poured into molds and cast as "blister copper," named after the appearance of its surface when bubbles of SO_2 are evolved upon cooling. The bars of blister copper are usually further purified by electrolysis; Figure 5.1. The impure copper is used as anode, and pure copper is obtained at the cathode with dilute solutions of sulfuric acid as electrolyte. If the voltage is carefully regulated, metals less active than copper will not go into solution at the anode but will collect in the bottom of the cells as anode sludges. These sludges are worked over to recover appreciable quantities of silver, gold, selenium, and tellurium—valuable by-products which reduce the cost of very pure copper. Furthermore, exact control of voltage allows only copper to plate out at the cathode, any more active metals remaining in solution. By this process 99.9 per cent pure copper is obtained.

Since gold and silver occur in much lower concentrations, the concentration or extraction of these metals presents different problems. The latest processes for the extraction of both of these metals involve the use of dilute solutions of sodium cyanide. In the presence of oxygen both silver and gold are dissolved:

$$4Au + 8CN^- + O_2 + 2H_2O \rightarrow 4Au(CN)_2^- + 4OH$$
$$4Ag + 8CN^- + O_2 + 2H_2O \rightarrow 4Ag(CN)_2^- + 4OH^-$$
$$Ag_2S + 4CN^- + \tfrac{1}{2}O_2 + H_2O \rightarrow 2Ag(CN)_2^- + S + 2OH^-$$

The remaining impurities may be filtered off and the solution worked for the metals by reduction with an active metal, such as zinc or aluminum.

In ancient times, and occasionally today, silver was obtained from its ores by cupellation. The process consists of roasting a lead compound with the silver ore, yielding an alloy of lead and silver. The alloy is placed in a cupel (a small cup made of bone ash) and heated in an air blast. The lead is oxidized to litharge, PbO, which melts and is swept out by the air blast, leaving a button of pure silver behind.

PHYSICAL PROPERTIES OF THE ELEMENTS

Copper, silver, and gold are much denser and have much higher melting and boiling points than the alkali metals. Commercially, the most important physical property of copper is its high electrical conductivity (see Table 5.1). Also important are the high ductility and malleability of all of these metals, which makes them easy to work in the production of wires, coinage, and jewelry. It is of interest that copper and gold are the only two *metals* in the entire periodic table that are highly colored.

TABLE 5.1

Electrical Conductivity of Some Common Metals Compared with Copper As 100 at 20°C

Silver	104
Copper	100
Gold	70
Aluminum	65
Sodium	37
Tungsten	31
Zinc	28
Iron	17
Platinum	16
Tin	15
Mercury	8
Lead	8

CHEMICAL PROPERTIES AND COMPOUNDS

These elements have the outer electron structure $(n - 1)d^{10}ns^1$, and so we expect and find an oxidation state of $+1$. However, even though the inner d sublevel is full, it can lose electrons to give higher valencies. In none of the succeeding B subgroups can the d orbitals lose electrons to form chemical compounds, and so the outer transition series of elements end with copper, silver, and gold. Thus, we arrive at the chemical definition of an outer transition element: an element whose valence electrons can come from two different principal quantum levels.

Copper forms two series of compounds, the copper(I) and the copper(II). The copper(I) ion exists only in minute concentration in solution, and all copper(I) compounds either are insoluble or have the metal tied up in a stable complex ion. There are many soluble and insoluble copper(II) compounds. With silver, on the other hand, the $+1$ state is the only common one. A few $+2$ compounds and one $+3$ compound exist, but they are unstable and powerful oxidizing agents. Silver in no way can be said to be intermediate between copper and gold, for with gold there are again two oxidation states of about equal stability, the $+1$ and $+3$. The former resembles copper(I) in that it exists in insoluble or complex compounds only. The latter forms covalent bonds only and does not exist as the free ion.

All of the oxidation states of these elements have a strong tendency towards covalent bond formation. This is in accordance with their non-rare-gas type of electron configuration, as stated in Fajans' fourth rule. Thus, the resemblance between the coinage metals and the alkali metals is slight, being limited merely to the value of the $+1$ oxidation state. The characteristics even of the $+1$ compounds are very different in the two subgroups, and there is no counterpart in the A subgroup of the higher valences in the B subgroup. The coinage metals form many stable complex compounds, while the alkali metals do not. The coordination number is variable; the most common are 2 for Cu^I, Ag^I, Au^I and 4 for Cu^{II}, Ag^{II}, Au^{III}.

Complex Ion Formation

Before taking up the detailed chemistry of the coinage metals, we must first look more closely at complex ion formation. A familiar example from qualitative analysis is the formation of the soluble diamminesilver ion when ammonia water is added to silver chloride:

$$\underline{AgCl} + 2NH_3 \rightarrow Ag(NH_3)_2{}^+ + Cl^-$$

A complex ion then is an ion made up of several atoms held together by chemical bonds. Generally, there is one atom in the center of the complex, the central atom, which is surrounded by the complexing groups, the ligands. The whole complex ion then bears a charge which is the sum of the charges of the groups that associated to form it.

The question immediately arises of how complex ions differ from radicals, such as the sulfate ion, defined on p. 27. In actual fact there is no fundamental difference between the two, but the different names are sometimes used to indicate a difference in the manner of formation and dissociation. Thus, the sulfate ion is not formed from a S^{++++++} ion (which does not exist) and four O^{--} ions, nor does it dissociate to any extent to give oxide ions. The diamminesilver ion, on the other hand, is formed from the Ag^+ ion and two NH_3 molecules, and it is dissociated, albeit slightly, into its components. The latter fact is also made use of in qualitative analysis when silver chloride is reprecipitated from ammoniacal solution by the addition of acid:

$$Ag(NH_3)_2 \rightleftharpoons Ag^+ + 2NH_3$$

$$+ \qquad\qquad +$$
$$Cl^- \qquad\qquad 2H^+$$

$$\downarrow\uparrow \qquad\qquad \downarrow\uparrow$$

$$\underline{AgCl} \qquad 2N\overset{}{H_4^+}$$

There are many other groups which will act as ligands. We have already seen that ionic compounds dissolve in water by virtue of the hydration of the ions. Hydration of this sort involves water as a ligand.* Other common ligands are the halide and pseudohalide ions, the nitrite ion, and the thiosulfate ion. In addition, there are a number of ligands which form more than one bond to the central atom, such as ethylenediamine (abbreviated en),

$$CH_2—CH_2$$
$$| \qquad |$$
$$NH_2 \quad NH_2$$

It forms two bonds to the central atom through the two nitrogen atoms. This type of ligand is called a "chelate" (Greek *chele* for claw). For example, copper(II) ion usually has a coordination number of four in complexes, so that it gives with ammonia the tetramminecopper(II) ion, $Cu(NH_3)_4^{2+}$, with the planar structure:

$$NH_3$$
$$|$$
$$H_3N—Cu—NH_3$$
$$|$$
$$NH_3$$

Only two ethylenediamine molecules coordinate with the copper(II) ion, but each of these bidentate (Greek for two-toothed) ligands satisfies two coordination positions to give the bisethylenediaminecopper(II) ion, $Cu(en)_2^{2+}$, with the planar structure:

$$CH_2—NH_2 \quad H_2N—CH_2$$
$$| \qquad\quad \diagdown \diagup \qquad |$$
$$\qquad\qquad Cu$$
$$| \qquad\quad \diagup \diagdown \qquad |$$
$$CH_2—NH_2 \quad H_2N—CH_2$$

* All the water molecules in solid hydrates are not necessarily bound to the cation as ligands. For instance, in $CuSO_4\cdot5H_2O$, four water molecules act as ligands to the copper(II) ion, while the fifth takes a lattice position between the tetraaquocopper(II) ions and the sulfate ions. The formula is most properly written, $Cu(H_2O)_4SO_4\cdot H_2O$.

Another common bidentate ligand is the oxalate ion: in rarer instances, the sulfate and carbonate ions will act as chelating groups.

The type of bonding in complex compounds can be either ionic or covalent. Thus, in the hydrated sodium ion the attraction is mainly electrostatic between the cation and the water dipoles, while in the hexaaquochromium(III) ion the six water molecules are held covalently to the central atom. Also, the bonding is covalent in $Fe(CN)_6^{---}$, but ionic in FeF_6^{---}. The determination of the type of bonding is a subject for more advanced study. It is sufficient for the present purpose to know that in complex compounds the central atom and its ligands are bound together as a unit. The relative stability of the unit can be rationalized according to Fajans' rules. Thus, we would expect an easily polarized anion, such as iodide, to be a better complexing agent than a smaller anion, such as chloride. Of course, steric factors enter into the stability also in a way which is difficult to predict. If the central atom has a large polarizing power, complete transfer of electrons may take place with easily polarized ligands. For example, copper(II) ion forms a chloro complex, but the iodo complex decomposes into copper(I) iodide and iodine.

When a complex is formed, energy is released, and the resulting compound is more stable than its components. This stabilization is reflected in the oxidation potential of the element (see below). For example, the silver(II) ion in AgF_2 is a powerful oxidizing agent, liberating ozone from water. When complexed with pyridine, C_5H_5N, however, to give the $Ag(C_5H_5N)_4^{++}$ ion, it is stable in water. Other unstable oxidation states of many metals can exist only in complex compounds; for example, Mn^I in $K_5Mn(CN)_6$.

Practically all of the elements in the periodic table will form complex compounds, but the tendency is most marked in the later transition elements and in the elements immediately following the transition elements. It is expected that the elements in the center of the periodic table will form the most complexes because of their non-rare-gas type of configuration. Thus, the Ca^{++} and Cd^{++} ions are of equal charge and very nearly equal size, yet complex ions of cadmium are more numerous and more stable than those of calcium.

Chemical Reactions of the Elements

These metals are not nearly as electropositive as the alkali metals; they are relatively inert chemically. The inertness increases from copper to gold, so that objects of gold retain their luster for years. Since they are all below hydrogen in the E.M.F. series of the elements, they do not release hydrogen from dilute acid solution. Neither are they attacked by bases. Copper will dissolve slowly in hot, concentrated hydrochloric acid, however, because the reaction is driven to completion by the removal of the copper(I) ions when they are complexed by the excess chloride:

$$2Cu + 4HCl \rightarrow 2HCuCl_2 + H_2$$
$$\text{(and other chlorocuprate(I) complexes)}$$

Copper also corrodes rapidly in the presence of ammonia and air, again by virtue of complex ion formation. Copper and silver dissolve in oxidizing acids: slowly in hot, concentrated sulfuric acid, with the evolution of SO_2; readily in cold, dilute nitric acid, with the evolution of NO. Gold resists even hot, concentrated nitric acid, and it takes aqua regia (three parts concentrated HCl to one part concentrated HNO_3) to bring it into solution:

$$Au + 4HCl + 3HNO_3 \rightarrow HAuCl_4 + 3NO_2 + 3H_2O$$

Gold will also dissolve in chlorine water, probably to form soluble chlorohydroxoaurate(III) complexes: $AuCl_4^-$, $AuCl_3OH^-$, etc.

The halogens react with all of these elements, the nature of the product depending upon the temperature and the relative amounts of the reactants. Copper with limited chlorine gives copper(I) chloride and with excess chlorine at moderate temperatures (about 500°C) gives copper(II) chloride. At higher temperatures, the $CuCl_2$ is unstable and decomposes into CuCl and Cl_2. Only AgCl is produced from silver and chlorine, while gold gives gold(III) chloride at about 200°C and gold(I) chloride above that temperature. Fluorine is strong enough an oxidizing agent to convert silver to silver(II) fluoride. Iodine, on the other hand, gives the +1 iodide in all three cases, owing to the instability of the higher iodides, even at room temperature. Oxygen attacks copper only, yielding black copper(II) oxide at moderate temperatures and red copper(I) oxide above red heat. If the latter is cooled in air, it absorbs oxygen, forming the black oxide. Molten silver dissolves oxygen, but the gas is evolved upon freezing, leaving pockets in the solid. When heated in sulfur, copper and silver are converted to copper(I) or copper(II) sulfides, depending on the relative amounts of the two elements, and to silver sulfide. The latter compound is so very insoluble in water that it is produced by the action of moist hydrogen sulfide on silver:

$$2Ag + H_2S \rightarrow Ag_2S + H_2$$

Black silver sulfide is the tarnish which discolors cutlery. It is formed from minute amounts of sulfur compounds in the atmosphere and in food.

Univalent Compounds

Many compounds of copper, silver, and gold in the +1 state are quite similar. For example, the chlorides, bromides, iodides, and pseudo-halides* are all insoluble in water. Silver(I) fluoride is soluble, however, which by analogy account for the fact that pure copper(I) and gold(I) fluorides have not been prepared. That is, copper(I) fluoride would be soluble, but soluble simple copper(I) salts are unstable. Many soluble complex +1 compounds of all three elements can be made. The important difference in the univalent compounds is that many soluble silver salts can be made for which there are no corresponding copper(I) and gold(I) compounds.

Copper(I) halides are usually prepared by reducing the soluble copper(II) salt in the presence of the halide ions. The reducing agent can be copper, sulfur dioxide, or, in the case of the iodide and cyanide, the iodide and cyanide ions themselves:

$$Cu + CuCl_2 + 2HCl \rightarrow 2HCuCl_2$$
$$\text{(and other chlorocuprate(I) complexes)}$$
$$HCuCl_2 \xrightarrow{\text{dilution}} CuCl\downarrow + HCl$$
$$2CuSO_4 + 4KCN \rightarrow 2CuCN\downarrow + (CN)_2 + 2K_2SO_4$$

* The pseudo-halides are uninegative radicals which resemble the halide ions in their properties. Common examples are: cyanide, CN^-; cyanate and thiocyanate, OCN^- and SCN^-; azide, N_3^-.

The copper(I) halides are white. Solid copper(I) chloride has the zincblende structure, with 4:4 coordination (see Chapter 12). Its formula is best written CuCl. In the older literature it is sometimes seen written as Cu_2Cl_2, because the vapor is appreciably associated. There is no evidence for the dimerized ion, Cu_2^{++}, however, as there is for the diatomic mercury(I) ion, Hg_2^{++}, and so we write CuCl and Hg_2Cl_2 to show that the structures are different. The copper atoms are held together by two chlorine bridging atoms *in the vapor phase only*, while the mercury atoms are bonded directly to one another by a covalent bond in all phases and in solution. CuCl is soluble in complexing agents:

$$CuCl + 2NH_3 \rightarrow Cu(NH_3)_2^+ + Cl^-$$
$$CuCl + 4CN^- \rightarrow Cu(CN)_4^{---} + Cl^-$$
$$CuCl + 2Cl^- \rightarrow CuCl_3^{--}$$

Copper(I) oxide is a brick-red, insoluble compound prepared by reducing copper(II) complexes in basic solution. The appearance of its colored precipitate is used as a test for reducing sugars in Fehling's solution (an alkaline solution of copper(II) sulfate and Rochelle salt, sodium potassium tartrate, $NaKC_4H_4O_6 \cdot 4H_2O$). It dissolves in complexing media to give copper(I) complexes, but if one tries to prepare a simple salt from it by the addition of a non-complexing acid, disproportionation to copper(II) and copper metal results:

$$Cu_2O + H_2SO_4 \rightarrow CuSO_4 + Cu + H_2O$$

Insoluble silver salts, such as the halides, are made by adding a soluble halide to a solution of silver nitrate. In contrast to the copper(I) halides, there is a color gradation in the silver halides. Silver chloride is white, the bromide is a very pale yellow, and the iodide yellow. The solubility decreases with increasing atomic weight of the halide: AgCl > AgBr > AgI, with the pseudo-halides falling between the bromide and the iodide. In photography, film is fixed by dissolving out the unexposed silver halides with "hypo," sodium thiosulfate:

$$AgBr + 2S_2O_3^{--} \rightarrow Ag(S_2O_3)_2^{---} + Br^-$$

Ammonia forms a complex with silver ion which is stable enough to dissolve the chloride, but not the very insoluble iodide. The cyano complex is strong enough so that all the halides dissolve in a cyanide solution. Soluble silver salts can be made either from the metal, as is done for silver nitrate, or by precipitating brown, insoluble silver oxide from silver nitrate plus a strong base, filtering, and reacting the oxide with the suitable acid.

Gold(I) salts are made in similar fashion to the copper(I) compounds, or merely by heating gold(III) compounds:

$$AuCl_3 \xrightarrow{\Delta} AuCl + Cl_2$$

Higher Valence Compounds

In addition to direct synthesis, copper(II) oxide is also formed when a strong base is added to a hot solution of a simple copper(II) salt. The oxide does not absorb water to form the hydroxide, but the hydroxide can be produced by the addition of alkali to the copper(II) salt at room temperature. The hydroxide is blue-green in color and easily loses water to go to the black oxide; it is basic only, although in small quantity it is peptized by excess caustic to give a deep blue colloidal solution which is sometimes referred to as sodium cuprate. The hydroxide is also precipitated by ammonia, but it dissolves in excess to give a complex:

$$Cu^{++} + 2NH_3 + 2H_2O \rightarrow \underline{Cu(OH)_2} + 2NH_4^+$$
$$\underline{Cu(OH)_2} + 4NH_3 \quad \rightarrow \overline{Cu(NH_3)_4^{++}} + 2OH^-$$

Both the hydroxide and the oxide react with most of the common acids to form soluble salts. The simple copper(II) salts crystallize from aqueous solution as hydrates. $CuSO_4 \cdot 5H_2O$ is light blue and is called by the trivial name of "blue vitriol." $Cu(NO_3)_2 \cdot 6H_2O$ is blue also, whereas $CuCl_2 \cdot 2H_2O$ and $CuBr_2 \cdot 4H_2O$ are green. Thermal dehydration of the hydrated halides is difficult, since partial hydrolysis to basic salts takes place at relatively low temperature, and complete hydrolysis to the oxide occurs at elevated temperature:

$$CuCl_2 \cdot 2H_2O \xrightarrow{\Delta} CuO + 2HCl\uparrow + H_2O\uparrow$$

Dehydration to the anhydrous chloride can be accomplished by heating the hydrate in a stream of dry HCl gas. The blue hydrated sulfate is easily converted to the white anhydrous salt by heat alone, because H_2SO_4 is much less volatile than HCl.

Copper(II) sulfide is a black substance, insoluble in water. It precipitates from solution when hydrogen sulfide is passed into a dilute acid solution containing copper(II) ions. The addition of aqueous ammonia to any soluble copper(II) salt gives an intense deep blue color, due to the formation of the tetramminecopper(II) ion:

$$Cu^{++} + 4NH_3 \rightarrow Cu(NH_3)_4^{++}$$

This reaction is frequently used as a qualitative test for the presence of divalent copper. Indeed, it can be used to determine the amount of copper present by measuring the intensity of the color.

Silver forms a few compounds in which it exhibits an oxidation number of $+2$. The most common of these are silver(II) oxide, formed by the action of potassium peroxydisulfate on silver nitrate in alkaline medium or by anodic oxidation of silver ion, and silver(II) fluoride, formed by direct synthesis. They are both powerful oxidizing agents.

When gold is dissolved in either aqua regia or chlorine water, the solution evaporated and the residue heated just over 100°C, red gold(III) chloride results. The anhydrous trichloride can also be made by direct synthesis. The tendency of trivalent gold to form four covalent bonds is so great that the trichloride exists as a dimer:

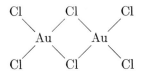

It is soluble in hydrochloric acid to form the complex tetrachloroauric(III) acid, $HAuCl_4$. The addition of a limited amount of base to the solution precipitates gold(III) hydroxide, which is soluble in complexing acids and excess base:

$$Au(OH)_3 + 4HCl \rightarrow HAuCl_4 + 3H_2O$$
$$\overline{Au(OH)_3 + OH^- \rightarrow Au(OH)_4^-}$$

Trivalent gold is easily reduced to the univalent state or to the metal. The trichloride decomposes into gold(I) chloride and chlorine above 200°C. At higher temperature, all the chlorine is lost. Hydrogen gas reduces tetrachloroauric(III) acid in solution to gold. If potassium iodide is added to the solution, gold(I) iodide precipitates:

$$HAuCl_4 + 3KI \rightarrow \underline{AuI} + I_2 + 3KCl + HCl$$

OXIDATION-REDUCTION POTENTIALS

We have seen that copper, silver, and gold do not release hydrogen from dilute acid solutions because they are below hydrogen in the E.M.F. series of the elements (Table 1.5). With elements such as these, however, which form many insoluble compounds and complexes, the concentration of the metal ion can be changed so drastically that reactions will go that would not be predicted by a cursory glance at the Standard E.M.F.'s. The relation between the E.M.F. of a reaction and the concentrations of the species involved is given by the Nernst equation:

$$E = E^0 - 2.303 \frac{RT}{nF} \log Q$$

$$= E^0 - \frac{0.059}{n} \log Q \quad \text{at } 25°C$$

where E is the E.M.F. under any conditions: E^0 is the Standard E.M.F. where all substances are at unit concentration—i.e., $Q = 1$; R is the gas constant; T is the absolute temperature; n is the number of electrons transferred; F is the faraday; and Q is the quotient of the product of the concentrations of the products each raised to the power given by their coefficients in the reaction to the product of the concentrations of the reactants each raised to the power given by their coefficients in the reaction.

For example, the E.M.F. of the half-reaction, $Cu = Cu^+ + e^-$, is:

$$E = -0.521 - 0.059 \log [Cu^+]$$

Actually the concentration of free copper(I) ions can never get to unity, so that $E^0 = -0.521v$ is a measure of an experimentally impossible situation. If chloride ions are present, the copper is tied up in an insoluble precipitate, $Cu^+ + Cl^- = CuCl$, for which $K_{SP} = 3.2 \times 10^{-7}$, or with an excess of chloride it is tied up in a complex, $Cu^+ + 2Cl^- = CuCl_2^-$, for which $K = \dfrac{[CuCl_2^-]}{[Cu^+][Cl^-]^2} = 2 \times 10^5$. Thus, there are very few free copper(I) ions when appreciable amounts of chloride are present. Then the half-reaction, $Cu = Cu^+ + e^-$, is shifted to the right, and E becomes larger because $[Cu^+]$ becomes smaller. Two other half-reactions can then be written:

for dilute chloride, $\quad\quad Cu + Cl^- = CuCl + e^-$, $E^0 = -0.137v$

for concentrated chloride, $Cu + 2Cl^- = CuCl_2^- + e^-$, $E^0 = -0.21v$

Thus, copper does not dissolve appreciably in 1 m HCl because the potentials are still below zero. However, in concentrated HCl— say, 10 m—the E.M.F. of the reaction:

$$Cu + H^+ + 2Cl^- = CuCl_2^- + \tfrac{1}{2}H_2$$

is positive even when $[CuCl_2^-]$ is as high as 0.1 m* (assuming H_2 concentration of unity):

$$E = E^0 - 0.059 \log \frac{[H_2]^{\frac{1}{2}}[CuCl_2^-]}{[H^+][Cl^-]^2}$$

$$= -0.21 - 0.059 \log \frac{0.1}{10^3} = +0.03v$$

Thus, copper will dissolve in 10 m HCl until its concentration is greater than 0.1 m.

The cyano complex of copper(I) is much more stable than the chloro complex, and so many fewer copper(I) ions exist in solution in equilibrium with it. Thus, it is seen in Table 5.2 that E^0 for the half-reaction producing $Cu(CN)_2^-$ is positive. Likewise, silver releases hydrogen from hydriodic acid because the formation of the very insoluble silver iodide reduces the concentration of the silver ions to a very small value.

Standard E.M.F.'s must then be used with caution in the prediction of chemical behavior. The condition of unit concentration

* The calculation is not exact unless activities are used instead of molalities. See footnote on page 32.

might be highly artificial, and account must therefore be taken of the actual species present in the solution.

TABLE 5.2
Standard Potentials of the Coinage Metals under Various Conditions

Half-Reaction	E^0
$Cu + 2CN^- = Cu(CN)_2^- + e^-$	0.43v
$Ag + I^- = \underline{AgI} + e^-$	0.151
$\frac{1}{2}H_2 = H^+ + e^-$	0.0000
$Cu + Cl^- = \underline{CuCl} + e^-$	−0.137
$Cu + 2Cl^- = \overline{CuCl_2^-} + e^-$	−0.21
$Ag + Cl^- = \underline{AgCl} + e^-$	−0.222
$Cu = Cu^{++} + 2e^-$	−0.337
$Cu = Cu^+ + e^-$	−0.521
$Au + 4CNS^- = Au(CNS)_4^- + 3e^-$	−0.66
$Ag = Ag^+ + e^-$	−0.7991
$Au = Au^{+++} + 3e^-$	−1.50
$Au = Au^+ + e^-$	−1.68

USES

Copper is used largely for electrical transmission. Small amounts of impurities greatly reduce its conductivity, as is shown in Figure 5.2, and so most of the copper produced is purified by electrolysis. Copper is also an important component of many alloys: brass, 4 parts Cu to 1 part Zn; bronze, 9 Cu to 1 Sn; monel metal, 7 Cu to 3 Ni. These alloys are more useful for fabrication uses, since they are all harder than pure copper. Copper kitchen utensils take advantage of the high heat conductivity and relative inertness of the metal.

For thousands of years silver and gold have been used to make coins and jewelry. Articles of pure silver or gold would be impractical because of the softness of both elements. They are alloyed with other metals, such as copper, in order to give them the needed strength to withstand the everyday use that coins and jewelry get. The purity of gold is measured in carats: 24K = pure gold.

With the advent of photography, silver has become useful as well as ornamental. The light-sensitive material in the emulsion of black-and-white film is mainly silver bromide, which is decomposed into the elements by light.

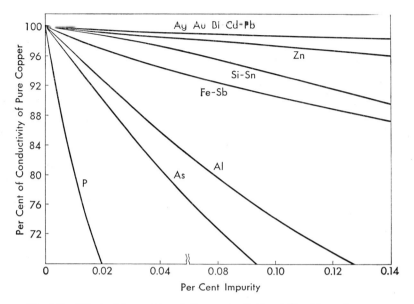

Fig. 5.2 Effect of impurities of the conductivity of Cu. (From Lawrence Addicks, Chem. and Met. Eng. *22*, 449, 1920.)

SUGGESTIONS FOR FURTHER READING

W. M. Latimer and J. H. Hildebrand, *Reference Book of Inorganic Chemistry*, 3rd ed., Macmillan, New York, 1951, Chapter VII.

W. M. Latimer, *Oxidation Potentials*, 2nd ed., Prentice-Hall, New York, 1952.

J. R. Partington, *Textbook of Inorganic Chemistry*, 6th ed., Macmillan London, 1950, Chapters XXXVII and XL.

M. E. Weeks, *Discovery of the Elements*, Journal of Chemical Education, Easton, Pa., 1956, Chapter I.

STUDY QUESTIONS

1. What happens when the following substances are mixed?
   (a) Au + conc. HNO_3 + conc. HCl
   (b) $CuCl$ + NH_3(aqueous)
   (c) AgI + NH_3(aqueous)
   (d) Cu + $CuSO_4$ + H_2SO_4
   (e) Au + O_2 + $NaCN$(aqueous)

2. Write balanced equations to show what happens when:
   (a) tetramminecopper(II) sulfate is treated with excess aqueous potassium cyanide.
   (b) air is blown through an ammoniacal solution of copper(I) chloride, turning the solution blue.
   (c) copper is dissolved in hot dilute nitric acid.
   (d) zinc is added to a solution of dicyanoaurate(I) ion.
3. Name the transition elements of the fourth period.
4. Why is it not possible to prepare CuI_2 and AuI_3?
5. By means of equations and a few words about conditions, show how to carry out the following conversions:
   (a) Make $K_3Cu(CN)_4$ from CuO.
   (b) Make $CuSO_4 \cdot 5H_2O$ from Cu.
   (c) Make Ag from Ag_2S.
   (d) Make $AuCl$ from Au.
   (e) Make $CuCl$ from a natural copper compound.
   (f) Make AgF from $AgNO_3$.
6. What oxidation states are exhibited by the coinage metals?
7. A metal ion is known to form a stable complex ion with the cyanide ion. How would the addition of $NaCN$ to a solution of this metal ion influence its electrode potential?
8. What are the three metals of highest electrical conductivity?
9. Name three reagents that will dissolve copper(I) chloride. Write balanced equations for the reactions.
10. List $CuCl$, $CuBr$, and CuI in order of increasing solubility.
11. Show how aqueous ammonia dissolves copper(II) oxide.
12. Given: $Cu = Cu^+ + e^-$, $E^0 = -0.521v$; $Cu + Cl^- = \underline{CuCl}$, $K_{SP} = 3.2 \times 10^{-7}$; $Cu + 2Cl^- = CuCl_2^-$, $K = 2 \times 10^5$.
    Calculate: E^0 for $Cu + Cl^- = \underline{CuCl} + e^-$ and E^0 for $Cu + 2Cl^- = CuCl_2^- + e^-$.

Chapter 6

Calcium, Strontium, Barium, and Radium

OCCURRENCE AND HISTORY

The group IIa elements are called the alkaline-earth metals. Sometimes magnesium is included as a member of the family, but it will not be discussed under that name in this text. For many years the oxides of the elements were thought to be elementary. Nonmetallic substances slightly soluble in water and unchanged by fire were called earths. Thus the oxides of the IIa elements were designated as earths. Later it was discovered that these earths give an alkaline reaction, and since then they have been called alkaline-earths.

None of the elements is found naturally in the free state, although many of their compounds are very abundant, making up some of the minerals most available to man. Limestone ($CaCO_3$) has been mined in many places on the earth for centuries. It is the most abundant mineral of calcium. Another commonly occurring form of calcium carbonate is marble. Gypsum ($CaSO_4 \cdot 2H_2O$), witherite ($BaCO_3$), strontianite ($SrCO_3$), heavyspar ($BaSO_4$), and fluorspar (CaF_2) are other minerals occurring in sufficient quantities to serve as sources of the elements. Dolomite ($CaCO_3 \cdot MgCO_3$) deposits are widespread also.

Radium is estimated to comprise only 10^{-10} per cent of the earth's crust. The important isotope is of mass number 226. It is radioactive, with a half-life of about 1600 years, and occurs in pitch-blende (impure U_3O_8) as a member of the decomposition series starting with uranium 238. Pitchblende used to be worked for its radium content for use in radiotherapy, with uranium as a by-product. Now, with the development of atomic bombs and atomic power, radium is a by-product of uranium extraction. About a kilogram of radium had been recovered from ores by 1950.

PREPARATION OF THE ELEMENTS

The most common method of preparing the elements is by the electrolysis of the fused halides. For example, the electrolysis of calcium chloride to which a little calcium fluoride has been added produces calcium at the iron cathode and chlorine at the carbon

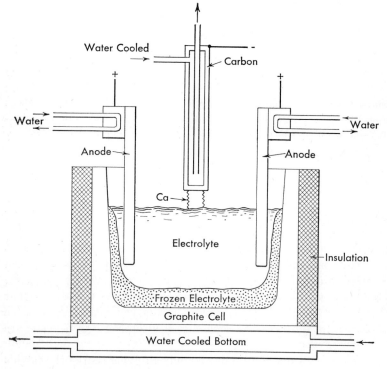

Fig. 6.1 Electrolytic preparation of calcium.

anode. The calcium plates onto the cathode in the solid state since the cells are operated somewhat below the melting point of the metal (see Figure 6.1). The metals are also deposited into a mercury cathode from aqueous solutions of their salts. The pure metal can be recovered by distilling the mercury off of the amalgam, the original method of isolation used by Sir Humphrey Davy in 1808. The latter method is impractical because of the difficulty of removing the last amounts of mercury.

PHYSICAL PROPERTIES OF THE ELEMENTS

These metals are relatively soft and ductile, with much higher melting points than the alkali metals. They are fair conductors of electricity, and all are denser than water.

CHEMICAL PROPERTIES AND COMPOUNDS

From the electronic configurations of these elements, it is expected that they will be very reactive. Indeed, they all lose two electrons easily to form dipositive ions of the preceding rare-gas type. The anticipated increase in electropositivity with increasing atomic weight in the group is observed. There is very little tendency towards covalent bond formation, and only in rare instances are complex compounds formed by the ions. The ions are colorless, and all compounds are white except those containing a colored anion.

Chemical Reactions of the Elements

The prediction of great chemical activity is borne out by the fact that these elements react readily with water, oxygen, sulfur, and the halogens:

$$Me + 2H_2O \rightarrow Me(OH)_2 + \overline{H}_2$$
$$2Me + O_2 \rightarrow 2MeO \text{ (peroxides may also form; see below)}$$
$$Me + S \rightarrow MeS$$
$$Me + X_2 \rightarrow MeX_2$$

The reactions are not as rapid nor as violent as are the corresponding reactions of the alkali metals, but they are sufficiently rapid so that the metals cannot be kept in air for any appreciable length of time. The elements also combine with nitrogen, hydrogen, and carbon at high temperature:

$$3Me + N_2 \rightarrow Me_3N_2$$
$$Me + H_2 \rightarrow MeH_2$$
$$Me + 2C \rightarrow MeC_2$$

The products are ionic compounds containing the N^{---}, H^-, and C_2^{--} ions, respectively, which give with water NH_3, H_2, and C_2H_2.

Oxides and Peroxides

The alkaline-earth metals form two series of binary oxygen compounds. The oxides are strongly basic, the basicity increasing with increasing atomic weight in the sub-group. This increase is illustrated by the relative affinities of the oxides for the acidic carbon dioxide in the reversible decomposition of the carbonates:

$$MeCO_3 \rightleftharpoons MeO + \overline{CO_2}$$

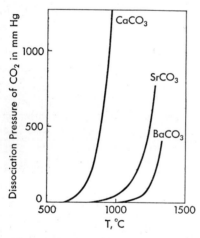

Fig. **6.2** Dissociation pressure of CO_2 over alkaline-earth carbonates.

Figure 6.2 shows the pressure of CO_2 in equilibrium with a mixture of carbonate and oxide as a function of the temperature. Since the barium ion is the largest of the three and hence the most electro-positive, its oxide is the most basic and shows the greatest affinity for carbon dioxide.

Calcium oxide can easily be prepared by heating the carbonate in a stream of air or steam to remove the CO_2. Strontium oxide is more difficult to prepare in this manner, and for barium oxide the method is impractical. Strontium and barium oxides are generally made by heating a mixture of the carbonates and carbon or by heating the nitrates to bright red heat in order to decompose any peroxides that may form:

$$BaCO_3 + C \xrightarrow{\Delta} BaO + 2\overline{CO}$$

$$Ba(NO_3)_2 \xrightarrow{\Delta} BaO + 2\overline{NO_2} + \overline{O_2}$$

The alkaline-earth oxides react vigorously with water to form the hydroxides. Considerable heat is evolved in this "slaking" process, showing the great affinity of the oxides for water. In fact, barium oxide is one of the best drying agents known. The hydroxides are only slightly soluble in water. The gradation in molar solubility is shown in Table 6.1.

TABLE 6.1
Solubility of Me(OH)$_2$ in Water at 20°C in Moles per Liter

Ca(OH)$_2$	0.02
Sr(OH)$_2$	.065
Ba(OH)$_2$	.22

The alkaline-earth metals also form peroxides of formula MeO_2. Another gradation among these elements can be seen in the further reactions of the oxides with oxygen. Barium oxide at dull red heat takes up oxygen from CO_2-free air under atmospheric pressure to give the peroxide. At bright red heat, the peroxide reverts to the oxide. Strontium oxide reacts further only with oxygen under pressure at moderate temperature. Calcium peroxide cannot be made by direct synthesis under any conditions. Barium peroxide was once used as an intermediate in the industrial production of hydrogen peroxide by reaction with sulfuric acid to precipitate the insoluble barium sulfate. This process has been superseded by electrolytic procedures.

All the alkaline earth peroxides can be prepared by adding a concentrated solution of hydrogen peroxide to a hot solution of a soluble salt, whereby the white, slightly soluble peroxide precipitates:

$$Ca^{++} + H_2O_2 \rightarrow \underline{CaO_2} + 2H^+$$

The peroxides are strong oxidizing agents.

Salts

The halides of the alkaline-earth elements are salt-like compounds with ionic lattices in the solid state. Table 6.2 shows that they exhibit the expected high melting points. With the exception of the fluorides, they are all quite soluble in water.

Calcium chloride is a by-product of the Solvay Soda Process. Direct synthesis yields all of the group IIa halides, but it is rarely used in view of the cost of the elements. The usual manner of preparing these halides consists of the action of hydrogen halide acid on the cheap, naturally occurring carbonates, followed by evaporation to yield the desired crystals:

$$MeCO_3 + 2HX \rightarrow MeX_2 + H_2O + CO_2\uparrow$$

This method gives hydrated crystals (except in the fluoride case), but thermal dehydration results in the anhydrous salt without the complications found with the hydrate of copper(II) chloride. Similar acid-base reactions can be used to prepare the hydrated nitrates, perchlorates, and acetates, but thermal dehydration will not always yield the anhydrous salt in these cases.

TABLE 6.2
Melting Points of MeX_2 in °C

	F	Cl	Br	I
Ca	1330	772	760	575
Sr	1190(?)	873	643(?)	402(?)
Ba	1280	962	847	740

The normal fluorides, sulfates, carbonates, and phosphates of IIa elements are only slightly soluble or insoluble in water. The carbonates and phosphates are soluble in strong acids to yield the more soluble acid salts.

$$MeCO_3 + H^+ \quad \rightarrow Me^{++} + HCO_3^-$$
$$Me_3(PO_4)_2 + 2H^+ \rightarrow 3Me^{++} + 2HPO_4^{--}$$

The sulfides of these metals are prepared by heating the anhydrous sulfate with carbon at a high temperature:

$$MeSO_4 + 2C \xrightarrow{\Delta} MeS + 2CO_2\uparrow$$

The alkaline-earth sulfides are extensively hydrolyzed by water,

$$2MeS + 2HOH \rightarrow Me(OH)_2 + Me(HS)_2$$

but neither product of hydrolysis is very soluble in water.

ANALYTICAL CHEMISTRY OF THE FAMILY

The solubilities of some of the common salts of the alkaline-earth elements are given in Table 6.3. Generally there is a regular gradation of solubility from calcium to barium. In a few cases, however, the change is not regular, but most of the irregularities are less if the molal solubilities are compared.

TABLE 6.3
Solubility of Alkaline-Earth Salts in gm Salt/100 gm H$_2$O

	F$^-$	Cl$^-$	Br$^-$	ClO$_3^-$	IO$_3^-$	NO$_2^-$	NO$_3^-$	Ac$^-$	SO$_4^{--}$	C$_2$O$_4^{--}$	I$^-$	CO$_3^{--}$
Ca	0.0016	74.5	143	194	0.25	85	129	34.7	0.2	0.0007	208	0.0015
Sr	.012	53	104(?)	175	0.26	65	69	41	.013	.0048	178	.0011
Ba	.16	35.7	104	34	0.022	70	9	73	.00024	.01	203	.0022

The quantitative separation of the alkaline-earth elements is one of the more difficult problems in inorganic chemical analysis, particularly on a macro scale. The separation of barium and calcium, based on solubilities alone, is relatively easy. For example, the difference in solubilities between either the sulfates or the oxalates is sufficient to effect a clean separation of the two elements in one or two precipitations. However, the presence of strontium midway between calcium and barium makes the separation of all three very difficult. Fractional crystallization and/or precipitation must be used.

Frequently use is made of the emission spectra of the alkaline-earth elements as a means of qualitative identification. Since some of the strong lines of each of the elements fall in the visible portion of the spectrum, they all give flame tests. Barium salts impart a green color to the flame, and salts of calcium and strontium show various shades of red.

THE SYSTEM CALCIUM CHLORIDE-WATER

Since calcium chloride forms several hydrates, this is a good place to study the general relationships among the various hydrates of the same salt. Calcium chloride hydrates of the following compositions have been reported: $CaCl_2 \cdot 6H_2O$, $CaCl_2 \cdot 4H_2O$, $CaCl_2 \cdot 2H_2O$, and $CaCl_2 \cdot H_2O$. In contact with a saturated solution, the transition from the 6-hydrate to the 4-hydrate occurs at 29.5°C, that from the 4-hydrate to the 2-hydrate at 39.2°C, and that from the 2-hydrate to the 1-hydrate at 175.5°C. This means that under equilibrium conditions the 6-hydrate crystallizes from aqueous solution below 29.5°, the 4-hydrate between 29.5° and 39.2°, and the 2-hydrate at temperatures above 39.2°.

As is expected, the equilibrium vapor pressure of water over the 6-hydrate is greater than that over the 4-hydrate for a given tem-

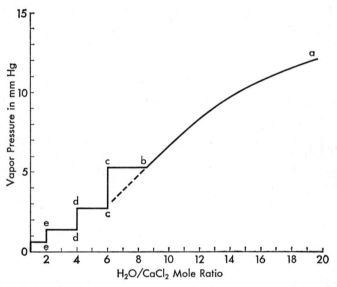

Fig. 6.3 Vapor pressure isotherm for the system $CaCl_2 - H_2O$ at 18°C.

perature. This can be seen by measuring the pressure of water over the $CaCl_2$—H_2O system while varying the ratio of H_2O to $CaCl_2$. Such an isothermal dehydration at 18°C is shown in Figure 6.3. Of course, at high values of $H_2O/CaCl_2$ the pressure approaches that of pure water, 15.5 mm, above point a in Figure 6.3. As the ratio is lowered, a more and more concentrated solution results, and the vapor pressure decreases continuously to b. At b crystals of the

6-hydrate start to separate. Along *bc* these crystals are in equilibrium with the saturated solution of calcium chloride. The vapor pressure remains the same while the amount of solution decreases and the amount of crystallized hydrate increases. At *c* only crystals of the 6-hydrate are present. Immediately the vapor pressure of the system drops discontinuously to a new value, which remains constant while calcium chloride 6-hydrate is being converted to calcium chloride 4-hydrate. At *d* only the 4-hydrate is present, and the vapor pressure drops again to a lower value, which remains constant between *d* and *e*. When all of the 4-hydrate is gone and only 2-hydrate crystals are present, *e* in the figure, another drop occurs. At higher temperatures the entire curve is displaced toward higher values of vapor pressure. In addition, the shape of the curve may be modified. For example, at temperatures slightly above 40°C the 6-hydrate and 4-hydrate portions of the curve disappear, since the 2-hydrate crystallizes from the saturated solution under these conditions.

The dotted extension of *ab* indicates the vapor pressure of supersaturated solutions of calcium chloride.

LIME AND ITS USES

The decomposition of calcium carbonate to lime, CaO, and carbon dioxide is carried out on an industrial scale in large furnaces called lime kilns. Lime produced this way is used to the extent of several million tons per year in the United States alone. Its chief uses are in making other chemicals, plaster, and paper and as a flux in metallurgical processes. "Agricultural lime" is in reality limestone.

One of the largest single uses of lime is in the production of acetylene. The lime is first reacted with carbon in electric arc furnaces at about 2500°C. The heat for such a furnace is furnished by striking an arc between carbon rods imbedded in the reaction mixture. The reaction

$$CaO + 3C \rightarrow CaC_2 + CO\uparrow$$

takes place. Water is then reacted with the calcium carbide to give acetylene:

$$CaC_2 + 2H_2O \rightarrow Ca(OH)_2 + C_2H_2\uparrow$$

Not all of the calcium carbide produced is used to make acetylene. Large quantities are used to make calcium cyanamide, by the absorption of nitrogen at 1000°C:

$$CaC_2 + N_2 \rightarrow CaCN_2 + C$$

The cyanamide is in turn the starting material for important industrial organic syntheses. Calcium cyanamide also reacts with high pressure steam to give ammonia (see Chapter 15).

OTHER COMPOUNDS OF INDUSTRIAL IMPORTANCE

Upon heating to about 100°C, gypsum loses some of its water of hydration in accordance with the following equation:

$$2CaSO_4 \cdot 2H_2O \rightarrow 2CaSO_4 \cdot \tfrac{1}{2}H_2O + 3H_2O$$

The resulting $\tfrac{1}{2}$-hydrate is known more commonly as "plaster of Paris." When plaster of Paris is mixed with water, the above reaction reverses, and the mixture sets back to the dihydrate. The setting is accompanied by a slight increase in volume, which explains the usefulness of plaster of Paris in making casts.

Barium sulfate is used to a limited extent as a white pigment in the paint industry. It is one of the constituents of lithopone. This pigment is made by reacting barium sulfide with zinc sulfate. The products are zinc sulfide and barium sulfate, both of which are white and water insoluble.

SUGGESTIONS FOR FURTHER READING

J. R. Partington, *Textbook of Inorganic Chemistry*, 6th ed., Macmillan, London, 1950, Chapters VII and XXXVIII.

M. E. Weeks, *Discovery of the Elements*, Journal of Chemical Education, Easton, Pa., 1956, Chapter XVII.

STUDY QUESTIONS

1. Starting with the carbonates, suggest laboratory methods of preparation for the chromates, sulfates, phosphates, hydroxides, oxides, nitrides, chlorides, perchlorates, and iodates of the alkaline-earths.

2. What flame tests are observed for these elements?

3. What happens to a lump of quicklime that is exposed to the atmosphere indefinitely?

4. Why is it that calcium chloride 6-hydrate may be dehydrated thermally, whereas copper(II) chloride 2-hydrate hydrolyzes under the same treatment?

5. Using Table 6.3, calculate solubility products for calcium iodate and barium iodate.

6. The solubility of barium sulfate is unaffected by changes in pH, whereas the solubility of barium carbonate is very much a function of pH. Explain.

7. Describe the action of surface water on limestone rock.

8. The capacity of some drying agents such as calcium chloride to remove water from air is a function of the drying temperature. Explain.

9. What comparison would you expect between the lattice energies of sodium chloride and calcium chloride? Since both of these salts are quite soluble in water, what comparison would you expect between the hydration energies of sodium ion and calcium ion?

10. A solution is known to contain sodium ion, strontium ion, and silver(I) ion, all as the nitrates. Suggest chemical means for separating the three cations.

11. What happens when the following substances are mixed?
    (a) $CaC_2 + H_2O$
    (b) $Ca(OH)_2 + $ excess CO_2(aqueous)
    (c) $BaO_2 + H_2SO_4$
    (d) $CaCN_2 + $ steam
    (e) $Sr_3(PO_4)_2 + $ excess HBr

12. By means of equations and a few words about conditions, show how to carry out the following conversions.
    (a) Make $SrCl_2$ from a naturally occurring strontium compound.
    (b) Make $Ca(NO_3)_2$ from $CaSO_4$.
    (c) Make $Ba(NO_3)_2$ from witherite.
    (d) Make $BaCl_2$ from $BaSO_4$.
    (e) Make Ra from $RaCl_2$.

13. Fifteen g of $Ba(OH)_2 \cdot 8H_2O$ are dissolved in 50 cc of warm water. The solution is divided into two equal portions, one of which is saturated with H_2S, and then recombined with the other half to make a solution of barium sulfide. To this 2.5 g of CS_2 are added with shaking, and 5.0 g of yellow barium trithiocarbonate crystallize and are recovered. What is the per cent yield?

Chapter 7

Zinc, Cadmium, and Mercury

OCCURRENCE AND HISTORY

Being elements of even atomic number, zinc, cadmium, and mercury are more abundant than their neighbors of odd atomic number, but zinc is the only one of the three that is at all abundant. All three occur principally as the sulfides. White zinc sulfide is usually colored by impurities in natural deposits, which are known by the names sphalerite or zincblende. Cadmium sulfide usually makes up a few tenths of one per cent of zinc ores; pure deposits are very rare. The largest deposits of cinnabar, HgS, red when pure, are found in Spain.

Of the three metals, only mercury antedates the Christian era, because cinnabar is widespread and yields mercury metal by the simplest means, heat:

$$HgS + O_2 \xrightarrow{\Delta} \overline{Hg} + \overline{SO_2}$$

Zinc and cadmium were not well recognized as elements until the eighteenth and nineteenth centuries, although zinc must have been used previously, since it has been found alloyed with copper in many ancient vessels.

PREPARATION OF THE ELEMENTS

The metallurgy of mercury is much less complicated than that of cadmium and zinc, since mercury is a noble metal (classically defined as a metal obtainable from its ores by heat alone, or, once

110

obtained, resistant to oxidation by heating in air; hence, noble). The sulfide ore of mercury is roasted in air, and the mercury vapors condense very easily.

Zinc and cadmium must be reduced to the metallic state by other means. Simple roasting in air yields their oxides:

$$2ZnS + 3O_2 \rightarrow 2ZnO + 2SO_2\uparrow$$
$$2CdS + 3O_2 \rightarrow 2CdO + 2SO_2\uparrow$$

The oxides are reacted with carbon in the form of coal or coke at about 1000°C to yield the metals and carbon monoxide. Since the boiling points of zinc and cadmium are below 1000°C, both metals volatilize in the process, and their vapors are condensed in small chambers above the reduction retorts. The zinc and cadmium may be separated by taking advantage of the difference in their boiling points. The products of this method are still impure. Recently electrolytic purification of zinc has been introduced, similar to the electrolytic refining of copper.

PHYSICAL PROPERTIES OF THE ELEMENTS

The melting and boiling points of these metals, shown in Table 7.1, are considerably lower than those of the preceding subgroup, a trend which is opposite to that which occurs in the a-subgroups.

TABLE 7.1
Some Physical Properties of the Group IIb Metals

	Density of the solid, g/cc	m.p., °C	b.p., °C
Zn	7.14	419	907
Cd	8.6	321	767
Hg	14.2	−39	357

Also the decrease in density from subgroup Ib, although not as abrupt as the change in fusibility, is the reverse of the change from Ia to IIa. All three metals are silvery in appearance. Pure zinc is relatively hard and brittle, but it becomes much less so in the temperature range 100–150°C. Cadmium is much more ductile than zinc.

Mercury is a unique element in many ways, in physical as well as chemical properties. It has the lowest melting point of any metal, and derives its common name of quicksilver from the fact that it is a liquid at room temperature. Its chemical inertness and high density make mercury an indispensable material in the laboratory. More startling, however, than its low melting point, for many other metals are seen to resemble it closely when temperatures are compared on the absolute scale, is its narrow liquid range, which is very short for a metal. Even at room temperature, its vapor pressure is appreciable enough—about 10^{-3} mm.—to make exposed mercury a health hazard upon prolonged exposure in a poorly ventilated room. The remarkable volatility to a monatomic gas shows the small interatomic forces in the liquid and the relative stability of the free atom. This stability is reflected in the chemical inertness and other chemical properties.

CHEMICAL PROPERTIES AND COMPOUNDS

With two electrons in the outer shell, all three elements should and do exhibit the oxidation number of $+2$. The penultimate d-sublevel is full and does not lose electrons to give higher oxidation numbers, as in the case of copper, silver, and gold. Thus, zinc, cadmium, and mercury are not transition elements in the chemical sense. The non-rare-gas type ions form many complexes, the greater tendency in this direction over subgroup IIa being the same as that already discussed in the comparison of subgroups Ia and Ib.

The $+2$ oxidation state is the only one observed for zinc and cadmium, but mercury shows its individuality again in exhibiting the $+1$ oxidation state also. The mercury(I) ion, which exists only as the dimer, ^+Hg—Hg^+, with a covalent bond between the two atoms, is another example of the stability of the mercury atom when it has an electron structure with two electrons in the 6s orbital. This covalent bonding of two atoms of mercury is a rare example among metals of a property which is more characteristic of nonmetals.

Zinc, cadmium, and mercury are more electropositive than the elements preceding them in their respective periods. The gradation within the subgroup is again the opposite of that in the a-subgroups, so that zinc is more active than cadmium which is more active than mercury. In fact, mercury lies below hydrogen in standard oxidation potential, and so will not, as zinc and cadmium do, displace hydrogen from dilute acids. None of the three is active enough to release hydrogen from water at room temperature. Since zinc oxide is amphoteric, while cadmium and mercury oxides are not, zinc metal will release hydrogen from solutions of alkali, whereas cadmium and mercury will not.

Chemical Reactions of the Elements

The reactions of these elements with oxygen illustrates well the various factors influencing the general reaction between metals and oxygen. Finely powdered zinc is pyrophoric, but strips of the metal will not combine with oxygen until heated to between 500 and 600°C. Thus, the particle size of the metal, which governs the surface area exposed, plays a major role in the reaction. Cadmium behaves much the same as zinc, but liquid mercury does not combine with oxygen at room temperature. If heated to between 300 and 350°, it will react to form mercury(II) oxide. If the oxide is heated another 100°, it decomposes into mercury vapor and oxygen. Thus, temperature and the thermal stability of the oxide are equally important in the reaction.

The elements also combine directly with the halogens and sulfur to give the $+2$ halides and sulfides. With excess mercury, the mercury(I) compounds are formed: e.g.,

$$Hg + Cl_2(\text{excess}) \rightarrow HgCl_2$$
$$2Hg(\text{excess}) + Cl_2 \rightarrow Hg_2Cl_2$$

The elements do not react with hydrogen, nitrogen, and carbon, nor do they form peroxides with oxygen.

As mentioned above, zinc and cadmium release hydrogen from nonoxidizing acids. Mercury is oxidized by hot, concentrated sulfuric acid to form mercury(II) sulfate with the evolution of sulfur dioxide. It dissolves in cold dilute or concentrated nitric acid, evolving NO or NO_2 respectively, to give mercury(II) nitrate with excess acid and mercury(I) nitrate with excess mercury.

Zinc plus aqueous alkali is a powerful reducing medium, giving "nascent hydrogen" which either combines with itself and comes off as a gas or reacts with any reducible substance present:

$$Zn + 2NaOH \rightarrow Na_2ZnO_2 + \overline{H}_2$$
$$4Zn + 7NaOH + NaNO_3 \rightarrow \overline{NH}_3 + 4Na_2ZnO_2 + 2H_2O$$

Oxides

When alkali is added to cold solutions of zinc and cadmium ions (not in excess for zinc), white flocculent precipitates of the hydroxides are formed which lose water very easily to go to the oxides. Mercury(II) oxide is produced directly without the intermediate hydroxide. The oxides can also be made by direct synthesis as described above, or by the thermal decomposition of the nitrates:

$$2Me(NO_3)_2 \xrightarrow{\Delta} 2MeO + 4\overline{NO}_2 + \overline{O}_2$$

The colors of these compounds are interesting. Zinc oxide is white at room temperature but turns yellow above 300°C, returning to the original white when cooled. Cadmium oxide is ordinarily brown but turns white when cooled to −190°C. The colors are presumably due to slight oxygen deficiencies in the compounds at the higher temperature. Mercury(II) oxide precipitated from aqueous solution is yellow; when prepared at high temperature by direct synthesis or by decomposition of the nitrate, it is red. The difference in color is thought to be due to no more than a difference in particle size.

The three oxides are insoluble in water but dissolve easily in most acids. Zinc oxide is the only one of the three which dissolves in excess base to give an anion. Zinc and cadmium oxides both dissolve in excess ammonia to give complex cations:

$$\underline{CdO} + 4NH_3 + H_2O \rightarrow Cd(NH_3)_4{}^{++} + 2OH^-$$

The behavior of mercury compounds with ammonia is very different (see below).

Halides

The halides of these metals are generally made by dissolving a basic compound such as the oxide or the carbonate in the hydrohalic acids. Upon evaporation, the soluble halides precipitate as hydrates, the insoluble ones come down as anhydrous salts. The hydrates must be dehydrated in a stream of dry HX gas; otherwise, basic salts result (cf. copper(II)). The anhydrous salts can also be obtained by direct synthesis.

All of the halides are white solids at room temperature except the iodides of mercury and cadmium and the bromide of cadmium. Mercury(II) iodide is a red solid below 126°C, at which temperature it changes to a yellow solid. The color change here is a true polymorphic change in which the two solids have different crystalline structures. Cadmium bromide is yellow, and cadmium iodide brownish. With the exception of the fluoride, the halides of divalent mercury have low melting points and are poor conductors of electricity in the liquid state. Even in aqueous solution, mercury(II) chloride behaves as a weak electrolyte, indicating the covalent nature of the bonding. This is a rare example of a weak salt. Most of the other halides of this subgroup are at least partially ionic, behaving as strong electrolytes in water. The melting points are given in Table 7.2.

TABLE 7.2
Melting Points in °C

HgF_2	645	CdF_2	1110	ZnF_2	872
$HgCl_2$	280	$CdCl_2$	568	$ZnCl_2$	275
$HgBr_2$	238	$CdBr_2$	585	$ZnBr_2$	390
HgI_2	257	CdI_2	381	ZnI_2	446

A large variation in water solubility is observed for these halides. Mercury(II) fluoride is moderately soluble in water, but it is extensively hydrolyzed to a basic salt, as are all the soluble ionic compounds of mercury(II). The solubilities of the other eleven halides are given in Table 7.3.

TABLE 7.3
Solubility in gms/100 gms of Water at Room Temperature

	F^-	Cl^-	Br^-	I^-
Hg^{++}		7.05	6.16	0.0059
Cd^{++}	4.34	115	115	85.5
Zn^{++}	1.62	420	488	730

Notice the enormous solubility of zinc chloride, bromide, and iodide.

Other Salts

The sulfates, nitrates, acetates, and perchlorates of the group IIb metals are soluble in water, the mercury salts being extensively hydrolyzed. Solutions of these salts are colorless, indicative of the fact that the simple hydrated ions of the IIb metals are colorless. The oxalates, carbonates, and sulfides are insoluble. When precipitated from dilute acid solutions by the addition of hydrogen sulfide, cadmium sulfide is yellow, zinc sulfide is white, and mercury sulfide is black. The slight solubility of the sulfides is used to separate these elements from other elements whose sulfides are more soluble. Black mercury sulfide is easily converted to the red form by digestion in a solution containing acetic acid and potassium thiocyanate.

The ammonium phosphates of zinc and cadmium are insoluble in neutral solution and can be used in the quantitative determination of the elements.

Complex Ions

Complex ions are numerous and stable for these post-transition metals. Usually the coordination number of the metal ions is 4 with a tetrahedral arrangement of ligands, but it may reach 6 in the more stable chelates. Examples of complex ions, generally formed by mixing the constituents in aqueous solution are:

$Zn(CN)_4^{--}$	ZnI_4^{--}	$Zn(NH_3)_4^{++}$	$Zn(C_2O_4)_2^{--}$	$Zn(en)_3^{++}$
$Cd(CN)_4^{--}$	$CdBr_4^{--}$	$Cd(NH_3)_4^{++}$	$Cd(C_2O_4)_2^{--}$	$Cd(en)_3^{++}$
$Hg(CN)_4^{--}$	$HgCl_4^{--}$	—	$Hg(C_2O_4)_2^{--}$	$Hg(en)_3^{++}$

en = ethylene diamine, $NH_2—CH_2CH_2—NH_2$

The tendency to form complex ions increases from zinc to mercury, and as expected, among the halo complexes the iodides form the most readily. For example, cadmium sulfide is soluble in solutions of potassium iodide by virtue of the formation of the very stable tetraiodocadmate ion:

$$CdS + 4I^- \rightarrow CdI_4^{--} + S^{--}$$

In fact, when the soluble cadmium iodide alone is dissolved in water, iodo complexes are formed which appreciably reduce the electrical conductivity of the solution from that of a simple salt of formula, $A^{++}2B^-$. This phenomenon is called "autocomplex" formation. The existence of many different complex species in the solution is shown by the equilibria:

$$Cd^{++} + I^- \rightleftharpoons CdI^+$$
$$CdI^+ + I^- \rightleftharpoons CdI_2$$
$$CdI_2 + I^- \rightleftharpoons CdI_3^-$$
$$CdI_3^- + I^- \rightleftharpoons CdI_4^{--}$$

All of the CdI_n^{2-n} species are present in a simple solution of CdI_2 in amounts depending on the concentration. If excess KI is added to the solution, the equilibria are driven to the predominant formation of CdI_4^{--}. The insoluble mercury(II) iodide dissolves easily in potassium iodide solution with the formation of the soluble potassium tetraiodomercurate(II). Even in the solid state, red mercury(II) iodide exists in a layer structure built up of HgI_4 tetrahedra which share corners with other HgI_4 tetrahedra.

The electronic configurations of complex ions deserves further mention here. The cadmium ion is formed by the loss of two electrons from the cadmium atom:

Cd $\quad 1s^22s^22p^63s^23p^63d^{10}4s^24p^64d^{10}5s^2 \rightarrow$
$$Cd^{++} \quad 1s^22s^22p^63s^23p^63d^{10}4s^24p^64d^{10}$$

The ion has a residual electron affinity in its fifth quantum level, so that a complex results in the presence of iodide ion:

$$Cd^{++} + 4 : \overset{\cdot\cdot}{\underset{\cdot\cdot}{I}} : ^- \rightarrow : \overset{\cdot\cdot}{\underset{\cdot\cdot}{I}} : \overset{\overset{\cdot\cdot}{\cdot\cdot}{I}{\cdot\cdot}}{\underset{\underset{\cdot\cdot}{\cdot\cdot}{I}{\cdot\cdot}}{Cd}} : \overset{\cdot\cdot}{\underset{\cdot\cdot}{I}} : ^{--}$$

The cadmium atom now has a share in eight more electrons to give it the stable electron structure of xenon:

$$CdI_4^{--} \quad 1s^22s^22p^63s^23p^63d^{10}4s^24p^64d^{10}5s^25p^6$$

A comparison of the calcium ion with the cadmium ion shows

that Ca^{++} cannot possibly achieve a rare-gas type structure by gaining a reasonable number of electrons, whereas Cd^{++} does it easily. Thus, autocomplex formation is unimportant in a solution of calcium chloride, the ions moving about in solution more or less at random. In cadmium chloride solutions, as in iodide solutions, there are chloro complex ions, such as $CdCl_4^{--}$, in addition to the hydrated cadmium and chloride ions. It is seen then that chloride ions are able to compete successfully with water molecules for positions around the cadmium ion but not for positions around the calcium ion.

That there is some fundamental difference between the cadmium and calcium ions is shown in still another way. Anhydrous calcium chloride and anhydrous cadmium chloride will both absorb gaseous ammonia to form ammines, $Ca(NH_3)_6Cl_2$ and $Cd(NH_3)_4Cl_2$. Solution of the ammines in water results in the decomposition of the calcium ammine, but not that of cadmium:

$$Ca(NH_3)_6Cl_2 + xH_2O \rightarrow Ca(OH_2)_x^{++} + 2Cl^- + 6NH_3$$
$$Cd(NH_3)_4Cl_2 \xrightarrow{\text{H}_2\text{O}} Cd(NH_3)_4^{++} + 2Cl^-$$

Evidently the ammine complex of cadmium is more stable than the aquo complex, while the situation is just the reverse in the case of calcium, even though the ionic radii are very nearly the same (see Figure 1.6). Again, a considerable difference is evident between ions of rare-gas configuration, Ca^{++}, Sr^{++}, Ba^{++}, and the so-called 18-electron ions, Zn^{++}, Cd^{++}, Hg^{++}.

Divalent mercury does not form ammine complexes with ammonia except under special conditions. Rather ammonobasic salts are usually produced:

$$HgCl_2 + 2NH_3(\text{aqueous}) \rightarrow \underline{HgNH_2Cl} + NH_4^+ + Cl^-$$
$$\text{white}$$
$$2HgO + NH_3 + H_2O \rightarrow \underline{(HOHg)_2NH_2OH} \text{ (Millon's base)}$$
$$\text{yellow}$$

With aqueous ammonia to which has been added ammonium chloride, a less basic medium than aqueous ammonia alone, or with ammonia gas, normal ammines can be made:

$$HgCl_2 + 2NH_3 \rightarrow Hg(NH_3)_2Cl_2$$
$$\text{white}$$

Mercury(I) Compounds

Compounds of univalent mercury are generally prepared by careful reduction of mercury(II) compounds. The reducing agent may be sulfur dioxide, tin(II) ion, or elemental mercury itself (see also the reactions above of excess mercury with oxidizing agents):

$$2HgCl_2 + Sn^{++} + 4Cl^- \rightarrow Hg_2Cl_2 + SnCl_6^{--}$$

$$2HgBr_2 + SO_2 + 2H_2O \rightarrow Hg_2Br_2 + 4H^+ + 2Br^- + SO_4^{--}$$

$$Hg(NO_3)_2 + Hg \quad\quad \rightarrow Hg_2(NO_3)_2$$

A black insoluble precipitate, sometimes called mercury(I) oxide, comes down when alkali is added to a mercury(I) compound. It is really an equimolar mixture of the element and mercury(II) oxide, colored black by the finely divided mercury:

$$Hg_2^{++} + 2OH^- \rightarrow Hg + HgO + H_2O$$

Only simple mercury(I) compounds are known, and they are all strongly ionized in solution, unlike many of the mercury(II) salts. Since the hypothetical base, $Hg_2(OH)_2$, is stronger than HgO, solutions of mercury(I) salts are not so greatly hydrolyzed as those of the soluble ionic compounds of divalent mercury. The nitrate, perchlorate, and fluoride are soluble and slightly hydrolyzed in water; the sulfate, carbonate, and other halides are insoluble.

Univalent mercury can be reduced to the metal—by tin(II) ion, for example—or can be oxidized to the +2 state—by, for example, concentrated nitric acid. In fact, most mercury(I) compounds disproportionate rather easily, as in the reaction above with alkali. All attempts to prepare complex compounds also result in disproportionation:

$$Hg_2Cl_2 + 2NH_3 \rightarrow Hg + HgNH_2Cl + NH_4Cl$$

The most common compound of mercury(I) is the white insoluble chloride, commonly called calomel. Unlike soluble mercury compounds, it is nonpoisonous and indeed was used for many years in medicine as a purgative.

Mercury(I) ion adds another to the list of ions which form in-

soluble chlorides, bromides, and iodides. All of the others lie close
to Hg in the periodic table, as may be seen below.

Ib	*IIb*	*IIIb*	*IVb*
Cu^+			
Ag^+			
Au^+	Hg_2^{++}	Tl^+	Pb^{++}

USES

Compounds of mercury are used as pharmaceuticals, fungicides,
and pigments. Elementary mercury is used as the cathode in the
amalgam type electrolytic cell described in Chapter 4. The liquid
metal also finds varied uses in scientific apparatus. In 1951 the U.S.
production of mercury and its compounds was about 275 tons,
which was only about one-eighth of the domestic need.

Cadmium is used chiefly as a protective coating for other metals,
principally steel. Production in the U.S. amounts to only 4000 tons
per year, most of it resulting as a by-product of zinc production.

About 600,000 tons of zinc are produced in the United States
annually, a quantity sufficient to meet two-thirds of the need. Zinc
is a constituent of many alloys; brass alloys in particular use up
a large portion of the zinc produced. In addition, substantial quantities are used to galvanize iron articles; that is, to cover them with
a rust-preventing coat of metallic zinc (see Chapter 24). Zinc metal
is the case and anode of dry cells (see Chapter 23). Compounds of
zinc find uses as pigments, preservatives, and fluxes.

SUGGESTIONS FOR FURTHER READING

J. R. Partington, *Textbook of Inorganic Chemistry*, 6th ed., Macmillan,
    London, 1950, Chapter XXXIX.
N. V. Sidgwick, *The Chemical Elements and their Compounds*, Oxford, Lon-
    don, 1950, pp. 262–333.
M. E. Weeks, *Discovery of the Elements*, Journal of Chemical Education,
    Easton, Pa., 1956, Chapters I, IV, and XVII.

STUDY QUESTIONS

1. Suggest two distinct means of galvanizing an iron pail.
2. A solution is known to contain chlorides of zinc, cadmium, and
mercury. How might the three elements be separated from each other?

3. Compare the results of heating $BaCl_2 \cdot 2H_2O$ and $CdCl_2 \cdot 2H_2O$ to several hundred degrees.

4. Give two different ways that mercury(I) chloride can be prepared from mercury(II) chloride.

5. Why might you expect the HgI_4^{--} ion to be more stable than the HgI_3^- ion?

6. Write a balanced equation for the reaction between aqueous ammonia and calomel.

7. From a mixture of solid oxides of zinc, cadmium, and mercury, what reagent will:

(a) dissolve one and leave the other two as a residue?

(b) dissolve two and leave one as a residue?

(c) dissolve all three?

8. Starting with zinc, cadmium, and mercury metals, suggest methods to prepare the following substances: $HgCl_2$, $CdCl_2 \cdot 2H_2O$, $ZnSO_4 \cdot 7H_2O$, CdS, K_2HgI_4, Hg_2SO_4, and ZnC_2O_4.

9. What happens when the following substances are mixed?

(a) $CdCl_2 + NH_3$(aqueous)

(b) $ZnCl_2 + NaOH$

(c) $Cd + NaOH$

(d) $Hg + NaOH$

(e) $Hg(NO_3)_2 +$ excess $SnCl_2$

10. By means of equations and a few words about conditions, show how to carry out the following conversions:

(a) Make K_2CdI_4 from Cd

(b) Make $ZnCl_2$ from $ZnSO_4$

(c) Make Hg_2Cl_2 from cinnabar

(d) Make yellow HgO from red HgO

(e) Make K_2ZnO_2 from Na_2ZnO_2

Chapter 8	# Beryllium, Magnesium, Boron, and Aluminum

OCCURRENCE AND HISTORY

While compounds of beryllium, magnesium, boron, and aluminum have been used by man for many centuries, the details of their chemistry were not known until well into the nineteenth century. The isolation of the elements themselves was accomplished at about the same time as Davy's work on the preparation of the alkali metals in the early 1800's.

Of the four, aluminum and magnesium are very abundant, being the first and sixth most abundant metals respectively; beryllium and boron are relatively rare. None occur naturally in the elementary state; the large majority of the natural compounds are complex silicate minerals. Talc, asbestos, and meerschaum are typical magnesium silicates. Feldspar, $KAlSi_3O_8$ and clay, the product of the weathering of feldspar in which the potassium is leached out by air and water, are among the most abundant minerals on earth. A few, less abundant minerals are more economical sources for the extraction of the elements. Cryolite, Na_3AlF_6; bauxite, $Al_2O_3 \cdot xH_2O$; carnallite, $MgCl_2 \cdot KCl \cdot 6H_2O$; dolomite, $MgCO_3 \cdot CaCO_3$; and magnesite, $MgCO_3$, are all mined in a relatively pure condition. Sea water, in which magnesium, after sodium, is the most abundant cation, is now an important source of magnesium. It is extracted by the precipitation of the hydroxide upon the addi-

122

tion of slaked lime. The chief source of beryllium is beryl, $3BeO\cdot$-$Al_2O_3\cdot6SiO_2$, of which the emerald is a variety of gem quality. The main source of boron is the extensive deposit of borax, $Na_2B_4O_7\cdot$-$10H_2O$, in Searle's Lake, California.

PREPARATION OF THE ELEMENTS

Beryllium, magnesium, and aluminum are prepared by the electrolysis of suitable fused salts, similar to the processes used to prepare the alkaline-earth metals. For example, the electrolysis of

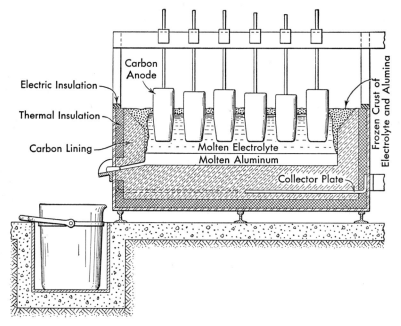

Fig. 8.1   The production of aluminum.

fused carnallite at about 700°C yields magnesium. Boron is difficult to prepare, but it can be isolated by the reduction of boron oxide with potassium, which gives an amorphous brown powder, or by the reduction of the bromide with hydrogen on a hot tantalum filament, which gives black crystals.

The Hall Process for the production of aluminum is of great

importance to an industrial economy. As a result of the development of the present method, the price of aluminum has dropped from twenty dollars to twenty cents per pound. The process consists of electrolyzing aluminum oxide dissolved in molten cryolite at a temperature of about 1000°C. Large steel boxes lined with carbon, which acts as the cathode, are used to hold the electrolyte. Baked carbon blocks form the anodes. Molten aluminum is deposited at the cathodes and is tapped or siphoned off from the cells. Oxygen is released at the anodes and reacts with them to form carbon monoxide with some carbon dioxide:

$$Al_2O_3 \xrightarrow{\text{elect.}} 2Al + \tfrac{3}{2}O_2$$

(see Figure 8.1).

PHYSICAL PROPERTIES OF THE ELEMENTS

These elements are all of low density. Magnesium and aluminum melt below red heat, while much higher temperatures are required to fuse beryllium and boron. Beryllium, magnesium, and aluminum have the physical as well as chemical characteristics of metals; that is, they are good conductors of electricity and have a silvery appearance when freshly cut or scratched. An adhering oxide film makes their surfaces dull when exposed to air. The combination of abundance, corrosion resistance, and high tensile strength make aluminum and magnesium valuable structural materials, especially where strength per unit weight is important. Boron is very hard and brittle, and it is practically a nonconductor of electricity.

CHEMICAL PROPERTIES AND COMPOUNDS

The only oxidation numbers taken by these elements are their respective group numbers. The sizes of their atoms and ions, however, are equally as important as their charges in determining the chemistry of the elements. Since the atoms of these typical elements are small to begin with, variations in size are large in terms of percentage change and bring about great changes in chemical properties. Thus, beryllium, with a small divalent ion, resembles aluminum, with a larger trivalent ion, more than it does magnesium. In fact, it was thought for many years that beryllium was a trivalent element on the basis of its general chemical properties. The same diagonal relationship in the periodic table exists to some extent between lithium and magnesium and between boron and silicon:

$$\begin{array}{cccc} \text{Li} & \text{Be} & \text{B} & \text{C} \\ & \searrow & \searrow & \searrow \\ \text{Na} & \text{Mg} & \text{Al} & \text{Si} \end{array}$$

The very small ions of the first few second period atoms have about the same deforming power as the larger third period atoms with a charge of one greater, and so the same tendencies in chemical properties. For this reason, these four elements from two different groups are discussed together in this chapter rather than with the elements of their respective groups. The diagonal relationship should be borne in mind throughout the study of these elements, and correlations should be made between lithium and magnesium, on the one hand, and between boron and silicon, on the other. With the larger atoms in the long periods the size changes are not so significant, and the resemblances are more vertical than diagonal.

As would be expected from the size and charge relationships, magnesium forms more ionic compounds than beryllium and aluminum, while most boron compounds are covalent. Magnesium has a basic oxide, and therefore exists in ionic compounds as a cation only. Since beryllium and aluminum oxides are amphoteric, the elements are found in both anions and cations. Boron, with an acidic oxide, forms anions only, when its compounds ionize. The tendency towards complex formation follows the behavior of the oxides. These elements, with small but rare-gas type ions, are about midway between the early a- and b-subgroups in this respect.

Chemical Reactions of the Elements

When the surfaces of these elements are exposed, they are very active. For instance, their oxidation potentials are all above hydrogen—even above zinc—in the E.M.F. series of the elements. On the other hand, the elements are remarkably stable in air and water at ordinary temperature because of the formation of an insoluble, closely adhering layer of oxide on the surface which protects the underneath portion from further reaction. Once ignited in air at high temperature, however, they burn with great vigor to form oxides and nitrides. In pure oxygen, the oxides BeO, MgO, B_2O_3, and Al_2O_3 are formed; in pure nitrogen, the nitrides Be_3N_2, Mg_3N_2, BN, and AlN result. They will also release hydrogen from hot steam.

Magnesium and aluminum corrode rapidly in salt water, a medium in which the oxides are slightly soluble. If the surface of the metals is amalgamated by rubbing it with moist mercury(II) chloride, the oxide coating will not stick, and the metals will release hydrogen from cold water.

All four elements react vigorously with the halogens at moderate temperatures to give the corresponding halides. Hydrogen does not attack the elements at any temperature, but an interesting series of volatile boron hydrides (B_2H_6, B_4H_{10}, B_5H_9, B_5H_{11}, B_6H_{10}, $B_{10}H_{14}$, and others) can be prepared by other means, such as the reaction of magnesium boride with acid:

$$Mg_3B_2 + 6HCl \rightarrow 3MgCl_2 + B_5H_9, \text{ etc.} \uparrow$$

The formation of volatile, binary hydrides by boron, the only one of these four elements to do so, is another instance of the resemblance between boron and silicon.

Magnesium, beryllium, and aluminum react with most strong acids to liberate hydrogen and form salts of the acids. As expected, magnesium reacts the most vigorously. Aluminum and beryllium show a peculiar reluctance to react with nitric acid, a phenomenon called "passivity." It is presumably due to the inability of nitric acid to dissolve the oxide films protecting the metals. Aluminum will dissolve rapidly in nitric acid containing a few drops of hydrofluoric acid.

Beryllium and aluminum, having amphoteric oxides, dissolve in aqueous alkali also, to give hydrogen and beryllates or aluminates. Magnesium with a basic oxide is unreactive towards alkali. Boron is inert to most chemical reagents except at elevated temperatures, and it takes fused sodium hydroxide to dissolve boron.

Oxides and Salts

The oxides of beryllium, magnesium, and aluminum are white refractory (difficultly fused) substances. Boron oxide resembles silicon dioxide in physical properties in that although it is somewhat lower melting it easily forms glasses, especially upon the addition of alkalis. Magnesium oxide is a moderately strong base even though it is only sparingly soluble in water. Beryllium and aluminum oxides are much weaker bases and much less soluble in water. Nevertheless, salts of all three elements can be made by the dissolution of the oxides in sufficiently strong acids. Freshly precipitated oxides dissolve in acids readily, but ignited oxides are dissolved only with prolonged digestion:

$$MgO + 2HX \rightarrow MgX_2 + H_2O$$
$$Al_2O_3 + 6HX \rightarrow 2AlX_3 + 3H_2O$$
$$BeO + 2HX \rightarrow BeX_2 + H_2O$$

If the acid is strong enough to prevent hydrolysis, the hydrated salts may be crystallized from solution. Halides, nitrates, sulfates, and perchlorates may be prepared in this manner. Salts of weak acids such as acetates and sulfides cannot be made this way. If aluminum acetate is prepared by another method and placed in water, it hydrolyzes completely to hydrous aluminum oxide and acetic acid:

$$2Al(C_2H_3O_2)_3 + (3 + x)H_2O \rightarrow Al_2O_3 \cdot xH_2O\downarrow + 6HC_2H_3O_3$$

Magnesium salts do not hydrolyze to such a great extent. This can be verified very simply by testing separately the pH of 0.1-N solutions of magnesium chloride, beryllium chloride, and aluminum chloride. The magnesium chloride solution is slightly acidic, but the other two are much more acidic, indicating more extensive hydrolysis.

Boron "salts" of acids do not exist, which indicates that boron oxide is a weaker base than aluminum oxide. Indeed, the oxide of boron is a weakly acidic oxide, forming salts such as sodium tetraborate, $Na_2B_4O_7$. These salts hydrolyze to give basic solutions:

$$B_4O_7^{--} + 5H_2O \rightleftharpoons 2H_2BO_3^- + 2H_3BO_3$$
$$H_2BO_3^- + H_2O \rightleftharpoons H_3BO_3 + OH^-$$

The addition of strong acid to borax gives a solution of the weak but soluble boric acid and the sodium salt of the added acid. Since boric acid is less soluble in cold water, it is prepared by cooling the solution.

Beryllium and aluminum oxides, being amphoteric, show acidic character also, albeit even weaker than that of boron oxide. Salts such as sodium beryllate and sodium aluminate hydrolyze in the same way as sodium borates and to a greater extent. Even as weak an acid oxide as carbon dioxide is able to displace aluminum oxide from its sodium salt. Bubbling the gas into a solution of the aluminate precipitates the hydrous oxide:

$$2NaAl(OH)_4 + 2CO_2 + (x - 3)H_2O \rightarrow \underline{Al_2O_3 \cdot xH_2O} + 2NaHCO_3$$

On the other hand, sodium hydrogen carbonate precipitates the hydrous oxide from the acidic solution of aluminum chloride:

$$2AlCl_3 + 6NaHCO_3 + (x - 3)H_2O \rightarrow$$
$$\underline{Al_2O_3 \cdot xH_2O} + 6NaCl + 6CO_2\uparrow$$

Magnesium oxide has almost no acidic properties.

Basicity of Hydroxides

The general relationships for the basicity of the oxides of the elements have already been given on page 34. Let us now look at this property in more detail. In aqueous solution the behavior of oxides can be rationalized by considering the X—O—H type of linkage, where X is the element whose oxide is under consideration. If this grouping splits at the X—O bond, then the hydroxide acts as a base:

$$X\text{—}O\text{—}H \rightarrow X^+ + OH^-$$

If it splits at the O—H bond, an acid results:

$$X\text{—}O\text{—}H \rightarrow XO^- + H^+$$

A familiar example of the first type of behavior is NaOH, and of the second, HOCl. The hydroxides of some elements, such as beryllium and aluminum, can split at either bond, depending on the environment. They are amphoteric.

The relative tendencies of the X—O—H group to split in the two ways shown above depend upon the attraction of the central atom or ion for electrons, that is, its electronegativity. If X is a large ion of small positive charge, it has little attraction for electrons, which then tend to be displaced toward and strengthen the

O—H bond, and the hydroxide is basic. If X is a small ion of higher positive charge, the electrons are pulled towards and strengthen the X—O bond. The O—H bond is then weakened, and the hydroxide acts as an acid by splitting off a proton.

This explanation is another example of the type of reasoning about the polarity of bonds used in Fajans' rules (page 25). If X is such that the X—O bond is mainly ionic, that bond tends to ionize in water. If the X—O bond is predominantly covalent, it does not split in water, being then less polar than the O—H bond. The reader should at this point apply this theory to explain the gradation in basicity of oxides previously mentioned and the variations in the acid-strengths of oxy-acids given on pages 60 to 62.

The above reasoning is well illustrated by the hydroxides of the four elements beryllium, magnesium, boron, and aluminum. They have been shown to exhibit a gradation in basicity:

$$Mg(OH)_2 > Be(OH)_2 \simeq Al(OH)_3 > B(OH)_3$$

The ionic radii from Figure 1.6 are:

Be^{++}	0.31Å	B^{+++}	0.20
Mg^{++}	$.65$	Al^{+++}	$.50$

It can be seen that the relatively large magnesium ion with dipositive charge has the most polar X—O bond and so is the most basic. The smallest trivalent boron ion gives an acidic hydroxide, $B(OH)_3$, commonly written H_3BO_3 to show its acidic character. The amphoteric beryllium and aluminum are in between, the larger charge of the aluminum being offset by its larger size.

Hydrous Oxides vs. Hydroxides

When base is added to dilute solutions of magnesium chloride, beryllium chloride, and aluminum chloride, white flocculent precipitates are formed in each case:

$$Mg^{++} + 2OH^- \rightarrow \underline{Mg(OH)_2}$$
$$Be^{++} + 2OH^- \rightarrow \underline{Be(OH)_2}$$
$$Al^{+++} + 3OH^- \rightarrow \underline{Al(OH)_3}$$

The above equations are generally used to describe the reactions, but they do not tell the true story concerning the nature of the precipitates. If the precipitate of aluminum hydroxide is filtered quickly, air-dried, and analyzed, no definite composition is observed. The percentage of water in the precipitate varies from one experiment to the next. Consequently, it is more correct to write the formula of the precipitate as $Al_2O_3 \cdot xH_2O$, where x may be a number as great as 30 or 40. Such precipitates are misnamed as hydroxides and are better called hydrous oxides, to indicate their indefinite composition. Hydrous oxides must not be confused with hydrates, such as $CuSO_4 \cdot 5H_2O$, where the 5 is a definite number. The word hydrous means that the x varies a great deal, depending upon conditions that cannot be controlled in ordinary laboratory procedure. Thus, x is not a whole number, but rather a continuous variable. A hydrous oxide is identified by its flocculent character. True hydrates have vapor pressure isotherms (see pages 105ff.) with the step-by-step variation shown in Figure 8.2(a), whereas the hydrous oxides have vapor pressure isotherms with the continuous variation shown in Figure 8.2(b).

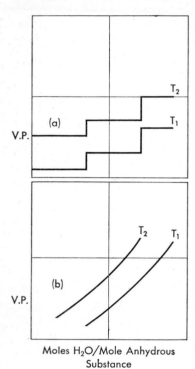

Moles H_2O/Mole Anhydrous Substance

Fig. 8.2 Vapor pressure isotherms of (a) hydrates and (b) hydrous oxides.

It should not be concluded that definite hydroxides of aluminum, etc., are unknown. They are rare, but they can be prepared by special means; many occur naturally in small natural deposits.

Halides

In the case of barium, strontium, and calcium the halides are all salt-like and can be crystallized from aqueous solution easily. The halides of magnesium, beryllium, aluminum, and boron show progressively less salt-like properties. Magnesium chloride 6-hydrate can be crystallized from solution. On heating, the substance loses 4 of the 6 waters of hydration easily, but on further heating, the 2-hydrate loses both water and hydrogen chloride, leaving a basic salt:

$$MgCl_2 \cdot 2H_2O \xrightarrow{\Delta} MgCl_2 + 2H_2O\uparrow$$
$$MgCl_2 \cdot 2H_2O \xrightarrow{\Delta} MgO + 2HCl\uparrow + H_2O\uparrow$$

Magnesium chloride is still salt-like enough so that the anhydrous compound can be prepared from the hydrate under carefully controlled conditions, such as heating in a stream of dry HCl gas.

Even though beryllium and aluminum salts are more hydrolyzed than magnesium salts are, it is still possible to crystallize hydrated halides of beryllium and aluminum from water containing an excess of hydrohalic acid. The hydrated crystals decompose on heating to lose hydrogen halide and leave the oxides:

$$2AlCl_3 \cdot 6H_2O \xrightarrow{\Delta} Al_2O_3 + 6HCl\uparrow + 9H_2O\uparrow$$

The anhydrous compounds cannot be prepared by dehydrating the hydrates under any conditions. They can be made by direct synthesis.

Boron halides cannot be crystallized from water. Made by direct synthesis, they are completely hydrolyzed when put in solution:

$$BCl_3 + 3H_2O \rightarrow H_3BO_3 + 3HCl$$

The boron halides are then largely covalent, whereas those of magnesium are largely ionic. Further evidence for this gradation in bond-type appears in the melting points of the halides of the four elements, given in Table 8.1.

TABLE 8.1
Melting Points of Some Metal Chlorides

Compound	Melting Point
$MgCl_2$	712°C
$BeCl_2$	440°C
$AlCl_3$	178°C (sublimes)
BCl_3	−107°C

As in the case of the Me—O bonds, the smaller the size and the larger the charge of the cation, the more covalent will be the bond between that ion and some anion.

Hydrolysis

When anhydrous halides, such as $MgCl_2$, $AlCl_3$, $BeCl_2$, and BCl_3, are dissolved in water, it is believed that hydrolysis reactions proceed by the following mechanism:

(1) Water molecules orient themselves with respect to the charged species making up the halide. Take a case: $AlCl_3$, while not an ionic compound, is not purely covalent either. The valence electrons of the Al atoms are greatly shifted to the more electronegative Cl atoms, giving rise to considerable polarity, $+$ at the Al and $-$ at the Cl. Water molecules are dipoles, the two H atoms making nearly a tetrahedral angle with the O atom:

This results in a center of $-$ charge at the O and a center of $+$ charge between the hydrogens. Thus the O end of a water molecule is attracted towards the positive Al and the H end toward the negative Cl. The net result is the separation and hydration of the Al^{+++} ions and the Cl^- ions.

(2) From Chapter 1, it can be seen that the Cl^- is a rather large ion and so cannot be expected to exert much influence on a water molecule. On the other hand, the Al has a $+3$ charge and is relatively small. It is able to exert a great influence on the water molecules surrounding it. This influence is so great as to weaken the H—O bond in the water, permitting the following type of reaction to occur:

$$Al(OH_2)_6^{+++} + H_2O \leftrightarrows Al(OH)(OH_2)_5^{++} + H_3O^+$$

setting free hydronium ions. This reaction is reversible, and its equilibrium constant can be measured. As is expected, no such reaction with the Cl^- is observed.

The same general rule governs the hydrolysis of hydrated cations as applies to the basicity of hydroxides. The smaller the ion and the greater its positive charge, the greater its influence on its water molecules of hydration will be. Thus:

$$Mg(OH_2)_4{}^{++} + H_2O \rightleftharpoons Mg(OH)(OH_2)_3{}^+ + H_3O^+ \quad \left. \begin{array}{l} \text{increasing} \\ \text{hydrolysis} \end{array} \right.$$

$$Be(OH_2)_4{}^{++} + H_2O \rightleftharpoons Be(OH)(OH_2)_3{}^+ + H_3O^+$$

$$Al(OH_2)_6{}^{+++} + H_2O \rightleftharpoons Al(OH)(OH_2)_5{}^{++} + H_3O^+$$

until BCl_3 is hydrolyzed completely and irreversibly in water and the hydrated B^{+++} ion does not exist at all.

USES

Aluminum and magnesium are being used in ever-increasing quantities as structural metals. Just short of a million tons of aluminum metal were produced in the United States in 1951. In the same year the national production of magnesium metal was a little less than 50,000 tons. However stand-by facilities are available that could treble the output of magnesium. Both metals are much lighter than iron, and they can rival the strength of iron in alloys with the proper elements.

The metal aluminum can be put to rather unique use by virtue of the very great heat of formation of its oxide. Such large quantities of heat are liberated when aluminum oxide is formed that aluminum is capable of reducing the oxides of most of the other metals. This reaction is called the Goldschmidt reaction. Its use is in welding, since a mixture of Fe_2O_3 and Al will react with the liberation of enough heat to melt the resulting iron and permit it to flow into the cracks that are to be welded.

Magnesium metal finds use as a "getter" in the outgassing of vacuum tubes. Not only does the ignited metal absorb oxygen to form magnesium oxide, but it also absorbs nitrogen to form magnesium nitride. Magnesium oxide made from dolomite is used on a large scale by the steel industry as a basic lining for furnaces. Two very common household drugs are compounds of magnesium; namely, Epsom salts, $MgSO_4 \cdot 7H_2O$, and milk of magnesia, which is a suspension of magnesium oxide in water.

Aluminum sulfate forms highly hydrated double salts with all of the alkali metal sulfates except lithium. These salts are called alums, are isomorphous with one another, and have the formulae $Me_2SO_4 \cdot Al_2(SO_4)_3 \cdot 24H_2O$. Not only can a number of univalent cations occupy the Me^+ position in these salts, but Fe^{+++} and Cr^{+++} can replace the Al^{+++}. Most of the alums are quite soluble in hot water but much less soluble in cold water. They are therefore easy to prepare and purify by recrystallization. Alums have been made since the time of the early Roman Empire, and probably before that. If it is recalled that all aluminum salts are extensively hydrolyzed in water solution, the uses for alums are immediately apparent:

$$Al(OH_2)_6^{+++} + H_2O \rightleftharpoons Al(OH)(OH_2)_5^{++} + H_3O^+$$
$$Al(OH)(OH_2)_5^{++} + H_2O \rightleftharpoons Al(OH)_2(OH_2)_4^+ + H_3O^+$$
$$Al(OH)_2(OH_2)_4^+ + H_2O \rightleftharpoons \underline{Al_2O_3 \cdot xH_2O} + H_3O^+$$

They can serve as sources of hydrogen ions, which is their function in baking powders and fire extinguishers. In addition, since the hydrous aluminum oxide has excellent adsorbing qualities, alums are used as clarifying agents in water purification and as mordants in the dye trade.

The most important compound of boron is borax. It is useful as a cleansing agent by virtue of its hydrolysis to a mildly basic solution. When fused, it forms an acidic glass which will dissolve basic metal oxides, some of which impart a characteristic color to the melt; hence its use in the "borax-bead" tests in analytical chemistry and as a flux in soldering and welding. The boron hydrides are being extensively investigated at present as possible high-energy, low-weight rocket fuels. The very weak boric acid serves in medicine as an eye-wash.

Beryllium compounds find very limited use. The gem emerald has been mentioned, and the element is a minor constituent of a few alloys.

SUGGESTIONS FOR FURTHER READING

G. D. Parkes and J. W. Mellor, *Mellor's Modern Inorganic Chemistry*, new ed., Longmans, Green, New York, 1939, Chapters XXVII and XXIX.

O. K. Rice, *Electronic Structure and Chemical Binding*, McGraw-Hill, New
York, 1940, pp. 421–438.

M. E. Weeks, *Discovery of the Elements*, 6th ed., Journal of Chemical
Education, Easton, Pa., 1956, Chapter XIX.

STUDY QUESTIONS

1. Write a balanced equation to show the reduction of NO_3^- ion to NH_3
by aluminum in boiling NaOH solution.

2. Look up a satisfactory method for the separation of beryllium and
aluminum salts.

3. The Hall Process uses pure aluminum oxide. Bauxite contains
impurities of iron and silicon oxides. How are they removed to leave pure
oxide for cell use?

4. Suppose separate samples of $AlCl_3$, $FeCl_3$,   *Ionic Radii in Å*
$MnCl_2$, and $InCl_3$ were dissolved in separate beakers Al^{+++} 0.50
such that 0.1-molar solutions resulted in each case. Fe^{+++} 0.60
All of the solutions are acidic as a result of hydrolysis. In^{+++} 0.81
List the solutions in order of decreasing pH. Explain Mn^{++} 0.80
your reasoning.

5. Which do you think requires the higher temperature to decompose
into metal oxide and carbon dioxide, limestone or magnesite? Why?

6. What happens when:
   (a) A solution of $AlCl_3$ is added to a solution of ammonia?
   (b) $NaAlO_2$ is treated with strong hydrochloric acid?
   (c) $BeCl_2$ is added to excess NaOH solution?

7. Write the formulae for as many different alums as you think exist.
Look up the color and solubility of each in a handbook.

8. Offer an explanation for the fact the complex ion BF_4^- is quite stable
whereas BCl_4^- does not exist.

9. Ga_2O_3 is amphoteric. Sc_2O_3 is basic only. Is this as you might
expect? Why, or why not?

10. Describe in detail your mental picture of what happens when
barium oxide dissolves in water.

11. A sample of magnesium nitride yielded a quantity of ammonia
(on hydrolysis with water and subsequent distillation) sufficient to neu-
tralize 100 ml of 0.25-molar HCl. How many grams of ammonia were
produced? How many grams of magnesium nitride must have been used
to yield this quantity of ammonia?

12. What simple chemical test would distinguish between Mg and Al?

13. What happens when the following substances are mixed?
   (a) H_3BO_3 + HCl(aqueous)

    (b) $Al(OH)_3 + HCl$(aqueous)

    (c) $BeSO_4 +$ excess $NaOH$(aqueous)

    (d) $MgSO_4 +$ excess $NaOH$(aqueous)

    (e) $Mg_3N_2 + H_2O$

14. By means of equations and a few words about conditions, show how to carry out the following conversions:

    (a) Make $AlCl_3$ from $AlCl_3 \cdot 6H_2O$.

    (b) Make Mg_3N_2 from dolomite.

    (c) Make B_2H_6 from borax.

    (d) Make $Al(ClO_4)_3 \cdot 6H_2O$ from alum.

    (e) Make BCl_3 from H_3BO_3.

15. In terms of the relative polarity of the X—O—H bonds, give the reason for the orders of basicity in the following series of compounds:

    (a) $NaOH > Mg(OH)_2 > Al(OH)_3 > Si(OH)_4$

    (b) $Ba(OH)_2 > Sr(OH)_2 > Ca(OH)_2 > Mg(OH)_2 > Be(OH)_2$

    (c) $MnO > Mn_2O_3 > MnO_2 > Mn_2O_2$

    (d) $HClO > HClO_2 > HClO_3 > HClO_4$

Chapter 9   Group IIIa

ELEMENTS IN THE GROUP

Group IIIa contains many more elements than any other sub-group in the periodic table. We have seen in Chapter 1 that after lanthanum the 4f-sublevel begins to fill, giving 14 inner transition elements before hafnium, the group IVa element in the sixth period, is reached. These 14 elements and lanthanum are arbitrarily placed in group IIIa below scandium and yttrium in order to preserve the general outline of the periodic table. They do form a series with very similar properties, the most notable of which is that the tri-valent oxidation state is the most stable for all of them. The name "rare earths"* is generally used for these elements, but yttrium, and sometimes even scandium, are included under that name. The more precise term, "lanthanides," stands for elements 57–71 inclusive.

In the seventh period the situation is even more complicated. Element 89, actinium, certainly belongs in group IIIa, but the next element, thorium, belongs at least as properly in group IV as in group III on the basis of its chemical properties and electron configuration. Beyond thorium it is clear that a series similar to the lanthanide series is developing, in which electrons are filling the

---

* The term "earth" strictly means oxide, and the elements should be identified as "rare-earth elements" or "rare-earth metals" and their compounds as "rare-earth-element salts" or "rare-earth-metal salts." Common usage shortens these to "rare earths" for the elements themselves, "rare-earth salts," etc. Even the redundant "rare-earth oxides" is used. The same kind of thing happens with the alkali metals and alkaline earth elements. The meaning is usually clear from the context, and since the student will encounter a variety of usage in his outside reading, we shall follow both strict and common usage in this text.

5f-sublevel. The irregularities are much greater at the beginning of the actinide series than at the beginning of the lanthanide series, however, and the regular group properties are not the most characteristic of the elements until after uranium. Indeed, the separation from one other of the elements following actinium is much easier than the separation of the early lanthanides because of the greater differences in chemical properties. We still arbitrarily put all the known elements after actinium into group IIIa, because element 104, if it is ever made, will belong below hafnium in group IVa. We shall call actinium and all the known elements after it the "actinides," with the understanding that the series, at least in the beginning, is not nearly so regular as the lanthanide series. It is profitable, nevertheless, to keep the chemistry of thorium in mind when studying group IVa and uranium with group VIa.

OCCURRENCE AND HISTORY

The elements of subgroup IIIa are found in widely distributed deposits which are always mixtures of the elements. Most of them are not really very rare—silver is less abundant than 18 out of the 31—but the absence of large quantities of concentrated ores plus the great chemical similarities among many of them make the isolation of the pure individual elements extremely difficult in most cases.

The rare earths have been loosely divided into two groups on the basis of their occurrence together in ores and of their separation by the fractional precipitation of double sulfates of the trivalent ions and sodium ion. Named for the most abundant element in their principal ores, they are the cerium group, with slightly soluble double sulfates $[Na_2SO_4 \cdot (C.E.)_2(SO_4)_3 \cdot 2H_2O]^*$ consisting of La, Ce, Pr, Nd, (Pm), Sm, and Eu, and the yttrium group, with more soluble sulfates consisting of Y, Gd, Tb, Dy, Ho, Er, Tm, Yb, Lu, and Sc when the last is present. The most common rare-earth deposits are of two kinds, phosphates and silicates. Two well-known phosphate ores are monazite, composed principally of cerium group earths bearing varying amounts of thorium silicate, and xenotime, rich in yttrium group elements. Allanite, cerite, and gadolinite are typical

---

* The abbreviations R.E., C.E., Y.E. are generally used for rare earth, cerium earth, and yttrium earth respectively.

silicate ores, the first two containing predominantly cerium group earths, while the latter is a good source of yttrium group earths and scandium. Promethium does not occur on earth since its longest-lived isotope has a half-life of only about 30 years, not nearly long enough for it to have survived during the 5 billion years or so of the earth's existence. It has been isolated in milligram quantities from the fission products of uranium. The relative abundances of the individual lanthanides, given in Table 9.1, are an excellent example of the generalization made in Chapter 1 that elements of even atomic number are more abundant than the adjacent elements of odd atomic number.

TABLE 9.1
Relative Abundance of Rare Earths

Name	Atomic Number	Symbol	Percentage of the Family (average)
Lanthanum	57	La	7
Cerium	58	Ce	31
Praseodymium	59	Pr	5
Neodymium	60	Nd	18
Promethium	61	Pm	?
Samarium	62	Sm	7
Europium	63	Eu	0.1
Gadolinium	64	Gd	7
Terbium	65	Tb	1
Dysprosium	66	Dy	7
Holmium	67	Ho	1
Erbium	68	Er	7
Thulium	69	Tm	1
Ytterbium	70	Yb	7
Lutetium	71	Lu	1.5

Of the actinides, only thorium and uranium occur in appreciable quantities; note that they both have even atomic numbers. They are radioactive, but possess isotopes with half-lives comparable to the age of the earth. Their more important naturally occurring isotopes are given in Table 9.2.

The principal ore of uranium is pitchblende, impure U_3O_8, which contains, besides other oxides of uranium, some thorium silicate and all the radioactive decay products of uranium and thorium in relative amounts directly proportional to their half-lives. That is, helium and all the elements between uranium and lead are present

TABLE 9.2

The Naturally Occurring Isotopes of Thorium and Uranium

Symbol	Percentage Abundance	Half-life
^{232}Th	100	1.4×10^{10} years
^{234}U	0.0058	2.48×10^5 years
^{235}U	0.715	7.13×10^8 years
^{238}U	99.28	4.49×10^9 years

in pitchblende, but some only in minute amounts. Actinium and protoactinium were discovered in pitchblende, as we have seen francium was. The elements beyond uranium have been produced artificially in recent years by means of cyclotrons and nuclear reactors. A list of the longest-lived or best-known isotopes of the remaining actinides is given in Table 9.3.

TABLE 9.3

Some Isotopes of the Actinides

Name	Atomic No.	Isotope	Half-life
Actinium	89	^{227}Ac	22.0 years
Protoactinium	91	^{231}Pa	3.43×10^4 years
Neptunium	93	^{237}Np	2.20×10^6 years
Plutonium	94	^{239}Pu	2.44×10^4 years
Americium	95	^{243}Am	8.8×10^3 years
Curium	96	^{245}Cm	1.2×10^4 years
Berkelium	97	^{249}Bk	290 days
Californium	98	^{249}Cf	400 years
Einsteinium	99	^{253}E	19 days
Fermium	100	^{254}Fm	3.3 hours
Mendelevium	101	^{256}Mv	few hours
—	102	—	

The story of sub-group IIIa is a fascinating narrative in the history of chemistry which is not complete even today because of the controversy which still exists about the position of thorium, protoactinium, and uranium in the periodic table. We can only mention some of the highlights here. The beginning was made by John Gadolin in 1794 with the announcement of the discovery of a new earth, yttria. It was actually a mixture of oxides; indeed, the history of the rare earths is full of examples of mixtures, mistakenly being regarded as pure compounds. More than a century was required to sort out and isolate all the natural rare earths. In some cases many thousands of fractional crystallizations and precipitations were necessary to separate adjacent pairs of elements. When scandium was isolated in 1879, it was found to have the properties predicted by Mendelejeff for ekaboron. In fact, it was not known for certain how many rare earths there should be until the work of Bohr on atomic structure and of Moseley on atomic numbers in the second decade of this century. For an interesting result of this knowledge, see the discussion of the discovery of hafnium in Chapter 13.

The tremendous growth of nuclear science is evidenced by the fact that neptunium, the first transuranic element, was not discovered until 1940, but by 1957 102 elements had been listed.

Since the rare earths, including scandium and yttrium, form a regular series about which much knowledge has accumulated over the years, we shall discuss them first as a group. Then the general features of the actinides will be mentioned for comparison with the lanthanides, and the chemistry of the well-known thorium and uranium will be taken up in some detail.

THE RARE EARTHS

PREPARATION OF THE ELEMENTS

The rare earths are very electropositive elements, and are therefore prepared by methods similar to those used in the preparation of magnesium and the alkaline earths. A good small-scale method is to electrolyze an alcoholic solution of the anhydrous chloride using a mercury cathode, thereby forming an amalgam. The rare-earth metal is left as a residue after removing the mercury by vacuum distillation at high temperature.

PHYSICAL PROPERTIES OF THE ELEMENTS

The rare earths are high-melting metals, the melting point increasing with atomic number in the lanthanides. The usual decrease in atomic and ionic radii in going across a period is exhibited by the lanthanides (see Figure 9.1). Europium and ytterbium are off the smooth curve, but this is because they crystallize in the cubic system, whereas all the others form hexagonal close-packed lattices,

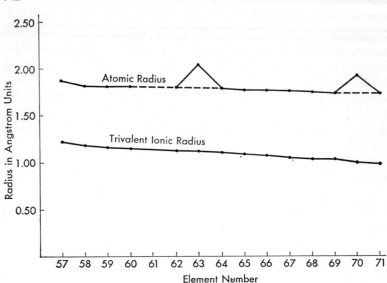

Fig. 9.1 Radii of the landthanides.

and the radii are calculated from the atomic volumes of the usual elementary form. The net effect of the small but steady decrease in atomic volume, or increase in density, for so many elements in one place shows up as an interesting result in the atomic sizes and densities of the other elements in this vicinity of the periodic table. From Table 9.4, it can be seen that in the groups preceding the lanthanides, a steady gradation in atomic volume is observed,

TABLE 9.4
Densities and Atomic Volumes of Group IIIa and Elements Next to It

	Ca	Sc	Ti
density (g/cc)	1.6	2.5	4.5
atomic volume (cc/gram atom)	26	18	11
	Sr	Y	Zr
	2.6	4.3	6.5
	34	21	14
	Ba	La–Lu	Hf
	3.5	6.2 9.7	13.1
	39	22 18	14

whereas zirconium and hafnium are the same size. A great increase in density results in the sixth period after the lanthanides.

This decrease in size is called the "lanthanide contraction." Its chemical effects are more startling than those on physical properties. Because of it, the second two elements in the later a-subgroups resemble each other much more than they do the first. In fact, zirconium and hafnium are so similar chemically that their separation is more difficult than that of two adjacent rare earths. The similarity extends, with decreasing effect, across into group VIII. We shall see it many times in the chemistry of the remaining a-subgroups.

CHEMICAL PROPERTIES AND COMPOUNDS

The +3 oxidation state is the most stable for scandium, yttrium, and the lanthanides, and it is the only oxidation state for most of them. In this state there is a very close similarity in chemical properties, especially between adjacent elements in the lanthanide series. This similarity results from the fact that their electron configurations differ only in inner subshells, principally in the 4f orbitals. The +3 ions form strongly basic, but insoluble, oxides, somewhere between magnesium and calcium oxides in basicity. With ions of the same charge and outer electron configuration (s^2p^6) as these, differences in basicity can be related accurately to the ionic size. We expect and find, then, a decrease in basicity from lanthanum to lutetium, with yttrium falling near holmium. Scandium, the smallest, is the least basic, although even it, unlike aluminum, is not amphoteric. With the outer electron configuration of xenon, these ions are not expected to be strong complex formers. They are not, but the +3 charge gives rise to a moderate tendency in this direction. Of special interest are the citrate complexes used in ion-exchange separations (see below).

Some of the lanthanides exhibit oxidation states other than the group valence of +3. The only stable higher valence is that of cerium(IV), but praseodymium and terbium show some tendency to go to higher states, although not to stoichiometric compounds. The lower state of +2 is relatively easily achieved by europium and ytterbium, less easily by samarium. These departures are easily rationalized in terms of the electron configurations; conditions of relative stability are completely empty, completely full, and half-full subshells. Note that gadolinium +3 ion is the rare-earth ion with a half-full 4f sublevel. The element just before it, europium, reaches this configuration in the +2 ion: terbium, just after it, reaches it in the +4 state. Cerium, and to a lesser extent praseodymium, go to the empty 4f condition of lanthanum in higher oxidation states: ytterbium goes to the full 4f subshell of lutetium in the +2 ion.

Chemical Reactions of the Elements

The metals, once prepared, are very active. They react with water to liberate hydrogen, and with oxygen to form oxides: cerium, praseodymium, and terbium going higher than the sesquioxides (*sesqui-*, a Latin prefix meaning one and a half). With halogens and sulfur, halides and sulfides are produced. The nitrides, hydrides, and carbides of these elements, made by direct synthesis at high temperature, are different from those of the alkaline earth elements, as are those of the other transition elements. Rather than being ionic or covalent compounds which obey our usual ideas of stoichiometry, they are interstitial compounds in which the nonmetal atoms occupy spaces between the metal atoms in the metallic lattice. We have seen this type of compound in Chapter 3.

Oxides

The hydrous oxides are precipitated by adding a base to a soluble rare-earth salt. Thermal dehydration gives the sesquioxides generally. A suspension of lanthanum oxide in water absorbs carbon dioxide to form the carbonate, which is a good indication of its basic strength. The oxides are readily soluble in most acids. They are insoluble in bases, although they may appear to dissolve through colloid formation by peptization.

Chlorides

The hydrated chlorides, with six or seven waters of crystallization, can be crystallized from aqueous solution. Thermal dehydration to the anhydrous salt must be carried out in a stream of dry hydrogen chloride gas in order to prevent hydrolysis. The anhydrous chlorides, except cerium, may also be prepared by heating the oxides with a large excess of ammonium chloride, followed by sublimation of the excess reagent. The hydrolysis of the chloride is prevented by the excess of the acidic ammonium chloride:

$$La_2O_3 + 6NH_4Cl \xrightarrow{\Delta} 2LaCl_3 + 3\overline{H_2O} + 6\overline{NH_3}$$

Simple Salts

Salts of the rare-earth elements can generally be prepared by acid-base reactions followed by crystallization of the hydrated compound for the soluble ones, or by precipitation for the insoluble ones. The halides (except the fluorides), nitrates, perchlorates, and bromates are very soluble; the sulfates are soluble (2 to 50 g. of R.E.$_2$(SO$_4$)$_3$·8H$_2$O per 100 g. of water at 20°C); the carbonates, phosphates, fluorides, and oxalates are insoluble in water and all except strongly acid solutions. In analytical procedures, the rare earths are usually precipitated as oxalates of uncertain hydration, and determined by ignition to the oxides.

The colors of the hydrated trivalent ions show an interesting periodicity; the colors of the elements the same distance from the end of the series are the same, and the intensity of color goes through two maxima: see Table 9.5.

TABLE 9.5
Colors of Hydrated Rare Earth Ions

Symbol	At. No.	Color of $Me(OH_2)_x^{+3}$	At. No.	Symbol
La^{+++}	57	←——————— colorless ——————→	71	Lu^{+++}
Ce^{+++}	58	←——————— colorless ——————→	70	Yb^{+++}
Pr^{+++}	59	←—— yellowish —— green —— pale ——→	69	Tm^{+++}
Nd^{+++}	60	←—— red-violet —— —— rose ——→	68	Er^{+++}
Pm^{+++}	61	←——————— yellow ——————→	67	Ho^{+++}
Sm^{+++}	62	←——————— pale yellow ——————→	66	Dy^{+++}
Eu^{+++}	63	←——————— pale pink ——————→	65	Tb^{+++}
Gd^{+++}	64	←——————— colorless		

The physical properties of the rare-earth ions have been subject to intense study because many of them are determined by the 4f electrons which, being rather deep inside the atom, are freer from outside disturbances than the physically active electrons of other ions. Among the many interesting properties are the magnetic properties of the ions and their absorption spectra.

Double Salts and Fractional Crystallization

There are a large number of compounds in inorganic chemistry which fall into the class of double salts. These are solid compounds in which more than one cation or more than one anion are present in stoichiometric proportions. Examples of the former type are more numerous: the alums; the sodium-rare earth sulfates, $Na_2SO_4 \cdot R.E._2(SO_4)_3 \cdot xH_2O$; the magnesium-cerium earth nitrates, $3Mg(NO_3)_2 \cdot 2C.E.(NO_3)_3 \cdot 24H_2O$. The latter type is exemplified by lead chloride fluoride, $PbClF$. These double salts differ from true complex compounds, such as K_2HgI_4, in that no definite structural aggregates are formed either in the solid or in solution by the double salts. Hence their formulas are usually written with dots and not in the normal manner for complex compounds (see Appendix B). Actually, there is probably a complete gradation from one type to the other. The subject is a field of very active research in inorganic chemistry today.

The two double salts of the rare earths mentioned above are particularly useful in separation procedures for isolating the individual elements. They are neither very soluble nor very insoluble in water, so that they can be easily crystallized, and advantage can be taken of slight differences in solubility in separating the elements. Of course, a clean separation in one, or even a few, crystallizations cannot be achieved. We have seen that the double sodium sulfates of the cerium group are less soluble than those of the yttrium group. This separation is carried out by dissolving the oxides in the least possible amount of nitric acid and adding anhydrous sodium sulfate to the solution until the neodymium color has disappeared from the solution. (A handy instrument for this test is a hand spectroscope.) The separation is not perfect, but it is adequate for rough separation into the cerium and yttrium groups. The double magnesium nitrates are then used to separate the cerium earths. Many fractional crystallizations must be used to effect even a partial separation into individual components. The method is tedious and time-consuming, but necessary in rare-earth separations. A typical scheme for a fractional crystallization is shown in Figure 9.2.

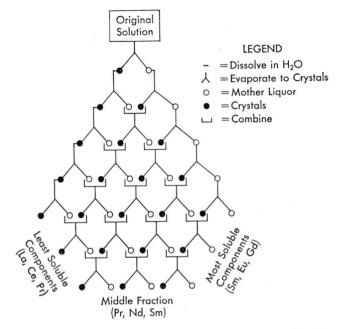

LEGEND

− = Dissolve in H_2O
人 = Evaporate to Crystals
○ = Mother Liquor
● = Crystals
⊔ = Combine

Least Soluble Components (La, Ce, Pr)

Most Soluble Components (Sm, Eu, Gd)

Middle Fraction (Pr, Nd, Sm)

Fig. 9.2 Separation of cerium earths by fractional crystallization.

Other Oxidation States

Cerium forms a series of $+4$ compounds, almost all of which are complex or insoluble. When base is added to a soluble cerium(III) salt, the colorless sesquioxide precipitates, but it soon becomes colored owing to oxidation by air, and eventually goes to the yellow hydrous dioxide. Anhydrous cerium(IV) oxide can be made by heating the hydrous oxide, or merely by igniting in air the cerium(III) salt of any volatile acid. (This behavior gives rise to errors in the determination of rare earths by ignition of the oxalates to the oxides when cerium is present; the presence of praseodymium and terbium has the same effect.) The oxide is soluble in strong acids. It oxidizes hydrochloric acid to chlorine, but merely dissolves in sulfuric or nitric acids to give sulfato or nitrato complexes. The hexanitrato-cerate(IV) ion, a good oxidizing agent, is often used instead of permanganate in oxidimetry. With very strong bases, cerates can be formed, such as Na_2CeO_3.

The existence of a stable $+4$ valence for cerium makes it possible to separate the element from the other cerium earths quantitatively in a one-step process. A nitric acid solution of the earths is nearly neutralized with calcium carbonate and the cerium oxidized by boiling with potassium bromate. If the acidity is right, the cerium hydrolyzes as it is oxidized and precipitates as the slightly soluble basic cerium(IV) nitrate, while the others remain in solution. Thus, in addition to being the most abundant, cerium is the most easily separated of the group.

The higher valences of praseodymium and terbium are prac-tically limited to the oxides. The sesquioxides upon ignition in an oxidizing atmosphere take up more oxygen, but they do not go to definite compounds.

Samarium, europium, and ytterbium compounds can be con-verted to the divalent state in the wet way by electrolysis or reduc-tion with amalgamated zinc in a Jones reductor (see Chapter 13), or in the dry way by heating in a stream of hydrogen. They may be partially reduced in the ignition of an oxalate precipitate, leading to an error opposite to that caused by cerium, etc. As might be expected by analogy with barium, the carbonates and sulfates are insoluble, the former serving as a useful starting material for many other $+2$ salts. The europium(II) salts, when precipitated and dried, are stable towards oxidation by dry air. Advantage is taken of these lower oxidation states to effect less tedious separations of these elements from the other earths.

ION EXCHANGE

The rapid development of ion-exchange chromatography has rejuvenated the chemistry of the rare earths. Using this technique in combination with classical fractional crystallization, it is possible to separate macro quantities of the individual earths in a fraction of the time formerly consumed.

For many years it has been known that cations in solution will exchange with cations in soils. In Chapter 12 it is shown that most silicates contain simple uni- or divalent cations bound ionically. When equilibrated with solutions containing other cations, exchange takes place. Water may be softened in this way, where calcium and magnesium ions in the water replace sodium or potassium ions in a "zeolite." The exchange capacity of a material is the number of equivalents of exchangeable cation per unit weight of material. The capacity of natural materials is limited. Recently synthetic organic ion-exchange resins have been developed that have much greater exchange capacity. In appearance the available resins vary in color from white to dark brown and may be obtained in particle sizes from 10- to 20-mesh* down to colloidal dimensions. Cation and anion exchangers are available in a wide range of acid or base strengths. In the former case, each little sphere is an organic polymeric network with a negative charge on the lattice, which charge is neutralized by cations within the body of the sphere. If the cations are all sodium ions, the resin is said to be in the "sodium form." If they are all hydrogen ions, it is said to be in the hydrogen form. The dry spheres of resin expand considerably when mixed with water, indicating that some water is absorbed into the resin, principally to hydrate the ions. Once swollen, however, any additional water forms a separate phase resulting in a slurry of the resin in water. If a solution of sodium chloride is mixed with a cation-exchange resin in the hydrogen form, an equilibrium will be established in which some of the sodium ions have replaced hydrogen ions in the resin, forming hydrochloric acid in the water phase. The system can be treated using the mass law:

$$HR + Na^+ \rightleftharpoons NaR + H_3O^+$$

where HR indicates hydrogen ion in the resin phase, NaR sodium ion in the resin phase, and Na^+ and H_3O^+ the ions in solution.

At equilibrium

$$K = \frac{[H_3O^+] \times [NaR]}{[Na^+] \times [HR]}$$

Equilibrium constants for many cations may be determined for a particular resin, establishing the relative replacing power of the

* A 10-mesh screen has 10 openings to the inch.

cations for that particular resin. Differences in equilibrium constants may be used to effect a separation of very similar cations. Suppose a long column is filled with an ion-exchange slurry forming a bed through which solutions will pass by gravity. Let the resin be in the hydrogen form, and sodium and potassium be the ions to be separated. The cations are absorbed on a small portion of the bed at the top of the column when the total resin exchange capacity is large relative to the equivalents of sodium and potassium. Then a dilute solution of hydrochloric acid is passed through the column.

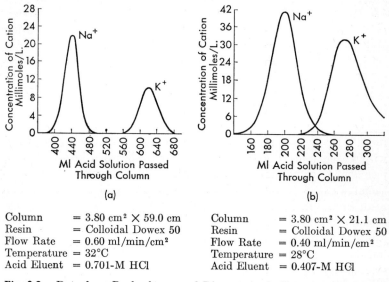

Column	= 3.80 cm² × 59.0 cm	Column	= 3.80 cm² × 21.1 cm
Resin	= Colloidal Dowex 50	Resin	= Colloidal Dowex 50
Flow Rate	= 0.60 ml/min/cm²	Flow Rate	= 0.40 ml/min/cm²
Temperature	= 32°C	Temperature	= 28°C
Acid Eluent	= 0.701-M HCl	Acid Eluent	= 0.407-M HCl

Fig. 9.3. Data from Beukenkamp and Rieman, Anal. Chem. *22*, 582 (1950).

As the acid solution reaches the bed, it will replace some Na^+ and K^+ in the resin by H^+, but by slightly different amounts because of the different equilibrium constants. The solution carries the Na^+ and K^+ farther down the column, where some Na^+ and K^+ will replace H^+ in that part of the bed which is in the hydrogen form. As more fresh acid solution is fed into the top of the column, more Na^+ and K^+ will be carried farther down the column, but the two ions will be carried at different rates because of the difference in equilibrium constants. The acid solution will eventually "elute" both cations from the column, but not at the same time. Plotting the concentration of Na^+ and K^+ in the effluent as a function of the amount of solution passed through the column, typical elution curves shown in Figure 9.3 are obtained. Notice that all of the Na^+ is eluted before the K^+ in 9.3(a), whereas some cross con-tamination occurs in 9.3(b). Rate of flow of solution through the column, length of the column, pH of eluent solution, particle size of resin, and temperature are factors determining the positions and shape of the elution curves.

The rare earths can be separated by the same technique. Actually it is more convenient to carry out rough separations by means of fractional crystallization and take fractions containing only a few elements for separation on a column. It is necessary to use complex-ing agents, usually citrate ion, in the eluent solution for rare-earth separations in order to obtain favorable equilibrium constants, since the tripositive ions are more strongly adsorbed by the resin than are the alkali ions.

USES

The rare earths find limited use, the most familiar being in an alloy of the metals with iron called misch metal used in cigarette lighter flints. The alloy showers sparks when scratched. Ceric oxidimetry has been mentioned. A mixture of praseodymium and neodymium, called didymium and once thought to be one ele-ment, colors glass blowers' glasses pink and absorbs out the yellow sodium-D lines. A former large use of the oxides was in gas-mantles.

THE ACTINIDES

The actinide series is not nearly so regular as the lanthanide series. Only two of the elements, thorium and uranium, are available to the average chemist for study, and extensive work on them has just become possible in the past few years. The results so far indi-cate that a "rare-earth series" is present in the seventh period, but at the beginning, at least, it is much more irregular than the one of the sixth period. Figure 9.4 shows the known oxidation states of these elements; those underlined are especially stable, those in parentheses are rare.

Ac	Th	Pa	U	Np	Pu	Am	Cm	Bk	Cf	E	Fm	Mv
						2						
3	(3)		3	3	3	3	3	3	3	3	3	3
	4	(4)	4	4	4	(4)		4				
		5	(5)	5	(5)							
			6	6	6	6						

Fig. 9.4

The actinide with a half-full 5f subshell is curium, and there the +3 oxidation state is at last the most stable. For an up-to-date account of the chemistry of the actinides, the reader is advised to go to the latest literature. Any survey given here would be out of date by the time this text went to press.

THORIUM

The only stable valency of thorium is the +4 state. The white ThO_2, by virtue of the large size of the cation, is the most strongly basic dioxide known. It is basic only (compare CeO_2, HfO_2, PbO_2, etc.) and forms a series of salts with oxy-acids unknown for any other ion with such a high charge. These salts are hydrolyzed in aqueous solution, but hydrated nitrates, sulfates, and perchlorates can be isolated from strongly acid solutions. They are all white. The oxalate is insoluble and comes down with the rare earths in separation procedures. The white anhydrous chloride can be got by dry methods only, such as by passing chlorine over a hot mixture of the oxide and carbon:

$$ThO_2 + 2C + 4Cl_2 \xrightarrow{\Delta} ThCl_4 + 2COCl_2$$

Only a few complex compounds are known. The properties of thorium are best predicted by treating it as the *third* element in subgroup IVa; titanium as the first, and zirconium and hafnium identically as the second.

URANIUM

Uranium is a much more complicated element than thorium, and far more complicated than its analog in the lanthanide series, neodymium. It has many oxidation states, of which +6 is the most stable and +4 the next.

The Metal

Uranium is a very dense, silvery metal. Its tremendous military and commercial importance as the fuel in nuclear reactors is well known today. Actually the natural mixture of isotopes has to be enriched considerably in the 235 isotope before use as a bomb or nuclear fuel. This is accomplished by repeated gaseous diffusion of the hexafluoride, in which the lighter $^{235}UF_6$ diffuses faster than $^{238}UF_6$ by the square root of the inverse ratio of the molecular weights, 1.0043.

The pure metal is difficult to prepare, since it combines with carbon, hydrogen, and nitrogen. It is best made by the reduction of the tetrachloride with an active metal, such as calcium.

The metal is very reactive, burning in air when hot to give U_3O_8. It also reacts with the halogens, nitrogen, and sulfur upon heating. It dissolves in acids (except nitric, to which it is passive) to release hydrogen and form salts of the +4 oxidation state. Bases do not attack uranium.

The +6 Oxidation State

The red trioxide, UO_3, made as various hydrates by adding acid to a solution of a uranate or in the anhydrous state by heating uranyl nitrate, is amphoteric. It dissolves in acids to give a series of salts of the yellow uranyl ion, UO_2^{++}, which has a linear configuration, $O—U—O^{++}$. With bases, uranates are produced, such as $(NH_4)_2U_2O_7$ and Na_2UO_4 which condense like the chromates.

The white hexafluoride, which can be made by the fluorination of the tetrafluoride or other compounds in the presence of a catalyst, is a solid subliming at 56°C. It is the most volatile stable compound of uranium, and hence is the one used in gaseous diffusion separation. It is very reactive, giving, for example, UO_3 with excess water.

A series of complexes of the uranyl ion is also known: for example, $Na_2UO_2Cl_4$.

Pitchblende

This important naturally occurring compound is a mixture of the dioxide and the trioxide, $UO_2 \cdot 2UO_3$, and so is named uranium-(IV,VI) oxide, or more appropriately in the stoichiometric system, triuranium octoxide. It dissolves in acids to give the products expected of its components:

$$U_3O_8 + 8H^+ \rightarrow 2UO_2^{++} + U^{++++} + 4H_2O$$

With nitric acid it is oxidized completely to uranyl nitrate:

$$3U_3O_8 + 20HNO_3 \rightarrow 9UO_2(NO_3)_2 + 2\overline{NO} + 10H_2O$$

which can be crystallized as the 6-hydrate.

The +5 Oxidation State

Pentavalent compounds are relatively rare. When pitchblende is heated with carbon in a stream of chlorine, a mixture of the penta- and tetrachlorides is produced, from which the pentachloride can be sublimed owing to its greater volatility. It is unstable and loses chlorine on standing to give the tetrachloride. The pentafluoride can also be made.

The +4 Oxidation State

Uranium dioxide, made by reducing higher oxides by hydrogen, is a brown, high-melting solid which dissolves with difficulty in acids to give salts resembling thorium salts in basicity; that is, they are easily hydrolyzed, as is expected of salts of an ion with such a high charge. The salts are green (transition elements in intermediate oxidation states are invariably colored), and they also differ from those of thorium in that they are easily oxidized, going to uranyl compounds.

The tetrahalides are generally the product of the action of the halogens on uranium under ordinary conditions. They are extremely hydroscopic and dissolve in water to give hydrolyzed solutions. The dioxide is precipitated from these solutions by the addition of base.

In the tetravalent state, uranium also forms a series of complex compounds, such as K_2UCl_6.

The +3 Oxidation State

The group valency, if indeed uranium is best considered in group III, exists for uranium, but it is not at all common. Trihalides can be made by the reduction of higher halides with hydrogen. They evolve hydrogen from cold water, being oxidized to the +4 state. A few other compounds are known, all of which are also easily oxidized, even by cold water and room temperature air.

SUGGESTIONS FOR FURTHER READING

F. C. Nachod, ed., *Ion Exchange, Theory and Application*, Academic Press, New York, 1949.

D. W. Pearce *et al.*, *Inorganic Synthesis*, vol. II, pp. 29–73 (1946).

N. V. Sidgwick, *The Chemical Elements and Their Compounds*, Oxford, 1950, pp. 439–457, 1069–1096.

G. T. Seaborg and J. J. Katz, *The Actinide Elements*, McGraw-Hill, New York, 1954.

STUDY QUESTIONS

1. What happens in the following cases?
    (a) $La_2(C_2O_4)_3 + O_2$(heat)
    (b) $EuCl_3 + H_2$(heat)
    (c) $Tb + O_2$(heat)
    (d) $Pm_2(SO_4)_3 + H_2O$ electrolysis, Pt electrodes
    (e) $ScCl_3 +$ excess NaOH(aqueous)

2. By means of equations and a few words about conditions, show how to carry out the following conversions:
    (a) Make $Gd_2(SO_4)_3 \cdot 8H_2O$ from $Gd_2(C_2O_4)_3$.
    (b) Make CeO_2 from $CePO_4$.
    (c) Make Dy from Dy_2O_3.
    (d) Make $LaCl_3$ from $LaCl_3 \cdot 6H_2O$.
    (e) Make $2Pr(NO_3) \cdot 3Mg(NO_3)_2 \cdot 24H_2O$ from PrF_3.

3. Give the arguments for and against calling thorium a group III element.

4. Describe the chemical and physical processes used in making pure metallic ^{235}U from pitchblende.

5. What happens in the following cases?
   (a) $UCl_3 + H_2O$
   (b) $Th(SO_4)_2 +$ excess $NaOH$
   (c) $U + H_2SO_4$
   (d) $U + NaOH$
   (e) $UO_3 + NaOH$

6. By means of equations and a few words about conditions, show how to carry out the following conversions:
   (a) Make $ThCl_4$ from ThO_2.
   (b) Make UO_3 from U_3O_8.
   (c) Make UCl_4 from $UO_2(NO_3)_2 \cdot 6H_2O$.
   (d) Make $UO_2(NO_3)_2 \cdot 6H_2O$ from a naturally occurring uranium compound.
   (e) Make $Ac_2(SO_4)_3 \cdot 8H_2O$ from $Ac_2(C_2O_4)_3$.

Chapter 10

Gallium, Indium, and Thallium

OCCURRENCE AND HISTORY

Gallium, indium, and thallium are widespread on the earth's crust, but no concentrated ores have been discovered. Hence, they are regarded as rare elements; their abundances are: Ga, 15 ppm.; In, 0.1 ppm.; Tl 0.6 ppm. They were all discovered spectroscopically, in fact, before they were isolated. Indium and thallium are named for the colors they impart to a flame, indigo and green (Greek *thallos*, a young shoot). Gallium was named after his native France by de Boisbaudran when he observed its spectrum in 1875. Shortly thereafter Mendeleef published an article stating that gallium was probably the element, "eka-aluminum," which he had predicted earlier on the basis of his periodic table. It is interesting to observe how closely the brilliant Russian chemist, whom it is safe to admire because he pre-dates the present government, predicted the properties of gallium. Table 10.1 compares his predictions with the known facts.

Group IIIb elements are recovered as by-products of the production of other elements, especially those isolated from sulfide ores. The main sources of gallium are zinc blende and bauxite, showing that the element has undergone little geochemical fractionation from the chemically similar zinc and aluminum. Indium is usually associated with zinc blende and the tin ore, cassiterite, SnO_2. Thallium is recovered from the residues of pyrites that have been used in the manufacture of sulfuric acid.

TABLE 10.1

Properties Predicted for Ekaaluminum (Ea) by Mendeleef	Properties Found for Boisbaudran's Gallium (Ga)
Atomic weight about 68.	Atomic weight 69.9.*
Metal of specific gravity 5.9; melting point low; non-volatile; unaffected by air; should decompose steam at red heat; should dissolve slowly in acids and alkalies.	Metal of specific gravity 5.94; melting point 30.15; non-volatile at moderate temperature; not changed in air; action of steam unknown; dissolves slowly in acids and alkalies.
Oxide: formula Ea_2O_3; specific gravity 5.5; should dissolve in acids to form salts of the type EaX_3. The hydroxide should dissolve in acids and alkalies.	Oxide: Ga_2O_3; specific gravity unknown; dissolves in acids, forming salts of the type GaX_3. The hydroxide dissolves in acids and alkalies.
Salts should have a tendency to form basic salts; the sulfate should form alums; the sulfide should be precipitated by H_2S or $(NH_4)_2S$. The anhydrous chloride should be more volatile than zinc chloride.	Salts readily hydrolyze and form basic salts; alums are known; the sulfide is precipitated by H_2S and by $(NH_4)_2S$ under special conditions. The anhydrous chloride is more volatile than zinc chloride.
The element will probably be discovered by spectroscopic analysis.	Gallium was discovered with the aid of the spectroscope.

* The 1956 atomic weight is 69.72.

PREPARATION OF THE ELEMENTS

In contrast to aluminum, these elements are easily prepared from the oxides by reduction with hydrogen or carbon. Gallium metal is recovered as a residue from the distillation of zinc or by the electrolysis of the sodium-hydroxide leachings of bauxite. Indium and thallium are recovered from the extracts of the flue dusts of pyrite burners or zinc and lead smelters by many techniques, such as reduction with zinc dust, electrolysis, etc.

PHYSICAL PROPERTIES OF THE ELEMENTS

All three of these metals are silvery, and the heavier two are softer than lead. Like the alkali metals, they have low melting points, but they also have high boiling points, giving them an extremely large liquid range. Gallium, which liquifies on a hot day, tends to supercool easily, so that it is one of the two molten metals that can be held in the hand. It is different from mercury, however, in that it has a great tendency to wet other substances. Its miniscus in a glass tube is just the opposite of that of mercury, as shown in Figure 10.1.

Another point of interest about gallium is that it is one of those relatively rare substances, like water, for which the liquid is more dense than the solid at the melting point.

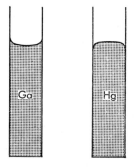

Fig. 10.1

CHEMICAL PROPERTIES AND COMPOUNDS

From the outer electron configurations, ns^2np, valences of $+3$ and $+1$ are expected for Ga, In, and Tl. The $+3$ oxidation state is exhibited by all three, and it is the more stable for Ga and In. The $+1$ state is more stable for thallium than the $+3$; it is rare for indium and gallium. This behavior is the beginning of the general trend in the b-subgroups, for which the lower valencies become *more* stable with increasing atomic number in the subgroup, just the opposite of the trend in the a-subgroups. Also, the stable oxidation numbers differ by 2 rather than the variation of 1 common in the transition elements. Thus, we have the stabilities $Tl^+ > Tl^{+++}$, $Pb^{++} > Pb^{++++}$, $Bi^{+++} > Bi^{+++++}$, etc.

There are, in addition, a few rare compounds of these elements in which the formal oxidation number is $+2$, such as $GaCl_2$. It is considered likely that they are compounds containing Ga in both $+1$ and $+3$ states; for example, $Ga^I[Ga^{III}Cl_4]$.

Chemical Reactions of the Elements

These elements are less active than the other elements of group III. They are unaffected by cold dry air or by water, but thallium gradually tarnishes in moist air. They burn in air upon heating, but the heats of formation of the oxides are less than for Al and the IIIa elements:

$$2Al + 3/2O_2 = Al_2O_3 \; (\alpha) \qquad \Delta H° = -399.1 \text{ kcal.}$$
$$2La + 3/2O_2 = La_2O_3 \qquad\qquad \Delta H° = -458$$
$$2Ga + 3/2O_2 = Ga_2O_3 \text{ (slow)} \qquad \Delta H° = -258$$
$$2In + 3/2O_2 = In_2O_3 \qquad\qquad \Delta H° = -222.5$$
$$Tl + O_2 \quad = \text{ mixture of } Tl_2O \text{ and } Tl_2O_3$$

Consequently, the reduction of the oxides is easier for IIIb than for IIIa, as we have seen.

The elements react with the halogens to give the trihalides, except thallium which forms only a monobromide and monoiodide. This behavior is reminiscent of copper. With sulfur, the sesqui-sulfides are formed upon heating:

$$2Tl + 3S \xrightarrow{\Delta} Tl_2S_3 + \text{heat}$$

All three metals are active enough to liberate hydrogen from acids:

$$2Ga + 6H^+ \rightarrow 2Ga^{+++} + \overline{2H_2}$$
$$2In + 6H^+ \rightarrow 2In^{+++} + \overline{3H_2}$$
$$2Tl + 2H^+ \rightarrow 2Tl^+ + \overline{H_2}$$

They also dissolve in bases, gallium and indium even more readily than in acids:

$$2Ga + 6OH^- + xH_2O \rightarrow 2GaO_3 \cdot xH_2O^{---} + \overline{3H_2}$$
$$2In + 6OH^- + xH_2O \rightarrow 2InO_3 \cdot xH_2O^{---} + 3H_2$$
$$2Tl + 2H_2O \qquad\qquad \rightarrow 2Tl^+ + 2OH^- + \overline{H_2}$$

+3 Oxides

The hydrous oxides of gallium and indium are precipitated from aqueous solutions of their salts by the careful addition of base, preferably ammonium hydroxide. Ignition of the hydrous oxides, or of any oxy-salt, gives the anhydrous sequioxides. Ga_2O_3 is white, In_2O_3 red-brown when hot and pale yellow when cold. When base is added to a solution of a thallium(III) salt, the black, anhydrous Tl_2O_3 precipitates directly. It loses oxygen slowly at 100°, rapidly at higher temperatures, to go to the +1 oxide.

In spite of the larger size of the cation, the amphoteric gallium oxide is more acidic than aluminum oxide: another example of the greater tendency of non-rare-gas type ions to form covalent bonds. (See page 25.) Hydrous gallium oxide will dissolve in excess ammonia, whereas hydrous aluminum oxide will not. Gallium can be separated from most other $+3$ cations on the basis of this marked acidity.

The acid strength of a hydrated cation, such as gallium, is given by the equilibrium constant for the reaction:

$$Ga(H_2O)_x^{+++} + H_2O \rightleftharpoons Ga(H_2O)_{x-1}(OH)^{++} + H_3O^+$$

with $\quad K = \dfrac{[Ga(H_2O)_{x-1}(OH)^{++}][H_3O^+]}{[Ga(H_2O)_x^{+++}]}$

A convenient way of tabulating acid strengths is to give the pK for each reaction of this type (pK is $-$ log K, just as pH is $-$ log [H], and so the lower the pK value, the higher is K, the further is equilibrium is to the right, and the greater is the acidity). One way of measuring pK's is to find the pH of solutions. Generally, second and higher order ionizations have to be taken into account, but for simplicity let us assume that the first ionization is the only important one. The pH of a 0.01m gallium perchlorate solution is 2.41, while that of 0.01m aluminum perchlorate is 3.42. To get the pK of $Ga(H_2O)_x^{+++}$, we calculate as follows:

$[H_3O^+] =$ antilog $(-2.41) = 3.9 \times 10^{-3} = [Ga(H_2O)_{x-1}(OH)^{++}]$

$[Ga(H_2O)_x^{+++}] = 0.01 - 3.9 \times 10^{-3} = 6.1 \times 10^{-3}$

$K = \dfrac{(3.9 \times 10^{-3})^2}{6.1 \times 10^{-3}} = 2.5 \times 10^{-3}$

$pK = 2.60$

For aluminum, the pK value is 4.85, giving a quantitative measure of the difference in acidity.

Indium oxide is mostly basic with only a very slight acidity. Thallium(III) oxide is basic only. The oxides, if not strongly ignited, dissolve in acid solutions from which hydrated salts can be crystallized. Gallium salts are strongly hydrolyzed (about like aluminum salts), indium salts less, while thallium(III) salts are rare because of the ease of reduction of the $+3$ ion.

+3 Halides

These are prepared by methods similar to the preparation of the aluminum halides: the hydrated salts are crystallized from water; the anhydrous halides must be prepared by dry methods. The anhydrous fluorides are ionic, high-melting solids; they are only very slightly soluble in water. The other trihalides of gallium and indium are low-melting, low-boiling solids, such as $GaCl_3$, m.p. 78°, b.p. 201°. They are much more soluble than the fluorides. Again like the aluminum compounds, they are dimerized in the vapor phase, e.g.:

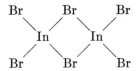

Since thallium(III) is easily reduced to thallium(I), only the anhydrous trifluoride and trichloride can be made, and $TlCl_3$ loses chlorine below 100°. When the hydrated tribromide is dehydrated in a vacuum, it loses bromine as well as water, going to what is apparently the dibromide, $TlBr_2$, but which is probably a complex salt of the +1 and +3 oxidation states; i.e., $Tl^I[Tl^{III}Br_4]$ (see below). A very unstable triiodide can be isolated also, but the most probable explanation for its existence is that it is thallium(I) tri-iodide, $Tl^+I_3^-$ (see Chapter 22 for a discussion of polyhalide ions).

Sulfides

The yellow gallium sulfide resembles aluminum sulfide in that it cannot be precipitated from aqueous solution under ordinary conditions, but must be prepared by dry methods (it is coprecipitated with zinc sulfide, which is the method by which Boisbaudran brought it down). Direct synthesis also gives the red In_2S_3 and black Tl_2S_3. The former may, in addition, be precipitated from aqueous solution in a yellow form. Thallium(III) is reduced by hydrogen sulfide:

$$2Tl^{+++} + 3H_2S \rightarrow \underline{Tl_2S} + \underline{2S} + 6H^+$$

Complexes

The $+3$ ions readily form complexes with halides, water, oxalate, ammonia, etc. Typical complex salts are:

Na_3GaF_6	K_3TlBr_6	$Ga(NH_3)_6Cl_3$ (made the dry way and
K_3InCl_6	$Cs_2Tl_2Cl_9$	decomposed by water, like the aluminum ammine)

The chloro complex of gallium cannot be made from aqueous solution, but it undoubtedly exists in nonaqueous media, since $GaCl_3$ is a good catalyst for the Friedel-Craft reaction, in which the $MeCl_4^-$ ion plays an essential role. The only really stable salts of thallium-(III) are the complex ones where the oxidation potential has been lowered to the point of stability.

Monovalent Thallium

Almost any reducing agent will reduce thallium(III) to thallium(I). The colorless Tl^+ ion resembles in some ways the alkali metal ions and in other ways the silver ion. The yellow thallium(I) hydroxide is quite soluble and a strong base; though not so strong as NaOH, it will burn the skin and etch glass. In this respect it resembles NaOH, yet it loses water at 100° to give the black thallium(I) oxide:

$$2TlOH \xrightarrow{\Delta} Tl_2O + H_2O$$

In this respect it resembles silver. The halides and sulfide are also more like the corresponding silver compounds; the sulfide, chloride, bromide, and iodide are only slightly soluble, whereas the fluoride is soluble. The chloride is white, but photosensitive. Even though the Tl^+ and Rb^+ ions are almost exactly the same size, the halides of Tl^+ have 8:1 coordination-number lattices in the solid state, while the Rb compounds have 6:1 lattices, again showing the greater coordination power of a non-rare-gas type ion.

The solubilities of the other Tl^I salts are like those of K, although they are generally not quite so soluble.

MAGNETOCHEMISTRY

Matter can be divided into three categories on the basis of its magnetic properties: diamagnetic substances, such as water, are repelled by a magnet; paramagnetic substances; such as $CuCl_2$, are attracted; and ferromagnetic substances; such as iron, are strongly attracted. Ferromagnetic attraction is of the order of 1000 times stronger than paramagnetic attraction, which in turn is about 1000 times stronger in magnitude than diamagnetic repulsion. Ferromagnetism occurs only in a few solid substances and will not be discussed further here. Diamagnetism is a property of all matter in all states. Paramagnetism may occur in solids, liquids, and gases also, but it only occurs for certain substances. When it does occur, it generally overcomes the inherent diamagnetism, and a net attraction to a magnet results.

Magnetism is of interest to the chemist because the paramagnetic moment of an atom, molecule, or ion arises from unpaired electrons in the particle. An unpaired electron is one which occupies an orbital alone. Having information about the number of unpaired electrons, then, we know how many electron pairs there are, either paired in the atom or paired in a bond with another atom. It takes energy to form an electron pair in an orbital, and therefore electrons do not pair unless energy considerations are favorable. For example, the fluorine atom has one unpaired electron, as can be seen by writing a circle for each of the orbitals and placing a dot in the circle for each electron in it:

$$2p \quad \odot \quad \odot \quad \ominus$$
$$2s \quad \odot$$
$$1s \quad \odot$$

The fluorine molecule is formed by two atoms sharing their odd electrons in an electron pair bond, the energy given off by forming the bond being greater than the energy required to pair the electrons. F_2 is diamagnetic.

When the five 3d orbitals are filling in the first transition series, the electrons do not pair until they have to—that is, until more than five electrons are in the sublevel. Of course, the sixth electron does not go into a higher sublevel, because that would take more energy than pairing it in an orbital with one of the first five. The 3d orbitals for a few transition metal ion are then:

	3d orbitals					Number of 3d electrons	Number of unpaired electrons
Sc^{+++}	◯	◯	◯	◯	◯	0	0
Ti^{++++}	◯	◯	◯	◯	◯	0	0
Ti^{+++}	☉	◯	◯	◯	◯	1	1
$Mn^{+++++++}$	◯	◯	◯	◯	◯	0	0
Mn^{++++}	☉	☉	☉	☉	◯	3	3
Mn^{++}	☉	☉	☉	☉	☉	5	5
Fe^{++}	☉	☉	☉	☉	☉	6	4
Fe^{+++}	☉	☉	☉	☉	☉	5	5
Co^{++}	☉	☉	☉	☉	☉	7	3
Ni^{++}	☉	☉	☉	☉	☉	8	2
Cu^{++}	☉	☉	☉	☉	☉	9	1
Cu^{+}	☉	☉	☉	☉	☉	10	0
Zn^{++}	☉	☉	☉	☉	☉	10	0

The electrons in inner sub-levels are all paired as are all the electrons in any filled sublevel. Unpaired electrons give rise to color and paramagnetism in many transition metal compounds.

Many problems in inorganic chemistry have been solved or helped to solution by magnetic studies. For example, mercury(I) compounds are all diamagnetic in gas, liquid, and solid states, showing that they cannot contain the isolated Hg^+ ion, which, having an odd number of electrons, would necessarily have at least one unpaired. The extra electron is, as we have seen, paired in a covalent bond to another mercury(I) ion. When the group IIIb chlorides lose chlorine, compounds which appear to be dichlorides are first formed. They cannot contain the simple +2 ions, however, because they are diamagnetic like the +3 and the +1 compounds. Two possibilities are apparent; either a metal-metal bond is formed, giving a structure such as

$$\begin{array}{ccc} Cl & & Cl \\ \diagdown & & \diagup \\ & Ga\text{---}Ga & \\ \diagup & & \diagdown \\ Cl & & Cl \end{array}$$

or the compounds are equimolar mixtures of the $+1$ and $+3$ states, $Ga^I[Ga^{III}Cl_4]$. The decision between these two alternatives was made in favor of the latter on the basis of other experimental results.

USES

These rare elements are very little used at present. Gallium-in-quartz thermometers were once made to replace mercury-in-glass thermometers for high temperature measurements, but the thermocouple has replaced them. Gallium was once considered as a heat-transfer medium, especially for nuclear reactors, but the fact that it wets many metals and even penetrates through them in some cases ruled it out. It does find limited application as an alloying element, most importantly now in the manufacture of transistors.

Thallium compounds are sometimes used as rodenticides, and the thallium(I) halides, by virtue of their good transparency in the infra-red region, can be made into useful optical crystals.

SUGGESTIONS FOR FURTHER READING

D. Mendeleef, Compt. rend., Vol. 81, p. 969 (1875).
P. W. Selwood, *Magnetochemistry*, 2nd ed., Interscience, New York, 1956.
N. V. Sidgwick, *The Chemical Elements and their Compounds*, Oxford, 1950, pp. 458–487.
M. E. Weeks, *Discovery of the Elements*, 6th ed., Journal of Chemical Education, Easton, Pa., 1956, Chapters XXIII–XXV.

STUDY QUESTIONS

1. From the data given in the text, calculate the pK of the $Al(H_2O)_x^{+3}$ ion.
2. What is the pH of a 0.03m Ga(III) solution?
3. What happens, if anything, in the following cases?
    (a) $Ga(ClO_4)_3 \cdot 6H_2O \xrightarrow{\Delta}$.
    (b) $TlF_3 + SO_2(aqueous) \rightarrow$
    (c) $Ga_2O_3 + CCl_4(heat) \rightarrow$
    (d) $In_2O_3 + NaOH(excess) \rightarrow$
    (e) $Tl^{+++} + I^- \rightarrow$
4. By means of equations and a few words about conditions, show how to carry out the following conversions:
    (a) Make Ga from Ga_2O_3.

(b) Make $Ga(ClO_4)_3 \cdot 6H_2O$ from Ga.

(c) Make TlF_3 from Tl_2O.

(d) Make $InCl_3$ from In_2S_3.

(e) Make $TlNO_3$ from Tl_2O.

5. Tell whether the following entities are diamagnetic or paramagnetic, and for the paramagnetic ones give the number of unpaired electrons:

(a) Cl_2 (f) Eu^{++} (k) S^{--}

(b) Ag^{++} (g) Yb^{++} (l) H^-

(c) Cr^{+++} (h) Ba^{++} (m) Re^-

(d) La^{+++} (i) Bi^{+++} (n) Al^{+++}

(e) $NaCl$ (j) V^{++} (o) SO_4^{--}

6. Outline the steps in a qualitative analysis scheme for the separation and identification of the elements in the following mixtures:

(a) K^+, Ag^+, Tl^+

(b) Al^{+++}, Ga^{+++}, Cu^{++}

(c) In^{+++}, Co^{++}, Tl^{+++}

Chapter 11   Carbon

Carbon is the fourteenth element in order of abundance on the surface of the earth, but, since it is essential to life processes at our temperature and pressure, it is one of the most important elements. It occurs in extensive deposits of carbonates, especially those of calcium and magnesium, in air as carbon dioxide, in small deposits of the pure element as graphite and diamond, and in the bodies of living and dead organisms. The last are found in various forms: coal, petroleum, natural gas, peat, etc.

Beginning with Boyle in about 1660 and continuing up to Lavoisier's time a century later, chemists developed the modern idea of a chemical element—a substance which cannot be decomposed into simpler substances—which replaced earlier Greek and alchemical ideas such as earth, fire, air, and water. It was at the end of this time that carbon was recognized as an element by many investigators. By then the division of chemistry into two branches, organic and inorganic, had taken place on the basis of whether a compound could be derived from an organism or not. It was thought that the organic compounds, which gave carbon dioxide and water upon burning, could only be synthesized in the metabolism of an organism. This idea was upset by Wöhler in 1828 when he made urea, a well-known organic compound, from ammonium cyanate, a well-known inorganic compound, merely by the application of heat:

$$NH_4CNO \xrightarrow{\Delta} CO(NH_2)_2$$

Thus, even though the name is an anachronism, organic chemistry refers to the chemistry of all carbon compounds. There are many, many organic compounds synthesized in the laboratory which do

168

not occur at all in living organisms. We shall take up in this chapter the element in particular along with a few of the simpler compounds which do not contain hydrogen.

PREPARATION OF THE ELEMENT

Carbon is produced in large quantity by the destructive distillation of coal, in which the coal is heated in the absence of air to drive off the valuable volatile products and leave behind coke. The destructive distillation of wood leaves behind charcoal, and many other forms of amorphous carbon are by-products of various industrial processes.

When pure carbon is needed in small quantities, it can be made by the pyrolysis of pure cane sugar:

$$C_{12}H_{22}O_{11} \xrightarrow{800°} 12C + 11\overline{H_2O}$$

PHYSICAL PROPERTIES OF THE ELEMENT

As is prominent for the nonmetals and probably characteristic of all the elements, carbon exhibits allotropy. There are two crystalline forms, graphite and diamond, and many noncrystalline or amorphous forms, such as coke, charcoal, soot, etc. In graphite the carbon atoms are arranged in flat layers, each layer consisting of atoms at the corners of a hexagonal network. These layers are stacked upon each other, as shown in Figure 11.1. The relatively short distance between an atom and its three nearest neighbors in its

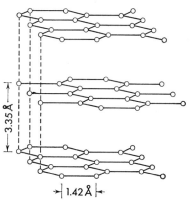

Fig. 11.1 Structure of graphite.

own layer, 1.42Å, compared to the wide separation of the layers, 3.35Å, shows that an atom is strongly bonded in its layer but that the bonding between the layers is weak. Since carbon has four valence electrons and normally uses them all in bonds, one electron per atom is left over after the three bonds in the layer are formed. These extra electrons behave somewhat like the valence electrons in metals discussed in Chapter 4. They are free to move about in the whole layer, contributing to the bonding within the layer and giving the rather weak bonding between the layers. This structure imparts some interesting and useful properties to graphite. It will adsorb gases which go in between the layers easily. If the adsorbed gases are removed by heating in a vacuum, however, graphite is not a good lubricant. When exposed to air again, it picks up gas, especially water vapor, and becomes a good lubricant, because the layers can then slip over one another easily. The "loose" electrons will conduct electricity, the conductivity of graphite at room temperature being about equal to that of lead. Moreover, the electrical conductivity decreases with increasing temperature, which is characteristic of metals.

In diamond, on the other hand, all four valence electrons are used by one atom to form four equal bonds to other carbon atoms arranged tetrahedrally around it. The resulting structure is shown in Figure 11.2. A perfect diamond crystal is in reality a single giant molecule. The bond lengths are all 1.54Å, indicating four strong bonds for each atom with no free electrons. The properties of diamond are clearly correlated with its structure. It is very hard, the hardest natural substance known, since all its atoms are held so tightly in the crystal. Among insulators, it is one of the best. It is transparent to light (cf. the black graphite), since there are no loosely bound electrons to interact with light quanta with energy in the visible range.

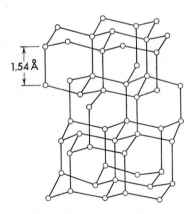

1.54Å

Fig. 11.2   Structure of diamond.

The amorphous varieties of carbon have very little regular structure. They are composed of microscopic regions with graphitic structure, which regions are more or less randomly arranged in the body of the material.

Diamond is the most closely packed form of carbon, with a density of 3.51 g/cc, while that of graphite is 2.25 and an average value for the amorphous varieties is 1.88. Graphite is, however, the thermodynamically stable form at one atmosphere pressure; diamond and amorphous carbon are metastable. Amorphous carbon, generally coke, is converted to graphite on a large scale by the Acheson process, in which a large electric current is passed through a pressed rod to heat it to a high temperature. An impractical but interesting fact is that diamonds fall into graphite upon heating to about 1000°, releasing a few hundred calories per mole. In both of these conversions, the high temperature merely speeds up the rate of the reaction, which is infinitely slow at room temperature. Since diamond is denser than graphite and contains more energy, it is to be expected by LcChatelier's principle that at high pressures and temperatures graphite can be converted to diamond. Many attempts over many years failed to bring about this conversion, until 1956, when it was achieved by heating graphite to very high temperature at very high pressure.

Carbon is the highest melting element; graphite begins to sublime at 3500° and melts at 3550°. The vapor pressure reaches 1 atm. at 4200°. All forms of carbon are insoluble in all common solvents. They do dissolve in many molten metals, especially iron, from which metal carbides and graphite crystallize upon cooling.

CHEMICAL PROPERTIES AND COMPOUNDS

From the electron configuration of $1s^2 2s^2 2p^2$ we expect and find oxidation numbers of $+4$ and -4. Actually strong covalent bonds, of which there are four, with a few exceptions such as CO, are generally formed by carbon in its compounds. These bonds may be to any nonmetal, including other carbon atoms, or to most of the metals, so that the concept of oxidation number is not very useful in organic chemistry. There are a few metal carbides in which carbon may exist as a monatomic ion, such as Al_4C_3.

The reason for the large number of organic compounds is that carbon is such a versatile covalent bond former. Since it will form chains of any length, double and triple bonds as well as single bonds, and rings, the variations are enormous.

Chemical Reactions of the Element

Carbon is quite inert at ordinary temperature, but when heated it reacts with many substances. It burns in air:

$$2C + O_2 \text{ (limited)} \xrightarrow{\Delta} 2CO$$
$$2CO + O_2 \text{ (excess)} \xrightarrow{\Delta} 2CO_2$$

and reduces many metal oxides to the metal:

$$Fe_2O_3 + 3C \xrightarrow{\Delta} 2Fe + 3\overline{CO}$$

With metals which form carbides, the product always contains some of the carbide, and when the carbon is in excess, the carbide may be the principal product:

$$CaO + 3C \xrightarrow{\Delta !} CaC_2 + \overline{CO}$$

The very electropositive metals give carbides containing the C^{-4} ion, or more usually the $C_2^{--}(^-C{\equiv}C^-)$ ion. With the transition elements interstitial carbides are formed, similar to the interstitial hydrides discussed in Chapter 3. (See the discussions under the individual metals for the course of specific reactions.)

Important commercially is the production of silicon carbide from sand and coke in an electric furnace:

$$SiO_2 + 3C \xrightarrow{\Delta\Delta} SiC + 2\overline{CO}$$

SiC has the diamond lattice with alternate carbon and silicon atoms and is very hard and hence useful as a grinding material.

The affinity of carbon for oxygen at high temperature is so great that it reacts with steam in the "water-gas" reaction at bright red heat:

$$C + H_2O \xrightarrow{\Delta} CO + H_2$$

Carbon Monoxide

This colorless, odorless, tasteless, low-boiling gas is the common example of a rare type of carbon compound, those in which carbon has less than four covalent bonds. The bonding has been a subject of theoretical speculation for many years, but the complete answer has not been given yet. One of the simplest proposals to understand is that postulating two covalent and one coordinate covalent bonds:

$$C \overset{\rightarrow}{=\!\!=} O$$

This model fits the experimental facts that carbon monoxide is diamagnetic and has a permanent dipole moment.

Carbon monoxide can be made in the laboratory by the dehydrating action of concentrated sulfuric acid on formic acid:

$$HCOOH \xrightarrow{\text{conc } H_2SO_4} CO + H_2O$$

Stable to air at room temperature, it burns or explodes when ignited. Two important commercial reactions are the catalytic hydrogenation to methyl alcohol,

$$CO + 2H_2 \overset{\text{cat}}{\underset{\Delta}{\rightarrow}} CH_3OH$$

and the purification of nickel by the formation of nickel carbonyl,

$$Ni + 4CO \xrightarrow{<100°} Ni(CO)_4$$

The latter is one of the most stable examples of a large class of compounds, the metal carbonyls, formed by the transition elements. In them the carbon atom coordinates with the metal atom to give what are formally zero-valent compounds of the metal. $Ni(CO)_4$ was the first discovered because it can be made with the CO at atmospheric pressure; the preparation of other carbonyls generally requires pressures of a few hundred atmospheres. Among the variety of carbonyls, the most stable are those conforming to the "inert-gas rule." This states that the E.A.N. (effective atomic number) of the metal atom, calculated by the summation of the number of electrons associated with it, is equal to that of the next inert gas. In calculating the E.A.N., the number of electrons in the free atom is augmented by two electrons for each CO molecule. Thus, for $Ni(CO)_4$ the E.A.N. of nickel is $28 + 4 \times 2 = 36$ (Kr). For cobalt, with an odd number of electrons, a dimer is formed, $Co_2(CO)_8$, presumably with a cobalt-cobalt bond. The E.A.N. of each cobalt is then $27 + 4 \times 2 + 1 = 36$. The following carbonyls conform to the inert-gas rule:

$Cr(CO)_6$	$Mn_2(CO)_5$	$Fe(CO)_5$	$Co_2(CO)_8$	$Ni(CO)_4$
$Mo(CO)_6$	—	$Ru(CO)_5$	$Rh_2(CO)_8$	—
$W(CO)_6$	$Re_2(CO)_5$	$Os(CO)_5$	$Ir_2(CO)_8$	—

There are other more complicated carbonyls, some of which conform to the rule and a few of which do not. In addition, mixed carbonyl hydrides, carbonyl halides, carbonyl ammines, carbonyl halide ammines, and carbonyl nitrosyl compounds of many metals can be made.

The carbonyls are low boiling (for example, $Ni(CO)_4$ is a colorless liquid freezing at $-25°$ and boiling at $43°$), which are soluble in benzene but not water. They decompose to the metal and CO when heated. They are extremely poisonous.

Other examples of the electron donor characteristics of carbon monoxide are its ability to replace other ligands in complex compounds, such as $K_3[Fe(CN)_5CO]$, and its toxicity, caused by its coordination to hemoglobin which then cannot carry oxygen in the blood.

Carbon Dioxide and Carbonates

Carbon dioxide, made by the action of acid on a carbonate or as a by-product of the fermentation industry, and the carbonates and hydrogen carbonates are familiar from any beginning course in chemistry. We have met CO_2 already in the Solvay Process (Chapter 4). It is a linear molecule with two double bonds from carbon to oxygen, $O{=}C{=}O$.

In general, carbonates are insoluble in water, with the exception of those of the alkali metals and ammonium, and it is only these ions whose hydrogen carbonates can be isolated in solid form. Hydrogen carbonates of other metals exist in solution when limited acid or CO_2 itself is added to a carbonate, but they are decomposed on boiling:

$$\underline{CaCO_3} + H_2O + \overline{CO_2} \rightleftharpoons Ca(HCO_3)_2$$

The sulfur analogs of these oxy-compounds exist also. Carbon disulfide, made by direct synthesis from sulfur vapor and coke at red heat, is a poisonous, inflammable liquid boiling at 46°. It is insoluble in water, but soluble in organic solvents. By reaction with basic sulfides, thiocarbonates are formed:

$$BaS + CS_2 \rightarrow \underline{BaCS_3}$$

Carbon Tetrachloride

Chlorine does not attack elementary carbon, and so CCl_4 is made by the chlorination of compounds. The most economic route to its production is the reaction between carbon disulfide and chlorine at red heat:

$$CS_2 + 3Cl_2 \xrightarrow{\Delta} CCl_4 + S_2Cl_2$$

The products are separated by fractional distillation, the by-product disulfur dichloride being used in the vulcanization of rubber. "Carbon tet" is a dense colorless liquid boiling at 76.8°. It is unreactive to most substances at room temperature, except such active metals as sodium, but at higher temperatures it is a good chlorinating agent and oxygen scavenger (see Chapter 13). It is a good solvent for many organic compounds.

$$\frac{x^2}{1-x} =$$

$$K_i = \frac{[H][CN]}{[HCN]}$$

Cyanides

The cyanide ion consists of a carbon atom triply bonded to a nitrogen atom, $C\equiv N^-$. Cyanides can be made in a number of ways, one of which is the high temperature reaction between carbon and calcium cyanamide, the latter coming from the reaction of nitrogen and calcium carbide:

$$CaC_2 + N_2 \xrightarrow{\Delta} CaCN_2 + C$$
$$CaCN_2 + C \xrightarrow{\Delta} Ca(CN)_2$$
$$\text{or } CaCN_2 + C + Na_2CO_3 \xrightarrow{\Delta} CaCO_3 + 2NaCN$$

The parent acid, HCN, is weak, $K_i = 7.2 \times 10^{-10}$ at 25°, and the soluble alkali cyanides therefore give solutions basic by hydrolysis. Pure hydrogen cyanide melts at $-13°$ and boils at 26°; the liquid is completely miscible with water.

$$KCN + H_2O \rightarrow [K][OH] + [HCN]$$
$$[HCN] \rightarrow [H] [CN]$$

We have seen that cyanide is classed as a pseudo-halide ion from its resemblance in many ways to the halogen ions. For instance, it can be oxidized to cyanogen, $(CN)_2$, about as easily as I^- can be oxidized to I_2, and cyanogen disproportionates in base similarly to I_2:

$$2CuSO_4 + 4KCN \rightarrow 2CuCN + \overline{(CN)}_2 + 2K_2SO_4$$
$$(CN)_2 + 2KOH \rightarrow \overline{KCN} + KCNO + H_2O$$

compare

$$2CuSO_4 + 4KI \rightarrow 2CuI + I_2 + 2K_2SO_4$$
$$I_2 + 2KOH \xrightarrow{\text{cold}} \overline{KI} + KIO + H_2O$$

Cyanide is a very good complexing agent for metal ions; these complexes are taken up with the individual metals. This complexing action makes cyanide very poisonous because of its deactivation of hemoglobin.

Cyanates and Thiocyanates

Gentle oxidation of cyanides results in cyanates:

$$KCN + PbO \xrightarrow{\Delta} KCNO + Pb$$

The soluble cyanate is extracted with water. The parent acid is about as strong as acetic acid, as seen from hydrolysis of its salts, but it is unstable, so that when a cyanate solution is acidified, decomposition takes place:

$$HCNO + H_2O \rightarrow NH_3 + CO_2$$

The cyanate ion is linear, with the carbon atom in the middle, $O{=}C{=}N^-$ or $^-O{-}C{\equiv}N$.

The sulfur analogs of cyanate can be made by fusing cyanides with sulfur:

$$KCN + S \xrightarrow{\Delta} KCNS$$

Again the parent acid is unstable.

The cyanate and more especially the thiocyanate ions are moderately good complexing agents for metal ions. The actual species have not been much studied, presumably because the solid compounds are difficult to isolate. A well-known one is the intense red complex between iron(III) ion and thiocyanate used in qualitative analysis to identify iron. Small amounts of iron can be determined quantitatively by this complex also, using various colorimetric techniques to measure the intensity of the color.

COVALENT BONDING

In a covalent bond electrons are partially transferred from one atom to another so that a pair is shared between them. It is of great interest to know which orbitals of the atom these shared electrons occupy, because orbitals have directional properties which then determine the structure of the molecule formed. For many chemical bonds it is found that the correct directions as known from structure determinations are not obtained if the orbitals described in Chapter 1 are taken as such. What has to be done is to hybridize the atomic orbitals available; that is, to make up a new set of orbitals from the old set by taking certain fractions of each of the old orbitals in each of the new orbitals. In this process the number of new orbitals is the same as the old, since the number of electron pairs does not change. The process is legitimate, because it can be shown in some cases that the new electron distribution as given by the new set of orbitals corresponds to a minimum of energy.

TABLE 11.1
Hybrid Bonding Orbitals

Number of Bonds	Hybrid Orbitals	Structure	Example
2	sp	Linear	$Ag(NH_3)_2{}^+$
2	p^2	Angular	H_2S
3	sp^2	Triangle	BF_3
3	p^3	Triangular pyramid	PH_3
4	sp^3	Tetrahedron	CH_4
4	dsp^2	Square	$Ni(CN)_4{}^{--}$
5	dsp^3	Triangular bipyramid	$Fe(CO)_5$
6	d^2sp^3	Octahedron	$AlF_6{}^{---}$

An example of hybridization is carbon, for which it is found that the minimum energy for four bonds is obtained from four hybrid orbitals made up of the one 2s and three 2p atomic orbitals directed to the corners of a tetrahedron. This is in fact the structure of C in CH_4, CCl_4, etc.

There are many kinds of directed covalent bonds in chemistry, organic and inorganic. It is convenient then to know what structures can be made from the orbitals available to the valence electrons. A list of some hybrid orbital sets and the resulting structures with examples is given in Table 11.1.

Uses

The uses of carbon and its compounds are legion, and any list that could be given here would be entirely inadequate. The largest single use is as the various fuels which have enabled man to develop his modern technology.

SUGGESTIONS FOR FURTHER READING

Many of innumerable organic chemistry textbooks.
W. M. Latimer and J. H. Hildebrand, *Reference Book of Inorganic Chemistry*, Macmillan, New York, 1940, Chapter XIII.

STUDY QUESTIONS

1. Calculate the pH of a 0.02m KCN solution.
2. Discuss the allotropy of carbon, with particular emphasis on the relation between the structures and the properties of the various forms.
3. Write a structural formula for cyanogen.
4. What happens, if anything, in the cases below?
    (a) $NH_4SCN \overset{\Delta}{\rightarrow}$
    (b) $Fe(CO)_5 \overset{\Delta}{\rightarrow}$
    (c) $NaHCO_3 + H_2SO_4 \rightarrow$
    (d) $KCN + dil\ H_2SO_4 \rightarrow$
    (e) $KCNO + dil\ H_2SO_4 \rightarrow$
5. By means of equations and a few words about conditions show how to carry out the following conversions:
    (a) Make $KAg(CN)_2$ from natural sources.
    (b) Make $BaCS_3$ from Ba, C, and S.
    (c) Make diamond from amorphous carbon.
    (d) Make CO from CO_2.
    (e) Make KCNO from C, N_2, and any other reagents not containing carbon or nitrogen.

Chapter 12 Silicon

OCCURRENCE

Silicon does not occur in elementary form, even though its compounds are very abundant. It is the next most abundant element on the earth's crust after oxygen, occurring largely as silicon dioxide and its derivatives, the silicates. Feldspar, mica, and asbestos are typical silicate minerals. These and many other minerals, crystallized in various proportions to form rocks, weather to give many other silicon compounds, of which the clays are the most common example. One gets an idea of the prevalence of silicon dioxide and the silicates from the abundances of the main constituents: O 46.5 per cent of the lithosphere, and Si 28 per cent.

PREPARATION OF THE ELEMENT

The element is prepared by the difficult reduction of the dioxide. If aluminum metal is the reducing agent, the silicon dissolves in the excess molten aluminum. Upon cooling and solidifying, the crystals of silicon may be freed of aluminum by leaching with acid. The aluminum dissolves, while acids do not attack silicon. On a large scale silicon dioxide is reduced with carbon. The dioxide is kept in excess to minimize the formation of the carbide.

A mixture of silicon and iron oxides is capable of reduction by carbon in an electric furnace, yielding an alloy of the two elements which is known as ferrosilicon. The alloy is produced in large quantity for use in making acid-resistant steel alloys. Many laboratory sinks and drainpipes are constructed of "duriron," a high-silicon, acid-resistant steel alloy.

High-purity silicon is made for use in transistors by the reduction of the tetrachloride with an active metal, such as sodium, magnesium, or zinc.

PHYSICAL PROPERTIES OF THE ELEMENT

Silicon exists in only one form, crystals with the diamond lattice. There are amorphous varieties described, but they are probably very small particles of the crystalline form. It is a high-melting, 1415°, solid with a metallic luster. The relatively low density of 2.4 g/cc (compare the 2.7 of the lighter aluminum) shows that the diamond lattice is not a particularly close-packed one.

The electrical properties of silicon are of great interest today with the advent of the solid radio tubes, the transistors. Silicon belongs to a large and growing class of substances known as the semiconductors. These have electrical resistances between the metallic conductors and the insulators, and are actually closer to the latter. At low temperatures all of the valence electrons of the silicon atoms are localized in the four bonds, so that they are not free to move and carry electricity. With increasing temperature, however, more and more of these electrons are promoted by thermal energy into a higher energy state, the conduction band, which belongs to the lattice as a whole in much the same manner as the energy levels of the valence electrons in a metal. Since electrons in the conduction band can carry electricity, the resistance of silicon decreases with increasing temperature, as does that of all semiconductors and insulators. The only difference between an insulator and a semiconductor is the size of the energy gap between the valence band and the conduction band. For diamond it is very large, resulting in a transparent insulator; for silicon it is less, and a shiny, opaque semiconductor results. The difference is of degree, not of kind.

Minute traces of impurities affect the conductivity of silicon markedly. If an atom of phosphorus with five valence electrons is substituted for a silicon atom, four bonds to four silicon atoms are formed and the fifth electron goes into the conduction band. Thus, one part per million of phosphorus in pure silicon gives many more conduction electrons than thermal agitation at room temperature, with a correspondingly large effect on the electrical resistance. The operation of a transistor is too complicated to go into here, but it depends on the addition of controlled amounts of impurities to a pure semiconductor.

CHEMICAL PROPERTIES AND COMPOUNDS

With the same outer electron configuration as carbon, silicon should be similar to it in chemical properties. They are alike in many ways, but the differences make them two very distinct elements. In the first place, bonds between silicon and oxygen are relatively much more stable than bonds between silicon and any other element, even silicon itself; whereas carbon bonds to oxygen are not so much more stable than bonds to other elements, including carbon itself. Secondly, silicon does not form double bonds, either to itself or to other elements. And, thirdly, the 3d orbitals are available in silicon for bonding electrons from a donor group. Actually, this last does not give rise to a large number of additional compounds: SiF_6^{--} is a rare example. What it does is to make it easier for silicon compounds to react with other species by forming reaction intermediates with more than four groups on the silicon.

Chemical Reactions of the Element

Silicon is a relatively inert substance, probably because it like aluminum is coated with an oxide film. At high temperature, it combines with oxygen and the halogens to give the dioxide and the tetrahalides respectively. It is inert to all acids except a mixture of nitric and hydrofluoric, which attacks it by combined oxidizing and complexing action:

$$Si + 4HNO_3 + 6HF \rightarrow H_2SiF_6 + 4\overline{NO_2} + 4H_2O$$

Silicon dissolves slowly in strong bases, liberating hydrogen:

$$Si + 2NaOH + H_2O \rightarrow Na_2SiO_3 + 2\overline{H_2}$$

It is insoluble in water but reacts with superheated steam, again liberating hydrogen. With active metals, silicides are produced:

$$Si + 2Mg \rightarrow Mg_2Si$$

or, more directly,

$$SiO_2 + 4Mg \rightarrow 2MgO + Mg_2Si$$

Silicon Dioxide and Glass

The inability of silicon to form double bonds is dramatically illustrated by the difference between silicon dioxide and carbon dioxide. The latter is a low boiling gas composed of discrete molecules, $O{=}C{=}O$, whereas the former is a high melting solid made up of SiO_4 tetrahedra linked together to form a giant molecule:

$$
\begin{array}{ccccccc}
 & | & & | & & | & \\
-\text{Si} & -\text{O} & -\text{Si} & -\text{O} & -\text{Si} & -\text{O} & - \\
 & | & & | & & | & \\
 & \text{O} & & \text{O} & & \text{O} & \\
 & | & & | & & | & \\
-\text{Si} & -\text{O} & -\text{Si} & -\text{O} & -\text{Si} & -\text{O} & - \\
 & | & & | & & | & \\
 & \text{O} & & \text{O} & & \text{O} & \\
 & | & & | & & | & \\
-\text{Si} & -\text{O} & -\text{Si} & -\text{O} & -\text{Si} & -\text{O} & - \\
 & | & & | & & | & \\
 & \text{O} & & \text{O} & & \text{O} & \\
 & | & & | & & | & \\
\end{array}
$$

The tetrahedra can be connected in various ways, so that polymorphism results. There are three crystalline varieties, quartz, trydimite, and cristobalite, and the supercooled liquid, amorphous silica (the -a ending is a common, nonsystematic nomenclature for oxides). With increasing temperature, the crystalline forms are stable in the order given, although the transitions from one to the other are slow. They each also have low and high temperature submodifications. Cristobalite melts at 1710°, but the substance softens about 200° lower because many modifications are present, and it can be shaped and molded at 1500°. Amorphous silica, or silica glass, is made by rapid cooling of the liquid. It exists as a metastable phase up to about 1000°, where it begins to devitrify. As a glass silica has a very low thermal coefficient of expansion, so that a red-hot piece can be plunged into water without cracking. By virtue of its high softening point and the fact that it transmits light of wave lengths well into the ultraviolet region, it is a useful, but expensive, material.

Silica is very slowly dissolved by sodium hydroxide solutions to form sodium silicate. At fusion temperatures the reaction proceeds rapidly, giving a melt which is soluble in water and sold under the name of "water glass." Water glass is used as a waterproofing compound and as sizing by the paper industry. The addition of strong acid to sodium silicate solution precipitates a white gelatinous mass of hydrous silicon dioxide. The precipitate is called silicic acid or gelatinous silica. Upon complete dehydration, a white granular form of silicon dioxide results. Partially dehydrated silicic acid is sold as silica gel for use as a drying agent.

Silicon dioxide exhibits no basic character. Therefore it does not react with acids, with the exception of hydrofluoric acid. In the latter case volatile silicon tetrafluoride is formed:

$$SiO_2 + 4HF \rightarrow SiF_4\uparrow + 2H_2O$$

As a nonvolatile acid oxide it is capable of displacing more volatile acid oxides from their salts. Thus, when sand is fused with sodium carbonate, a clear melt of sodium silicate is obtained, and bubbles of carbon dioxide can be seen leaving the liquid:

$$Na_2CO_3 + SiO_2 \rightarrow Na_2SiO_3 + CO_2\uparrow$$

By such processes glass is made. Excess silicon dioxide is soluble in molten sodium silicate. By varying the ratio of Na_2O to SiO_2 in the melt, glasses of various quality can be obtained. Substituting potassium carbonate for sodium carbonate produces a harder glass. Still other oxides are added to make glasses of better quality. Ordinary soft glass contains about 75 per cent SiO_2 and 25 per cent $Na_2O + CaO$, with small quantities of aluminum oxide. Pyrex Brand No. 774 is advertised as having the composition 81 per cent SiO_2, 12 per cent B_2O_3, 4 per cent Na_2O, and 2 per cent Al_2O_3. The higher the percentage of silica in the glass, the higher the melting point of the glass. Thus silica glass has the highest melting point of any silica-base glass.

Apparatus fabricated of glass is not attacked by most chemical reagents. However, vessels of some other material must be used for reactions involving hydrofluoric acid or soluble fluorides. Also, hot, concentrated caustic solutions slowly dissolve any kind of glass. Silica glass is much more slowly attacked by caustic than is soft glass or pyrex.

The Silicate Minerals

Next to carbon, silicon forms the greatest number of compounds of any element, but for very different reasons. The variety is due, in the case of silicon, to the large number of silicate minerals. Being so abundant, the silicates have been the subject of intensive investigation by soil chemists, geologists, and crystallographers. Chemical analysis establishes the composition of a material, but it is only since the advent of x-ray crystallography that the diversity and detail of the crystalline structure of the silicates has been shown.

The basic building block of the silicates is the SiO_4 tetrahedron. In silica a tetrahedron shares all four corner oxygen atoms with four other tetrahedra, so that each silicon atom is attached to four oxygen atoms and each oxygen to two silicons, resulting in the neutral formula, SiO_2. The tetrahedra may share corners in many different ways. One of the simplest is the sharing of two corners only to form a chain of formula $(SiO_3)_n^{-2n}$:

$$
\begin{array}{cccccccc}
& O & & O & & O & & O \\
& | & & | & & | & & | \\
-Si & -O- & Si & -O- & Si & -O- & Si & -O- \\
& | & & | & & | & & | \\
& O & & O & & O & & O
\end{array}
$$

A more structurally correct picture can be given in two dimensions by looking down on the top of each tetrahedron, so that three oxygen atoms appear at the corners of a triangle with a silicon and oxygen atom at the center, as shown in Figure 12.1. Since the chains are charged, positive ions must be present between the chains, acting to hold the structure together. A typical example of this type is enstatite, $MgSiO_3$. Such minerals are found to cleave easily along the lengths of the chains. Modifications of the chain structure lead to the asbestos minerals.

Another type of mineral results when three corners of each SiO_4 tetrahedron are shared with adjacent tetrahedra to form a layer structure: see Figure 12.2. Each silicon has one-half share in three oxygens and whole share in one, so that the formula of a layer is $SiO_{\frac{5}{2}}$, or $(Si_2O_5)_n^{-2n}$. Talc, $2MgSi_2O_5 \cdot Mg(OH)_2$ has this structure with layers of Mg^{++} and OH^- ions between the $Si_2O_5^{--}$ layers.

Modifications of this layer structure lead to the micas, which cleave easily into very thin sheets, and the clays.

Further variation exists because other elements can be substituted for the silicon in the tetrahedra. For example, if every fourth silicon atom in silicon dioxide is replaced by an aluminum atom, the formula $AlSi_3O_8$ results, but, since aluminum bears only a $+3$ charge, another positive ion must be present for electrical neutrality. Orthoclase, $KAlSi_3O_8$, has this arrangement, with the potassium ions accommodated in the many vacant spaces in the infinite lattice.

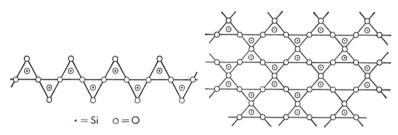

• = Si   ○ = O

Fig. 12.1 Plan view of SiO_4 tetra-hedra sharing corners.

Fig. 12.2 Plan view of SiO_4 tetra-hedra sharing 3 corners.

When one considers the various ways of packing and joining tetrahedra and the number of substitutions possible, the reasons for the variety of silicate minerals become evident.

As far as the immediate crust of the earth is concerned, the most common minerals are feldspars and clays. Pottery, structural brick, chinaware, cement, and a myriad of other ceramic products use clays and feldspars as raw materials. Weathering processes such as wind and water erosion break feldspars down into clays and sand. The following equation is typical of the way one feldspar, orthoclase, weathers to sand and a clay, kaolinite:

$$K_2O \cdot Al_2O_3 \cdot 6SiO_2 + 2CO_2 + 3H_2O \rightarrow$$
orthoclase $$2KHCO_3 + Al_2O_3 \cdot 2SiO_2 \cdot 2H_2O + 4SiO_2$$
                                    kaolinite   sand

Such processes are very slow, taking place over many thousands of years. Orthoclase, as well as the vast majority of natural silicates, is insoluble in water as far as ordinary laboratory tests go.

Halides

The tetrahalides of silicon can be prepared by direct synthesis, but in two cases other methods are employed more frequently. Warming a mixture of fluorspar and silica with excess concentrated sulfuric acid gives silicon tetrafluoride, a gas at room temperature:

$$2CaF_2 + SiO_2 + 2H_2SO_4 \rightarrow 2CaSO_4 + 2H_2O + SiF_4\uparrow$$

The tetrachloride is made by the chlorination of ferrosilicon or by the chlorination of a hot mixture of carbon and silica:

$$2C + SiO_2 + 2Cl_2 \xrightarrow{\Delta} SiCl_4\uparrow + 2CO\uparrow$$

Silicon tetrachloride is a colorless liquid, melting at $-70°C$ and boiling at $58°C$. It must be collected in the absence of moisture, since it hydrolyzes completely to silicic acid and hydrochloric acid:

$$SiCl_4 + (2 + x)H_2O \rightarrow SiO_2 \cdot xH_2O\downarrow + 4HCl$$

The tetrabromide and the tetraiodide behave like the tetrachloride, but the tetrafluoride hydrolyzes in a different manner, forming silicic acid and hexafluosilicic acid:

$$3SiF_4 + (2 + x)H_2O \rightarrow SiO_2 \cdot xH_2O\downarrow + 2H_2SiF_6$$

The latter is one of the few examples of six-coordinated silicon, presumably because fluoride ions are among the few anions small enough for six of them to fit around the rather small silicon. It does, however, show that silicon can use the 3d orbitals in bonding. Hexafluosilicic acid is a strong, soluble acid, having a series of typical salts, such as the alkali fluosilicates, which are slightly soluble in water. This type of compound is unique in another way; a salt reacts with a base to produce a salt and an acid:

$$Na_2SiF_6 + 4NaOH + (x - 2)H_2O \rightarrow 6NaF + SiO_2 \cdot xH_2O\downarrow$$

Among the products of the reaction between chlorine and silicon are found small quantities of Si_2Cl_6, Si_3Cl_8, etc. Si—Si bonds are necessary to explain the structure of these compounds.

$$
\begin{array}{ccc}
\text{Cl} & \text{Cl} & \\
| & | & \\
\text{Cl—Si—Si—Cl} & \text{and} & \\
| & | & \\
\text{Cl} & \text{Cl} &
\end{array}
\qquad
\begin{array}{ccc}
\text{Cl} & \text{Cl} & \text{Cl} \\
| & | & | \\
\text{Cl—Si—Si—Si—Cl} \\
| & | & | \\
\text{Cl} & \text{Cl} & \text{Cl}
\end{array}
$$

Mixed halides of silicon have been prepared also, such as SiF_2Cl_2, SiF_3Cl, $SiCl_2Br_2$, etc. Most of the halides and mixed halides of silicon are liquids or gases at room temperature, and all are very susceptible to hydrolysis.

Silanes

If silica is reduced with carbon in the presence of a basic flux such as lime, calcium silicide is produced. A number of metal silicides have been prepared. They behave as though the silicon has a -4 valence number. Magnesium silicide reacts with dilute hydrochloric acid to produce silane in small yields:

$$4HCl + Mg_2Si \rightarrow 2MgCl_2 + SiH_4\uparrow$$

Silane is a gaseous compound analogous to methane, but much less stable. In air it burns spontaneously, forming silica and water. It reacts with water to form silica and liberate hydrogen. The reaction with pure water is slow, but the reaction is very fast in alkaline solutions:

$$SiH_4 + 2H_2O \rightarrow SiO_2\downarrow + 4H_2\uparrow$$

Other members of the silane series, Si_2H_6, Si_3H_8, etc., are found also in the gaseous products of the reaction between magnesium silicide and hydrochloric acid. The bonding is essentially covalent:

$$
\begin{array}{c}
\text{H} \\
\cdot\cdot \\
\text{H : Si : H} \\
\cdot\cdot \\
\text{H} \\
\text{silane}
\end{array}
\qquad
\begin{array}{c}
\text{H}\quad\text{H} \\
\cdot\cdot\quad\cdot\cdot \\
\text{H : Si : Si : H} \\
\cdot\cdot\quad\cdot\cdot \\
\text{H}\quad\text{H} \\
\text{disilane}
\end{array}
\qquad
\begin{array}{c}
\text{H}\quad\text{H}\quad\text{H} \\
\cdot\cdot\quad\cdot\cdot\quad\cdot\cdot \\
\text{H : Si : Si : Si : H} \\
\cdot\cdot\quad\cdot\cdot\quad\cdot\cdot \\
\text{H}\quad\text{H}\quad\text{H} \\
\text{trisilane}
\end{array}
$$

Recently a new method has been developed whereby much better yields of purer silane are obtained. Lithium hydride reacts with aluminum chloride in ether to give lithium aluminum hydride. This reagent reacts, in the same solvent, with silicon tetrachloride to give silane:

$$4LiH + AlCl_3 \rightarrow LiAlH_4 + 3LiCl\downarrow$$
$$LiAlH_4 + SiCl_4 \rightarrow LiCl + AlCl_3 + SiH_4\uparrow$$

In the presence of a copper catalyst, elementary silicon and hydrogen chloride react to give mixtures of substituted silanes:

$$Si + 3HCl \xrightarrow[\;300°C\;]{Cu} SiHCl_3 + H_2$$
$$Si + 2HCl \xrightarrow[\;300°C\;]{Cu} SiH_2Cl_2 + H_2$$

plus small amounts of $SiCl_4$ and SiH_3Cl

The chlorosilanes have the same structural formulae as the silanes, with halogen substituting for some of the hydrogen. Such compounds, on hydrolysis, show the following behavior:

(The square brackets around the intermediate products indicate that the series of reactions is an easy way of visualizing the over-all reaction but does not necessarily represent the actual course of the reaction. Only the final product is definitely known.) This hydrolytic behavior followed by polymerization, when a double bond should be left as a result of dehydration, shows that silicon will not form double bonds with oxygen. Vigorous hydrolysis of these compounds with strong sodium hydroxide results in sodium silicate, sodium chloride, and hydrogen.

If the element silicon is reacted with methyl chloride in the presence of a copper catalyst, a mixture of methylchlorosilanes is obtained:

$$Si + CH_3Cl \xrightarrow[300°C]{Cu} \begin{array}{l} (CH_3)_3SiCl \\ (CH_3)_2SiCl_2 \\ CH_3SiCl_3 \end{array}$$

Alkylchlorosilanes can be prepared in another way also. Silicon tetrachloride reacts with methylmagnesium chloride in dry ether as follows:

$$\underset{\underset{Cl}{|}}{\overset{\overset{Cl}{|}}{Cl-Si-Cl}} + CH_3MgCl \rightarrow \underset{\underset{Cl}{|}}{\overset{\overset{Cl}{|}}{Cl-Si-CH_3}} + MgCl_2$$

One or more of the chlorines may be substituted in this manner by methyl groups. The methylchlorosilanes are volatile, colorless liquids. They are quite toxic. When the vapors come in contact with the surface of paper, glass, and ceramic materials, a reaction occurs between the water adsorbed on the surfaces and the silanes, leaving thin films of hydrolyzed methylsilane bound to the surfaces. The films are remarkably waterproof. Methylchlorosilanes are marketed under the name of "dri-film," and are used to produce water-repellent surfaces on paper, ceramic insulators, building materials, chemical glassware, etc.

It is important to note that the Si—Cl bond is split by water instantaneously. The Si—H bond can be hydrolyzed, but only with difficulty. The Si—C bond is much more stable to hydrolysis than the Si—H bond. For practical purposes it can be said that the Si—C bond is stable to hydrolysis.

SILICONES

The hydrolysis of methylchlorosilanes is similar to the pattern set in the chlorosilanes case. For example, when dimethyldichlorosilane is poured into water, the products of hydrolysis and polymerization consist of cyclic and straight chain polymers. By way of illustration, suppose some of the $(HO)_2Si(CH_3)_2$ resulting from the hydrolysis of $Cl_2Si(CH_3)_2$ condenses to form a five silicon chain by splitting out water between adjacent monomers:

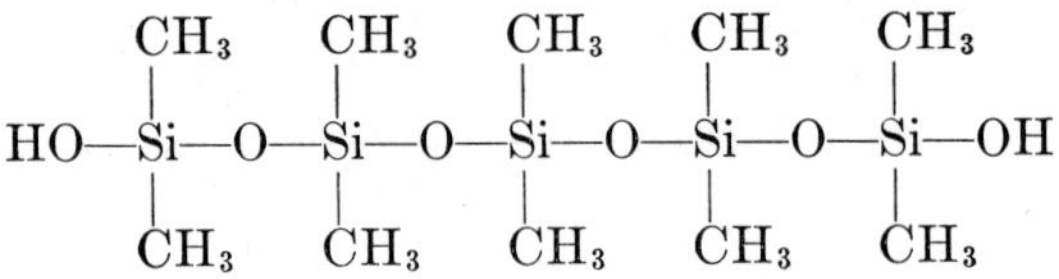

$$
\begin{array}{ccccc}
CH_3 & CH_3 & CH_3 & CH_3 & CH_3 \\
| & | & | & | & | \\
HO—Si—O—Si—O—Si—O—Si—O—Si—OH \\
| & | & | & | & | \\
CH_3 & CH_3 & CH_3 & CH_3 & CH_3
\end{array}
$$

The two ends of the chain could condense further, leaving a cyclical polymer:

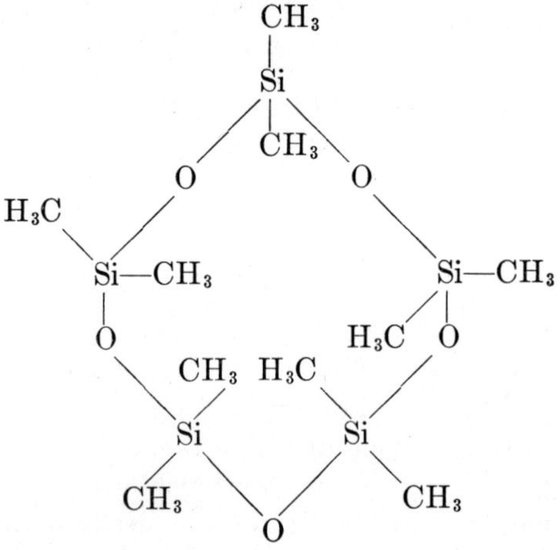

Or, if a little trimethylchlorosilane is present, it hydrolyzes to $(CH_3)_3SiOH$, which could condense with each end of the chain giving the following structure:

$$
\begin{array}{ccccccc}
CH_3 & CH_3 & CH_3 & CH_3 & CH_3 & CH_3 & CH_3 \\
| & | & | & | & | & | & | \\
H_3C-Si-O-Si-O-Si-O-Si-O-Si-O-Si-O-Si-CH_3 \\
| & | & | & | & | & | & | \\
CH_3 & CH_3 & CH_3 & CH_3 & CH_3 & CH_3 & CH_3
\end{array}
$$

The various products of polymerization are called silicones. The physical properties vary with the type of polymer and substituent groups (methyl, ethyl, etc.). The silicones are finding many uses in an amazing variety of ways. Resin polymers are used as insulation material in electrical installations. Some of the liquids make ideal all-weather lubricants, having very low temperature coefficients of viscosity. The "bouncing putty," in addition to being a fascinating toy, has been put in golf balls and is used by the medical profession as a therapeutic aid.

SUGGESTIONS FOR FURTHER READING

O. Hassel, *Crystal Chemistry*, translated from the German by R. C. Evans, Chemical Publishing Co., New York, 1935, pp. 44–55.

B. Mason, *Principles of Geochemistry*, Wiley, New York, 1952, Chapters 5 and 6.

E. G. Rochow, *An Introduction to the Chemistry of the Silicones*, Wiley 1946, New York.

A. F. Wells, *Structural Inorganic Chemistry*, Oxford, London, 1945, pp. 459–487.

STUDY QUESTIONS

1. Review the hydrolytic behavior of the following substances: SiF_4, $SiCl_4$, Cl_3SiH, $(CH_3)_2SiCl_2$, $(CH_3)_3SiCl$, and Na_2SiO_3.

2. Under what conditions may silicon be expected to liberate hydrogen from water or aqueous solutions?

3. The SiF_6^{--} ion exists whereas $SiCl_6^{--}$ does not. How do you explain this?

4. When 0.500 grams of impure sodium fluosilicate were dissolved in distilled water and titrated with 0.200-M NaOH, 40.0 ml. of the NaOH were required. The formula weight of Na_2SiF_6 is 188. Find:
   (a) the weight of Na_2SiF_6 in the sample
   (b) the percentage purity of the sample

5. How are some of the natural silicates used to soften water?

6. What happens, if anything, in the cases below?
   (a) $SiO_2 + NaOH$(fused) →
   (b) $Si + HF$(aqueous) →
   (c) $SiF_4 + HF$(aqueous) →
   (d) $SiCl_4 + HCl$(aqueous) →
   (e) $Si + H_2O$ →

7. By means of equations and a few words about conditions, show how to carry out the following conversions:
   (a) Make $SiCl_4$ from a natural silicon compound.
   (b) Make SiH_4 from SiO_2.
   (c) Make H_2SiF_6 solution from Si.
   (d) Make $(CH_3)_3SiCl$ from orthoclase.
   (e) Make ferrosilicon from SiO_2.

Chapter 13

Titanium, Zirconium, and Hafnium

OCCURRENCE AND HISTORY

The elements in group IVa are much more abundant than is generally recognized. Titanium is the ninth most abundant element, making up nearly 0.5 per cent of the earth's crust. Such common metals as chromium, tungsten, zinc, nickel, copper, and vanadium are all less abundant than zirconium, yet titanium is twenty times as abundant as zirconium. Even hafnium, which until recently was considered a very rare element, is more abundant than such well-known metals as cadmium, mercury, and bismuth.

Rutile, TiO_2, and ilmenite, $FeO \cdot TiO_2$, are the two principal minerals of titanium. Plentiful deposits of these minerals are located throughout the world. Zircon sand, $ZrSiO_4$, is the chief source of zirconium compounds. Hafnium occurs with zirconium in smaller amounts.

Although titania and zirconia have been recognized as such for over 150 years, the discovery of hafnium was announced by Coster and von Hevesy as late as 1923. The search for the element is historically interesting. For many years it was looked for among the rare earths. Moseley in his study of x-ray spectra had shown that the element of atomic number 72 was missing. Bohr then showed, on the basis of his theory of electron structure, that the rare-earth series ended with element 71, and accordingly he advised the chemist von Hevesy to look for element 72 in zirconium ores. With Coster, von Hevesy found it in the first ore they examined, identifying it by its characteristic x-ray lines. The discoverers named hafnium after Hafnia, an old name for Copenhagen, the city where it was discovered at the suggestion of a Copenhagen physicist.

Practically all natural zirconium materials contain hafnium. The ratio of hafnium to zirconium is usually 1 or 2 to 100. The discovery of hafnium showed that all previous work on zirconium was done on a mixture of the two elements. Thus the atomic weight of zirconium was lowered about one unit by the discovery of its congener, from which it had never been separated previously.

PREPARATION OF THE ELEMENTS

Titanium, zirconium, and hafnium metals are prepared in the pure state only with difficulty, since they are quite active elements at the temperatures which must be used in their preparation. They will combine readily with oxygen, nitrogen, and carbon at several hundred degrees. Consequently, when the dioxides of the elements are reacted with carbon at high temperatures, carbides as well as the free metals are formed. Calcium hydride has been used to prepare the pure metals, but the reaction must be carried out in an atmosphere of hydrogen at a rather high temperature:

$$CaH_2 + TiO_2 \xrightarrow[\Delta]{H_2} CaO + H_2O + Ti$$

Another method is the reaction between sodium and the tetrachlorides of the metals under pressure:

$$4Na + TiCl_4 \rightarrow 4NaCl + Ti$$

Recently the Kroll Process has been developed for the large-scale reduction of the tetrachlorides with magnesium. The metals so produced are relatively pure and can be worked for fabrication.

By means of the costly de Boer-van Arkel purification process, very pure titanium, zirconium, and hafnium have been made. In this process sponge metal, obtained from the Kroll Process, is placed in a chamber with some iodine. At about 400°C the iodine reacts with the titanium to form titanium tetraiodide, which is volatile at that temperature. The vapors of the tetraiodide come into contact with a tungsten wire, which has been sealed into the chamber and is heated to about 1100°C by passing a current through it. The tetraiodide decomposes, depositing titanium on the wire and setting the iodine free to go back and react with more titanium sponge. Gradually a bar of high-purity titanium is built up around the tungsten wire. Such a bar of titanium is much more ductile than sponge metal. The same process can be applied to zirconium and hafnium.

PHYSICAL PROPERTIES OF THE ELEMENTS

Titanium has a higher strength to weight ratio than steel and is as resistant to corrosion as the better stainless steels. As the price of titanium comes down, it will be put to a wider variety of uses. Certainly it can compete with stainless steel already in every way except price.

Zirconium and hafnium make desirable metals of construction also, but are much more dense.

CHEMICAL PROPERTIES AND COMPOUNDS

With two electrons in the penultimate d orbitals and two in the outer s, the group IVa elements have possible oxidation numbers of from 2 to 4. Actually, the group number is the most stable valence for all three elements; +3 titanium is easily made also, whereas Ti^{++}, Zr^{++}, Zr^{+++}, Hf^{++}, and Hf^{+++} are achieved with difficulty and are unstable. As is general for the transition elements, the lower oxidation states become less stable and the higher oxidation numbers more stable with increasing atomic number in a subgroup. This generalization goes on here to thorium, for which the lower valencies are very rare, if they exist at all.

Because of the increasing size of the ions going down the subgroup, the basicity of the oxides increases, except for the effect of the lanthanide contraction which makes zirconium and hafnium essentially identical in basicity. For this reason, zirconium and hafnium are more difficult to separate one from the other than two adjacent rare earth elements. Thus, the oxides in this group go from acidic to basic, with zirconium and hafnium acting as a single element in the middle:

Si^{++++}	0.41Å	SiO$_2$ acidic only, no reaction with acids
Ti^{++++}	0.68	TiO$_2$ amphoteric, reacts only slightly with acids
Zr^{++++}	0.87	ZrO$_2$ amphoteric, reacts only slightly with bases
Hf^{++++}	0.87	HfO$_2$ amphoteric, reacts only slightly with bases
Th^{++++}	1.10	ThO$_2$ basic only, no reaction with bases

Titanium, zirconium, and hafnium form a number of complexes, especially with chelating agents; the great complexing ability characteristic of transition elements is beginning to appear in this subgroup.

Chemical Reactions of the Elements

The metals are unreactive at room temperature, but they become active when heated. At high temperatures they combine with oxygen to give dioxides, the halogens to give tetrahalides, and with nitrogen, carbon, and hydrogen to give interstitial compounds. Titanium releases hydrogen from hot acids, forming titanium(III) salts:

$$2Ti + 3H_2SO_4 \xrightarrow{\Delta} Ti_2(SO_4)_3 + 3H_2\uparrow$$

With nitric acid, the insoluble dioxide is formed:

$$Ti + 4HNO_3 \rightarrow TiO_2\downarrow + 4NO_2\uparrow + 2H_2O$$

Zirconium and hafnium are even more inert, the complexing action of hydrofluoric acid or of aqua regia being required to dissolve them:

$$Zr + 7HF \qquad\qquad \rightarrow H_3ZrF_7 + 2H_2\uparrow$$
$$Hf + 4HNO_3 + 6HCl \rightarrow H_2HfCl_6 + 4NO_2\uparrow + 4H_2O$$

Dioxides

The dioxides of these elements are white insoluble compounds, which can therefore be made by neutralizing a solution of any salt. Hydrous titanium dioxide is easily soluble in aqueous bases to give titanates:

$$TiO_2 + 2NaOH \rightarrow Na_2TiO_3 + H_2O$$

Dilute acids, however, do not react with it; concentrated acid is necessary to bring it into solution:

$$TiO_2 + 2H_2SO_4 \rightarrow Ti(SO_4)_2 + 2H_2O$$

These reactions indicate that while TiO_2 is amphoteric, its acidic nature predominates. Hydrous zirconium and hafnium dioxides, on the other hand, dissolve in acids, but not bases, indicating their increased basicity.

The ignited oxides are quite refractory. They are practically insoluble in aqueous acid or base; fusion with an acidic or basic flux is required to dissolve them:

$$MeO_2 + 4KHSO_4 \xrightarrow{\Delta} Me(SO_4)_2 + 2K_2SO_4 + 2\overline{H_2O}$$
$$MeO_2 + 2NaOH \xrightarrow{\Delta} Na_2MeO_3 + \overline{H_2O}$$

Thorium dioxide does not react, even on fusion, with bases.

Both sodium titanate and titanium(IV) sulfate are extensively hydrolyzed in solution, the first to give a basic solution and the second to give an acid solution. Merely boiling a solution of sodium titanate is sufficient to precipitate some hydrous titania. Alkali zirconates and hafnates are almost quantitatively hydrolyzed to insoluble hydrous oxides at room temperature:

$$Na_2ZrO_3 + (x + 1)H_2O \rightarrow \underline{ZrO_2 \cdot xH_2O} + 2NaOH$$

The sulfates of zirconium and hafnium are not so greatly hydrolyzed and are soluble in water.

Titanium dioxide, like silicon dioxide, is trimorphic, and all three forms occur in nature:

$$\text{anatase} \xrightarrow{860°} \text{brookite} \xrightarrow{1040°} \text{rutile} \xrightarrow{1560°} \text{liquid}$$

Titania does not have the tendency, however, that silica does of forming glasses. When hydrous TiO_2 is ignited and rapidly cooled, rutile is formed. It has the high refractive index of 2.55 (compare ordinary glass, c. 1.5) which makes the fine powder look very white. Its largest use, as a pigment, is based on this property. Blended properly into paint, titanium dioxide has great hiding power and a hard surface. It shows good acid resistance and is nonblackening. In addition, titania is being incorporated in enamel surfaces for metals and in synthetic textile fibers as a delustering agent.

Titanium dioxide has a dielectric constant of about 100. Firing the dioxide with barium oxide or barium carbonate at 1500°C gives barium titanate, $BaTiO_3$, which has a dielectric constant of about 1000. Mixtures of barium and strontium titanates have dielectric constants in the vicinity of 10,000 under certain conditions. Such substances are called "ferroelectrics," being the electrical analogs of ferromagnetics. They are finding increasing use in solid state electronics.

Tetrahalides

When refractory oxides such as the dioxides of this subgroup are encountered, it is often convenient to convert them into more water-soluble compounds by reaction with carbon and chlorine. The oxide is mixed with carbon, and chlorine is passed over the heated mixture. The tendency of carbon to reduce oxides to metals plus the tendency of chlorine to combine with metals results in the production of the metal chloride and carbon monoxide:

$$MeO_2 + 2C + 2Cl_2 \xrightarrow{\Delta} MeCl_4 + 2CO$$

The halide sublimes or distills and collects in the cooler portion of the reaction chamber. This is a general method for preparing the halides of many elements from the oxides. In the case of the oxides of titanium, zirconium, and hafnium, it is possible to substitute carbon tetrachloride for the carbon and chlorine, simply passing carbon tetrachloride vapor over the oxides which are heated to 450°C:

$$MeO_2 + 2CCl_4 \xrightarrow[\Delta]{} MeCl_4\uparrow + 2COCl_2\uparrow$$

The iodides are best prepared by direct synthesis. The fluorides can be prepared by the action of hydrofluoric acid on the tetrachlorides.

Titanium tetrachloride is a colorless liquid boiling at 136°C. It is very hygroscopic, hydrolyzing instantly on contact with water. It is used to make smoke screens. Being a liquid, it can be sprayed into the air, when it reacts with the moisture in the air to give hydrogen chloride and titanium dioxide. The electrical conductance of liquid titanium tetrachloride is very small, indicative of covalent bonding. Fused thorium tetrachloride, on the other hand, exhibits the conductance of a salt-like substance. The tetrachlorides of zirconium and hafnium are white, hygroscopic substances that have conductances in the liquid state that are intermediate between those of titanium tetrachloride and thorium tetrachloride. Zirconium tetrachloride sublimes at 331°C, and hafnium tetrachloride sublimes at 317°C.

The tetrafluorides of this subgroup are less volatile, more salt-like compounds than the chlorides. Toward water they behave more like silicon tetrafluoride, forming fluo-complex acids. In fact, titanium tetrafluoride is soluble in solutions of potassium fluoride to form potassium hexafluotitanate. The latter can be crystallized from solution. Similar complexes of zirconium and hafnium are known, and, in addition, such ions as ZrF_7^{---} are permitted by the larger size of the Zr^{++++} ion.

Potassium hexachlorotitanate can be made in the absence of water by the reaction of $TiCl_4$ with KCl, but the compound is decomposed by water just as titanium tetrachloride is. As was found with silicon, the Ti—Cl bond is far more susceptible to hydrolysis than the Ti—F bond.

Solution Chemistry

When pure zirconium tetrachloride is added to water, it dissolves with a hiss, giving a clear solution; yet the resulting solution does not contain simple hydrated zirconium ions. $Ti(OH_2)_x^{++++}$, $Zr(OH_2)_x^{++++}$, and $Hf(OH_2)_x^{++++}$ ions are such strong acids that they hydrolyze immediately:

$$Zr(OH_2)_x^{++++} + nH_2O \rightleftharpoons [Zr(OH_2)_{x-n}(OH)_n]^{4-n} + nH_3O^+$$

Here n is a function of the concentration of metal ion and of hydronium ion, and varies from two to almost four in dilute solution. Thus, dissolving zirconium tetrachloride in water actually "makes" hydrochloric acid in larger molar concentration than the concentration of the zirconium species. Upon evaporation of the solution, white crystals of hydrated zirconyl chloride are obtained. The composition of the crystals is usually in accord with the formula $ZrOCl_2 \cdot xH_2O$, with x about 8. These crystals are soluble in water, and still further hydrolysis is detected by the low pH of the solution. The addition of ammonia to zirconium chloride solutions precipitates the hydrous oxide.

$$[Zr(OH_2)_{x-n}(OH)_n]^{4-n} + (4-n)NH_3 + 2H_2O \rightarrow$$
$$ZrO_2 \cdot xH_2O\downarrow + (4-n)NH_4^+$$

In the presence of sulfate ions the hydrolysis of the $Me(OH_2)_x^{++++}$ ions does not proceed so far. This is due to the substitution of SO_4^{--} ions for some of the H_2O molecules around the Me^{++++} ions. Probably a number of complex ions are present. Three simple possibilities are shown.

Under the influence of an electric field, some of the solute zirconium migrates to the cathode and some toward the anode. The above possibilities could explain such behavior.

If anions that form tight complexes with the Me^{++++} ions are added, hydrolysis is suppressed completely. For example, zirconium tetrachloride will dissolve in potassium fluoride solution without appreciable hydrolysis:

$$ZrCl_4 + 6(K^+F^-) \rightarrow 2K^+ZrF_6^{--} + 4(K^+Cl^-)$$

The cation hydration water is completely replaced by fluoride ions. Oxalate ions will do the same thing. The hydrolysis of $Ti(OH_2)_x^{++++}$ can be prevented by the addition of potassium oxalate, which forms the trioxalatotitanate ion:

$$Ti(OH_2)_x^{++++} + 3C_2O_4^{--} \rightarrow Ti(C_2O_4)_3^{--} + xH_2O$$

Peroxides

When hydrogen peroxide is added to a solution of a titanium salt, a very intense yellow color results; it can be used for the qualitative or quantitative analysis of either component. The exact composition of the colored species is not known, but it is probably peroxytitanic acid, H_2TiO_4. A hydrated peroxide can be precipitated from the solution with the formula $TiO_3 \cdot 2H_2O$. Various salts can also be made, such as, $Na_2TiO_5 \cdot 3H_2O$.

Lower Oxidation States

Titanium(III) forms a number of well-defined compounds, but our knowledge of the other lower oxidation states is practically limited to the halides.

The preparation of the tri- and di-halides of titanium, zirconium, and hafnium is accomplished by means of an ingenious apparatus that has wide application to reduction procedures, the Sainte-Claire Deville hot-cold tube. If hydrogen and titanium tetrachloride vapor are heated together, reduction occurs:

$$(a) \quad H_2 + 2TiCl_4 \xrightarrow{\Delta} 2HCl + 2TiCl_3$$

but at this high temperature $TiCl_3$ disproportionates:

$$(b) \quad 2TiCl_3 \xrightarrow{\Delta} TiCl_2 + TiCl_4$$

Also $TiCl_2$ undergoes reaction:

$$(c) \quad 2TiCl_2 \xrightarrow{\Delta} TiCl_4 + Ti$$

Thus the over-all result is the reduction of the tetrachloride to the metal. If the $TiCl_3$ produced in (a) could be "frozen" immediately, it would not disproportionate. This condition is realized in the hot-cold tube, which consists of an outer glass (or ceramic or metal) tube heated externally by means of electrical heating coils. A second tube is placed inside the outer tube and is cooled by running water through it; thus, a hot surface is maintained at the inside wall of the outer tube, and a cold surface is maintained on the outside wall of the inner tube. If H_2 and $TiCl_4$ are passed through this chamber, reaction (a) takes place near the surface of the outer tube. The $TiCl_3$ thus produced condenses as a solid on the inner tube, along with some $TiCl_4$. The latter can be removed following this operation by subliming it *carefully* away from the $TiCl_3$ (see Figure 13.1).

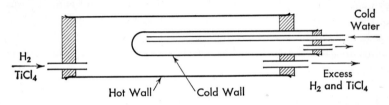

Fig. 13.1   Hot-cold tube.

All of the known $+2$ and $+3$ halides of titanium, zirconium, and hafnium are violet to black in color. They are very susceptible to pyrolysis. With the exception of trivalent titanium, they displace hydrogen readily from water. In suitable concentration and in the presence of a good catalyst, such as finely divided platinum, titanium(III) also releases hydrogen from water since the standard E.M.F. of the Ti^{III}-Ti^{IV} couple is negative:

$$Ti^{+++} + H_2O = TiO^{++} + 2H^+ + e^-   E^0 = -0.1v$$

On the other hand, aqueous solutions of Ti^{III} can be quite stable in the absence of oxygen or other oxidizing agents. A solution of titanium(IV) sulfate is reduced to titanium(III) sulfate electrolytically or by zinc metal. The latter reaction is conveniently carried out by passing the solution through a Jones reductor, illustrated in Figure 13.2. The zinc is amalgamated with a thin layer of mercury before use to cut down on the evolution of hydrogen in the acid solution by virtue of the high overvoltage of hydrogen on mercury. The eluant solution of trivalent titanium is violet and has good reducing powers. The titanium(III) ion can be stabilized by precipitating a slightly soluble salt, such as the alum, $RbTi(SO_4)_2 \cdot 12H_2O$. Other complexes isomorphous with those of chromium(III) and iron(III) are also known.

The lower oxides of titanium, Ti_2O_3 and TiO, can be made by the careful reduction of the dioxide.

TITANATE ESTERS

We have seen that hydroxides of metals with a charge greater than 2 cannot be prepared, at least by precipitation from solution. The higher hydroxides split out a molecule of water from two hydroxide radicals to give hydrous oxides, similar to the hypothetical behavior of the Si—O—H compounds discussed in the previous chapter. Thus, when titanium tetrachloride reacts with sodium hydroxide, orthotitanic acid, $Ti(OH)_4$, cannot be isolated; $TiO_2 \cdot xH_2O$ is the product.

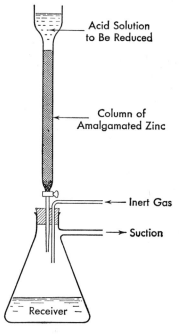

Fig. 13.2 Jones reductor.

When titanium tetrachloride reacts with sodium ethylate, on the other hand, an ester of orthotitanic acid can be isolated as a clear liquid. Its name is tetraethyl titanate:

$$TiCl_4 + 4NaOC_2H_5 \rightarrow Ti(OC_2H_5)_4 + 4NaCl\downarrow$$

The sodium ethylate is made by adding sodium to ethyl alcohol:

$$2Na + 2C_2H_5OH \rightarrow 2NaOC_2H_5 + H_2\uparrow$$

Other esters can be made this way by starting with other alcohols. Certain orthoesters of titanium can also be prepared by the reaction of titanium tetrachloride with alcohols directly, if ammonia is bubbled into the reaction mixture:

$$4ROH + TiCl_4 + 4NH_3 \rightarrow Ti(OR)_4 + 4NH_4Cl\downarrow$$

By way of comparison, silicon tetrachloride reacts with alcohols without the use of sodium or ammonia as condensing agents:

$$SiCl_4 + 4C_2H_5OH \rightarrow Si(OC_2H_5)_4 + 4HCl\uparrow$$

Orthoesters of zirconium and hafnium are prepared using the titanium procedures. All of these esters are soluble in organic solvents such as benzene, alcohols, and ethers, but they are decomposed rapidly by water:

$$(C_2H_5O)_4Ti + (2 + x)H_2O \rightarrow 4C_2H_5OH + TiO_2 \cdot xH_2O\downarrow$$

The alkyl titanates are used as paint vehicles and as waterproofing agents. Like the silanes, the titanate esters probably react with the surface moisture on the material to be waterproofed.

MIXTURES OF ZIRCONIUM AND HAFNIUM

All of the chemical and most of the physical properties of compounds of zirconium and hafnium are so similar that the separation of the two elements, which always occur together, has been a challenge since the discovery of hafnium. With the exception of isotope separation, no other separation problem is more difficult. Like the rare earths, they have been separated by tedious fractional crystallization processes and, more recently, by ion-exchange chromatography. When purchasing zirconium chemicals, one usually obtains the natural mixture of the two. This means that the average atomic weight of metal present is not 91.22, the accepted value for zirconium. Suppose in a sample of "zirconium" the weight ratio Hf/Zr is 0.025. Then in 100 grams of metal there are 2.44 grams of hafnium and 97.56 grams of zirconium.

$$\frac{2.44}{97.56} = 0.025$$

Then there are:

$$\frac{2.44 \text{ gms Hf}}{178.6 \text{ gms Hf/gm atom Hf}} = 0.0137 \text{ gm atoms Hf}$$

$$\frac{97.56 \text{ gms Zr}}{91.22 \text{ gms Zr/gm atom Zr}} = 1.0695 \text{ gm atoms Zr}$$

$$= \overline{1.0832 \text{ gm atoms metal}}$$

and $\dfrac{100 \text{ gms metal}}{1.0832 \text{ gm atoms metal}} = 92.32 = \text{av. at. wt. of metal}$

The molecular weight of $ZrCl_4$ prepared from such a sample of metal would be $92.32 + 4 \times 35.457 = 234.15$.

SUGGESTIONS FOR FURTHER READING

"Titanium Symposium," reprinted from *Industrial and Engineering Chemistry*, Vol. 42, pp. 214–268 (1950). Obtainable from the American Chemical Society.

R. C. Young, "The Sainte-Claire Deville Hot-Cold Tube and Some of Its Applications," *Journal of Chemical Education*, Vol. 20, p. 378 (1943).

STUDY QUESTIONS

1. Suggest a way to make an alum of titanium starting with titanium dioxide.

2. Which has the smallest ionic radius, Ti^{++++}, Ti^{+++}, or Ti^{++}?

3. If Ti compounds will liberate hydrogen from water, why will not titanium metal?

4. Suggest a way to make potassium hexafluohafnate starting with hafnium dioxide.

5. Design an apparatus for the preparation of pure titanium tetrachloride.

6. Would you expect $TiCl_4$ to hydrolyze to a greater extent than $ScCl_3$? Why or why not?

7. Write an equation to describe what happens when potassium hexachlorotitanate is put into water.

8. Describe the operation of a Jones reductor.

9. Which is the most basic oxide, Sc_2O_3, Y_2O_3, or La_2O_3?

10. What is the molecular weight of $HfCl_4$ made from a sample of HfO_2 in which the Zr/Hf is 0.022 by weight?

11. What happens in the cases below?
   (a) $TiO_2 + KOH$(fused)
   (b) $ThO_2 + KOH$(fused)
   (c) $ZrCl_4 + K_2C_2O_4$(aqueous)
   (d) $HfO_2 + C$(heat)
   (e) $Hf + HF$

12. By means of equations and a few words about conditions, show how to carry out the following conversions:
   (a) Make $TiCl_3$ from rutile.
   (b) Make $ZrCl_4$ from a natural zirconium compound.
   (c) Make Ti from ilmenite.
   (d) Make K_2TiCl_6 from Ti.
   (e) Make $ZrO_2 \cdot xH_2O$ from Zr.

Chapter 14

Germanium,
Tin,
and Lead

OCCURRENCE AND HISTORY

Since lead and tin are mentioned in the Old Testament, they apparently were well known in ancient times. Lead pipe and lead writing tablets were used in ancient Rome. Tin was used at an early date to protect copper vessels from corrosion. It follows that tin and lead ores must be reasonably widespread and easily smelted. Cassiterite, SnO_2, is the principal ore of tin, and galena, PbS, the principal ore of lead. Germanium, a rare element, was not discovered until 1886 by Winkler in argyrodite, $GeS_2 \cdot 4Ag_2S$. It was a matter of controversy after its discovery whether germanium, named after Winkler's fatherland, was Mendeleef's ekastibium, ekacadmium, or ekasilicon. A detailed study of its properties by Winkler showed it to be ekasilicon. Concentrated germanium ores do not occur; hence, it is called a rare element. It is found as the sulfide mixed with other sulfides. The principal source today is zinc ores containing up to 0.17 per cent germanium.

PREPARATION OF THE ELEMENTS

Group IVb elements are relatively easy to make by carbon reduction of the heated oxides, obtained by roasting the sulfides. Germanium thus obtained is a fine powder, since the operation is carried out below its melting point, whereas tin and lead form liquids which may easily be cast.

Actually when metals such as tin and lead are produced on a large scale, pure compounds are not used and the reactions are not simple. To produce lead, for example, purified galena is roasted, giving a mixed product:

$$PbS \xrightarrow[\Delta]{\text{air}} PbO, \text{ PbS, and } PbSO_4$$

The product is reduced with carbon, limestone being added as a flux for the silicate impurities in the ore. It is possible to reduce the purified ore with scrap iron also:

$$Fe + PbS \rightarrow Pb + FeS$$

A combination of methods is in general use, whereby the iron is generated in the smelter by adding oxide of iron to the smelt. Pure lead is quite soft, but the lead obtained from the average smelting process is much harder because of the presence of other metals (impurities from the ore, reduced along with the lead) dissolved in the lead.

It is an odd fact that the rare and little known germanium is now the purest substance known to man. Very pure material is needed for semiconductor applications (see Chapter 12), and a great effort has been made to purify germanium and silicon. The problem is somewhat easier for germanium than silicon because of germanium's lower melting point. The purification depends upon making single crystals. Chemically purified germanium in a graphite crucible is melted in an inert atmosphere, and a crystal is "pulled" by dipping in and then slowly removing a seed crystal. The resulting single crystal is further purified by "zone refining," whereby a thin molten zone is passed down the rod by suitable heating arrangements. The best heater is a radio frequency induction coil which heats by inducing eddy currents in the hot crystal held at the ends, thereby eliminating altogether the necessity for a possibly contaminating crucible. In this "floating zone" process, the impurities tend to collect in the molten zone and pass with it down the rod. By repeated passage of zones, germanium with 1 part in 10^{10} of electrically active impurity has been made.

PHYSICAL PROPERTIES OF THE ELEMENTS

Germanium exhibits the diamond lattice only, while lead occurs only in the metallic lattice. As might be expected, tin, being between the two, exhibits allotropy. From 13° to about 161° the β form, ordinary white metallic tin, is the stable modification. At 13° the β form is in equilibrium with the α form, gray tin, but the change is so slow as to be of little importance. If, on the other hand, white tin is cooled to temperatures of 50 or 60 degrees below zero, the change to gray tin is rapid. The gray form is quite brittle and crumbles to a powder under very little pressure. Thus tin roofs are of little value in very severe climates, because of this popularly called "tin-pest." From 161° to the melting point, γ or rhombic tin is the stable form, but again the change is slow.

The difference between the diamond and metallic lattices is reflected in the melting points of these three elements:

Ge	937.2°
Sn	231.8
Pb	327.4

The semiconducting germanium has a metallic appearance, a single crystal looking like a piece of stainless steel. It is, however, hard and brittle, whereas pure tin and especially lead are quite soft and malleable.

Chemical Properties and Compounds

Germanium, tin, and lead exhibit +2 and +4 oxidation numbers, in keeping with their outer electron configurations, ns^2np^2. There are also a large number of covalent compounds with hydrogen, halogens, and organic groups in which other oxidation numbers from -4 to $+4$ can be assigned to them; but here again, as in organic chemistry, the concept of oxidation number is not particularly useful. In the formation of these volatile, covalent compounds subgroup IVb resembles the typical elements of the group more than the IVa elements do.

Germanium(II) compounds are relatively unstable and have strong reducing properties. The +4 state is the unstable one for lead, while for tin the +2 and +4 states are about equally stable (recall the opposite trend in the a-subgroup).

There are relatively few complexes of germanium, tin, and lead, of which the halide complexes are the most significant.

Chemical Reactions of the Elements

Germanium, like the nonmetals, is not attacked by dilute acids, but it is more reactive toward acids than silicon, since it dissolves in concentrated oxidizing acids, sulfuric acid, nitric acid, and especially aqua regia:

$$Ge + 4HNO_3 + 6HCl \rightarrow H_2GeCl_6 + 4\overline{NO_2} + 4H_2O$$

The action of acids on the metallic tin and lead is complicated by overvoltage for hydrogen, which makes them appear less active than they thermodynamically are, and sometimes by the insolubility of the products which protect the underlying metal. Both are above hydrogen in the E.M.F. Series, but react only slowly with dilute acids. The reactions below illustrate their behavior toward acids:

$Sn + 2HCl(hot, conc.) \rightarrow SnCl_2 + \overline{H_2}$

$Sn + 2H_2SO_4(hot, conc.) \rightarrow SnSO_4 + \overline{SO_2} + 2H_2O$

$Sn + 4HNO_3(conc.) \rightarrow \underline{SnO_2} + 4\overline{NO_2} + 2H_2O$

$Sn + 4HNO_3 + 6HCl(conc.) \rightarrow H_2SnCl_6 + 4\overline{NO_2} + 4H_2O$

$Pb + HCl \rightarrow$ N.R. (because of the insolubility of $PbCl_2$)

$Pb + H_2SO_4(dil.) \rightarrow$ N.R. (because of the insolubility of $PbSO_4$)

$Pb + 3H_2SO_4(hot conc.) \rightarrow Pb(HSO_4)_2 + \overline{SO_2} + 2H_2O$

$3Pb + 8HNO_3(dil.) \rightarrow 3Pb(NO_3)_2 + 2\overline{NO} + 4H_2O$

$Pb + HNO_3(conc.) \rightarrow$ N.R. (because of the insolubility of $Pb(NO_3)_2$ in conc. HNO_3)

$2Pb + 4HC_2H_3O_2 + O_2 \rightarrow 2Pb(C_2H_3O_2)_2 + 2H_2O$

Germanium does not react with bases alone, but in the presence of an oxidizing agent it dissolves readily:

$$Ge + 2NaOH + 2H_2O_2 \rightarrow Na_2GeO_3 + 3H_2O$$

Tin and lead release hydrogen from hot bases alone, although slowly:

$$Sn + 2NaOH \rightarrow Na_2SnO_2 + \overline{H_2}$$

The group IVb elements do not combine with carbon, nitrogen, or hydrogen. No carbides or nitrides are known, but hydrides, and especially organic derivatives of the hydrides, are known. The hydrides decrease in stability from carbon to lead, until plumbane cannot be isolated. The hydrides can be made by reactions similar to those used in making silane (see Chapter 12). GeH_4 and SnH_4 are not so easily hydrolyzed by water as is SiH_4. Consequently SnH_4 has been prepared by reaction of sodium borohydride, $NaBH_4$, with $SnCl_4$ in aqueous media:

$$SnCl_4 + NaBH_4 + 3H_2O \rightarrow \overline{SnH_4} + H_3BO_3 + 3HCl + NaCl$$

Tetravalent Compounds

The dioxides of germanium and tin can be made by direct synthesis, but lead dioxide requires more drastic oxidizing conditions for its preparation.* Suitable methods are the anodic oxidation of lead(II) salts or the action of hypochlorite on lead(II) compounds in alkaline solution:

$$PbO_2^{--} + OCl^- + H_2O \rightarrow \underline{PbO_2} + Cl^- + 2OH^-$$

If red lead is extracted with nitric acid, the lead(II) dissolves, leaving PbO_2, but this is a rather inefficient method of preparation:

$$\underline{Pb_3O_4} + 4HNO_3 \rightarrow 2Pb(NO_3)_2 + \underline{PbO_2} + 2H_2O$$

Germanium(IV) and tin(IV) oxides are white while lead(IV) oxide is black.

These dioxides are acidic only, in the sense that while they react with bases to give germanates, stannates, and plumbates, they do not react with acids to give cationic species:

$$\underline{MeO_2} + 2NaOH \rightarrow Na_2MeO_3 + H_2O$$
$$\underline{MeO_2} + HNO_3 \quad \rightarrow N.R.$$

With the halogen acids, however, the dioxides dissolve to give the tetrahalides or halide complexes, depending on the acid concentration. The ability of the IVb elements to form halide complexes

* As a matter of fact, pure, stoichiometric PbO_2 has never been prepared. The best preparations of the compound are always oxygen deficient (see Chapter 18).

other than fluoro that are stable in water is in sharp contrast to silicon. It takes strong acid or strong base to keep these oxides in solution, the hydrous oxides being precipitated by neutralization:

$$GeO_3^{--} + 2H^+ + (x - 1)H_2O \rightarrow GeO_2 \cdot xH_2O$$
$$H_2SnCl_6 + 2NaOH + (x - 4)H_2O \rightarrow \underline{SnO_2 \cdot xH_2O} + 6NaCl$$

The lead case is complicated by the strong oxidizing properties of lead(IV). If PbO_2 is dissolved in cold HCl, the chloro complex is formed, but at room temperature or above chlorine is evolved:

$$\underline{PbO_2} + 6HCl(\text{cold}) \rightarrow H_2PbCl_6 + 2H_2O$$
$$\underline{PbO_2} + 4HCl(\text{room temp.}) \rightarrow \underline{PbCl_2} + \overline{Cl}_2 + 2H_2O$$

The fluoro complex is also unstable but known, while hydrobromic and hydriodic acids with lead dioxide or plumbates give lead(II) and the free halogen immediately. Lead dioxide is soluble in concentrated alkali to give plumbates:

$$\underline{PbO_2} + 2NaOH(\text{conc.}) \rightarrow Na_2PbO_3 + H_2O$$

The disulfides of germanium and tin can be precipitated from a hydrochloric acid solution of the tetravalent metals:

$$H_2SnCl_6 + 2\overline{H_2S} \rightarrow \underline{SnS_2} + 6HCl$$

Contrast the behavior of silicon whose disulfide is unstable in any aqueous solution. Germanium(IV) sulfide is white, like all germanium(IV) and tin(IV) compounds except the yellow tin(IV) sulfide. The disulfides are readily soluble in alkaline sulfide solution, forming thiogermanates or thiostannates:

$$\underline{GeS_2} + Na_2S \rightarrow Na_2GeS_3$$

The thio compounds are also formed when H_2S is bubbled into alkaline solutions of germanates or stannates. Acidification of solutions of the thio compounds leads to precipitation of the disulfides. Of course, lead disulfide does not exist, because such a strongly oxidizing cation cannot be part of the same compound with a reducing anion such as sulfide.

Compounds of the type MeX_4 can be prepared, but only in the absence of water, since they hydrolyze to basic salts and halide complexes. Germanium tetrachloride can, however, be distilled from solution in concentrated hydrochloric acid, a fact that caused Winkler to lose germanium and prolong his search when he evaporated HCl solutions of germanium to dryness in his analytical procedure.

The tetrahalides are usually made by direct synthesis. Except for the salt-like SnF_4, they are liquids or low-melting solids of covalent bond type; see Table 14.1.

TABLE 14.1
Melting Points of IVb Tetrahalides

	F	Cl	Br	I
Ge	sublimes −104	−50	26	144
Sn	sublimes 705	−30	31	144
Pb	—	−15	—	—

Lead tetrachloride is very unstable; it is reported to explode on heating to 105°.

Germanium (and perhaps tin) is similar to silicon and carbon in forming mixed halides, hydride-halides, and higher hydrides of the types GeF_3Cl, etc.; $GeHCl_3$, etc.; and Ge_2H_6, etc. In addition, since the metal-carbon bond is more stable than the metal-hydrogen bond, there are a large number of covalent compounds of germanium, tin, and lead with organic groups attached, such as $(CH_3)_2SnCl_2$, $Pb_2(CH_3)_6$, etc. The commercially important tetraethyl lead, $Pb(C_2H_5)_4$, is made in large quantity as an anti-knock agent for gasoline (1 to 3 cc. per gallon), by the reaction of an ethyl halide with sodium-lead alloy:

$$4C_2H_5X + Na_4Pb \rightarrow Pb(C_2H_5)_4 + 4NaX$$

In 1952 about 160,000 tons of lead were used to make high-test gas. These covalent compounds are not so stable as those of silicon; they are all rather volatile, combustible, and exceedingly toxic.

Divalent Compounds

The +2 oxides of these three elements are amphoteric, but they are more on the basic side than the dioxides. Divalent germanium compounds are not very stable under ordinary conditions. The black monoxide results from the hydrolysis of the dichloride, made from germanium and the tetrachloride:

$$Ge + GeCl_4 \rightarrow 2GeCl_2$$
$$GeCl_2 + H_2O \rightarrow GeO + 2HCl$$

The ease of oxidation of $+2$ germanium compounds is so great that their reactions are little known.

When an aqueous solution of a tin(II) or lead(II) salt is neutralized, the white hydrous monoxides precipitate, although colloid formation may make them difficult to filter. They can be dehydrated to the black SnO and orange-yellow PbO.

Tin(II) and lead(II) oxides dissolve in alkali to form stannites and plumbites. Tin(II) is especially unstable in basic solution, owing to the greater acidity of the $+4$ state, and sodium stannite solutions are therefore easily oxidized by air to stannate. Plumbite solutions are quite stable to oxygen.

The basic properties of tin(II) and lead(II) oxides are strong enough to permit of the crystallization of salts of strong acids, such as $SnCl_2 \cdot 2H_2O$, $PbCl_2$, and $SnSO_4$. The addition of hydrogen sulfide to slightly acid solutions of tin(II) and lead(II) ions results in the precipitation of the sulfides, black in both cases. These monosulfides are insoluble in sodium sulfide solution. The chromate, carbonate, and sulfate of lead are insoluble and are very often used as pigments. White lead, a basic carbonate of lead, is still a competitor of titanium dioxide for the white pigment market. The annual production of white lead is about 25,000 tons. Smaller amounts of lead chromate and lead sulfate are used as yellow and white pigments respectively.

Litharge, PbO, is a yellow pigment. Mixed with glycerin, it makes a fast-setting cement also. About 150,000 tons of litharge are produced annually. Careful roasting of litharge gives red lead, Pb_3O_4. About 35,000 tons of red lead are used per year in this country, mostly as a protective coating on metals and as a pigment.

THE LEAD STORAGE BATTERY

The lead storage battery is composed of a number of cells in series, each generating almost 2 volts. The cathode of each cell is lead, the active ingredient on the anode is lead dioxide, and the electrolyte is sulfuric acid. During discharge the following reactions take place:

At the cathode: $Pb + SO_4^{--}$ $\qquad\qquad\quad\rightarrow PbSO_4\downarrow + 2\ominus$
At the anode: $PbO_2 + 4H^+ + SO_4^{--} + 2\ominus \rightarrow PbSO_4\downarrow + 2H_2O$
Net reaction: $Pb + PbO_2 + 2H_2SO_4 \qquad\quad \rightarrow 2PbSO_4 + 2H_2O$

During discharge lead sulfate is deposited on both electrodes, and the concentration of sulfuric acid in the electrolytic solution is decreased. It is important that the lead sulfate coat on the electrodes securely, since during charging the reverse reaction takes place. If the lead sulfate flakes off the electrodes and falls to bottom of the cell, then it is unable to take part in the charging operation.

The Lewis Acid-Base Concept

If tin tetrachloride is reacted with potassium chloride in a non-aqueous solvent such as selenium oxychloride, the results are the same as if the reaction had been carried out in water:

$$SnCl_4 + 2(K^+Cl^-) \rightarrow 2K^+ SnCl_6^{--}$$

According to G. N. Lewis, the reaction may be likened to acid-base reactions, except that no hydrogen is present, the element upon which acids and bases rest for their existence in the proton concept. Actually many reactions involving no protons may be treated as neutralization phenomena, and the reactions may be followed by means of indicators, in the same manner as acid-base titrations in water solutions. Such being the case, it becomes necessary to expand somewhat the proton concept to include such reactions or to introduce entirely new definitions mutually satisfactory to both phenomena. To accomplish either of these, it is necessary to examine more closely the simple reaction:

$$H^+ + OH^- \leftrightharpoons H_2O$$

According to the proton concept, the H^+ has been donated by some acid to the OH^-, with the resultant formation of a covalent bond.

Looking at it electronically,

$$H^+ + \left[\; :\overset{..}{O}:H\; \right]^- \leftrightharpoons H:\overset{..}{O}:H$$

the oxygen has donated a share in a pair of its electrons to the proton, forming a coordinate covalent bond. Thus a base is a substance capable of donating a share in some of its electrons to form a coordinate covalent bond, and an acid is a substance capable of accepting a share in other electrons to form a coordinate covalent bond. If the sharing of electrons is made the basis of a definition of acids and bases, hydrogen becomes but a special case of a larger and more all-inclusive system of acid-base reactions. Viewed in this light, the reaction between tin tetrachloride and potassium chloride becomes

$$2\left(K^+ : \overset{..}{\underset{..}{Cl}}{:}^- \right) + \begin{matrix} :Cl: \\ :Cl : \overset{..}{Sn} : Cl: \\ :Cl: \end{matrix} \to 2K^+ \left[\begin{matrix} :Cl: \\ Cl \quad\quad Cl \\ Sn \\ Cl \quad\quad Cl \\ :Cl: \end{matrix} \right]^=$$

whereby the tin is the acid accepting a share in a pair of electrons from each of two additional chloride ions to form two more electron pair bonds.

The above example of acid-base reaction according to the so-called electronic or Lewis theory is what has been called complex compound formation in earlier chapters. Thus, all complex formation, and perhaps oxidation-reduction as well, would be classified as acid-base reactions using the electronic definition. While this sweeping definition is useful at times in correlating similar types of behavior, it is so general that the terms "acid" and "base" lose much of their precision. Furthermore, the quantitative aspects of acid-base reactions, such as the strengths of acids and bases, are not preserved in the Lewis system, since the strength is different from one reaction to another. In spite of these limitations, the concept is a useful one, and whether we call a reaction an acid-base reaction or not does not change our picture of the actual nature of the reaction. Current practice seems to use the terms "Lewis acid" and "Lewis base" when it is desired to focus on the electron acceptor or donor characteristics of reactants.

SUGGESTIONS FOR FURTHER READING

R. P. Bell, *Acids and Bases*, Metheun, London, 1952.
————, *Quarterly Reviews*, Vol. **1**, p. 113 (1947).
W. F. Luder and S. Zuffanti, *The Electronic Theory of Acids and Bases*, Wiley, New York, 1946.
P. C. L. Thorne and A. M. Ward, *Fritz Ephraim's Inorganic Chemistry*, Nordeman, New York, 3rd English ed., 1939, pp. 141–146, 320–328.
M. E. Weeks, *Discovery of the Elements*, 6th ed., Journal of Chemical Education, Easton, Pa., 1956, pp. 407–412.

STUDY QUESTIONS

1. Write an equation for the oxidation of an acid solution of tin(II) chloride by potassium permanganate.

2. Write an equation for the oxidation of sodium stannite by oxygen, the reaction taking place in solution.

3. A solution of sodium stannite reduces bismuth(III) hydroxide to metallic bismuth. Write the equation.

4. Suggest a reason why it is not possible to prepare PbS_2.

5. Which is the most acidic, GeO_2, SnO_2, or PbO_2? Explain.

6. Which is more acidic, GeO_2 or TiO_2? Explain.

7. A dilute acid solution contains the following species: Sn(II), Ge(IV), and Pb(II), all as chlorides. Suggest a procedure for separating the three.

8. A dilute acid solution contains the following species: Cu^{++}, Cd^{++}, Hg^{++}, Pb^{++}, and Sn^{++}, all as nitrates. Suggest a procedure for separating the five.

9. To a hydrobromic acid solution containing 27 grams of KBr are added 55 grams of $SnBr_4$. How many grams of K_2SnBr_6 could be obtained from the solution?

10. Write an equation to show the oxidation of divalent lead to lead dioxide by alkaline hypochlorite.

11. Lead dioxide oxidizes manganese from $+2$ to $+7$ in strong sulfuric and nitric acid solution. Write an equation for the reaction.

12. Explain, on the basis of the electronic concept of acids and bases, which is the acid and which the base in each of the following reactions:

   (a) $Zn^{++} + 4NH_3 \rightarrow Zn(NH_3)_4^{++}$

(b) $H^+ + NH_2^- \rightarrow NH_3$

(c) $SOCl_2 + K_2SO_3 \rightarrow 2KCl + 2SO_2$

13. To the extent that sodium stannate is soluble in water, would you expect it to hydrolyze? Why? How?

14. Either tin(II) or lead(II), but not both, will form a carbonate. Which one will? Why?

15. Consider lead and hafnium:

(a) Estimate their melting points.

(b) What compounds of these elements would you expect to find in nature?

(c) Assuming that both of these elements has a divalent state, which of the two would be more basic in that state?

(d) The oxide of which would be more difficult to reduce to the metal?

(e) Which would be the more difficult to oxidize to the maximum oxidation state?

(f) What is the maximum oxidation state for each of these elements?

16. What happens in the cases below?

(a) $Sn + conc.\ HNO_3$

(b) $Pb(NO_3)_2 + NaCl$(aqueous)

(c) $SnO_2 + NaOH$(aqueous)

(d) $Ge + H_2O_2 + NaOH$(aqueous)

(e) $SnCl_4 + HCl$(aqueous)

17. By means of equations and a few words about conditions, show how to carry out the following conversions:

(a) Make Na_2PbO_3 from a natural lead compound.

(b) Make $Pb(C_2H_3O_2)_2$ from Pb.

(c) Make $SnSO_4$ from a natural tin compound.

(d) Make $GeCl_4$ from GeO_2.

(e) Make SnH_4 from Sn.

18. By means of equations, show how ZnO in water is amphoteric on the basis of the Lewis concept of acids and bases.

19. Give an example of an acid-base reaction in the sense of Lewis's theory which would not be called an acid-base reaction according to the Bronsted-Lowry concept.

20. Compare briefly the relative stability of the various oxidation states of Ti, Zr, Hf, and Th, on the one hand, and Ge, Sn, and Pb, on the other.

OCCURRENCE AND HISTORY

Elementary nitrogen is the major constituent of the earth's atmosphere: about 75 per cent by weight and 78 per cent by volume. In the crust, however, it is a very minor, but nonetheless important, element: its compounds account for the order of 0.01 per cent by weight of the lithosphere and hydrosphere. Saltpeter, KNO_3, and Chilean saltpeter, $NaNO_3$, are the main natural inorganic compounds, which occur in a few localized deposits. Nitrogen is one of the essential elements in the metabolism of living organisms, and so a wide variety of natural organic compounds are known. Amino acids, the structural units of proteins, are of the general formula

$$\underset{NH_2}{\overset{H}{R-C-C}}\overset{O}{\underset{OH}{\diagdown}}$$

where R— stands for certain organic radicals.

Nitrogen compounds, such as ammonium chloride or sal ammoniac, have been known since ancient times. At the end of the eighteenth century, nitrogen as a constituent of air was recognized by several scientists, with priority going to the Scottish physician, D. Rutherford.

PREPARATION OF THE ELEMENT

Since there are many billions of tons of the element in the atmosphere, nitrogen is almost always obtained by purification from the other constituents in the air. When ordinary air is liquefied by successive compression, cooling and expansion, the liquid contains about 50 per cent oxygen, since nitrogen is more volatile than oxygen: N_2, b.p. $-196°$; O_2, b.p. $-183°$. Fractional distillation of the liquid can be made to give nearly pure nitrogen as the distillate and nearly pure oxygen as the residue. The gases are compressed in cylinders and sold. Tank nitrogen contains traces of oxygen, argon (b.p. $-186°$), and water vapor. It is suitable for most purposes, but if purer nitrogen is needed, the oxygen concentration can be reduced to a very low value by chemical means, such as passing the gas over hot copper or into alkaline pyrogallol solution. Subsequent drying with phosphorus(V) oxide gives quite pure gas; the inert argon is unobjectionable for all but the most exacting research purposes. When small quantities of extremely pure nitrogen are desired, it can be made by the careful thermal decomposition of a pure alkali or alkaline earth azide (see below for preparation of azides):

$$2NaN_3 \xrightarrow{300°} 2Na + 3N_2\uparrow$$

Very pure metal is a by-product.

PHYSICAL PROPERTIES OF THE ELEMENT

Nitrogen is composed of diatomic molecules with the atoms joined by a triple bond, $N\equiv N$. It is a colorless, odorless, tasteless, diamagnetic gas sparingly soluble in water which gives on strong cooling a colorless liquid and then a colorless solid (compare oxygen). Some of its physical properties are listed in Table 15.1.

TABLE 15.1
Some Physical Properties of Nitrogen

Melting Point	$-209.86°$
Boiling Point	$-195.8°$
Critical Temperature	$-147.1°$
Critical Pressure	33.5 atm
Critical Density	0.3110 g/cc
Density of Gas at STP	1.2506 g/l
Density of Liquid at b.p.	0.808 g/cc
Density of Solid at $-252°$	1.026 g/cc
Solubility in water at 0° and 1 atm	0.023 cc/100 g

CHEMICAL PROPERTIES AND COMPOUNDS

With the electron structure of $1s^2 2s^2 2p^3$, nitrogen can complete its octet (the octet rule is particularly applicable to second period elements) by gaining a share in 3 more electrons, or it can formally approach the electron configuration of helium by losing a share in its 5 valence electrons. In fact, it does both, and oxidation numbers from -3 to $+5$ are observed, with all the possible states in between also represented. Like carbon, covalent bonds are the rule, and the only monatomic ions are those in compounds of very electropositive metals, such as Li_3N. The concept of oxidation number is used with effect in nitrogen chemistry, unlike that of carbon, perhaps because a greater variety of oxidizing and reducing power is found among simple nitrogen compounds than among simple carbon compounds.

Very much a nonmetal, nitrogen has acidic oxides only. It does not form complexes in the way that metals do; rather, it acts as the electron donating atom; for example,

$$H \leftarrow NH_3{}^+, \ F_3B \leftarrow NH_3, \ Cu(\leftarrow NH_3)_4{}^{++}, \ Fe(CN)_5NO^{--},$$
$$Co(NO_2)_6{}^{-3}, \ Co(NH_3)_5NO_3{}^{++}, \text{ etc.}$$

Chemical Reactions of the Element

The nitrogen molecule, with its very strong triple bond, is quite stable at ordinary temperature. Thus, nitrogen is chemically inert unless energy in the form of heat or an electric discharge is supplied to activate it. At high temperatures, on the other hand, nitrogen is reactive. It combines with hydrogen at several hundred degrees in the presence of a catalyst to give an equilibrium concentration of ammonia in the Haber Process, which should be familiar to the reader who has studied elementary chemistry. It reacts with oxygen only at extreme temperature or in the presence of an electric discharge (the "smell of electricity" associated with electric motors with sparking commutators, or with thundershowers, is due to nitrogen oxides and ozone produced by the discharge). Even then only a small fraction of the reactants are converted:

$$N_2 + O_2 \underset{\text{discharge}}{\overset{2500°, \text{ or electric}}{\longleftarrow \longrightarrow}} 2NO - \text{heat}$$

Once seriously considered for the fixation of atmospheric nitrogen into compounds, this reaction is of no practical importance now because of the development of the more efficient Haber Process.

At elevated temperatures nitrogen combines with most metals to form nitrides. If the metal is an active one, only moderate temperatures are needed, and ionic nitrides containing the N^{---} ion are formed:

$$6Li + N_2 \xrightarrow{200°} 2Li_3N \qquad \text{(not for Na, K, Rb, Cs)}$$

$$3Mg + N_2 \xrightarrow{>300°} Mg_3N_2 \qquad \text{(also for Be, Ca, Sr, Ba)}$$

With less active metals, covalent nitrides are formed at high temperatures:

$$2Al + N_2 \xrightarrow{800°} 2AlN$$

$$2B + N_2 \xrightarrow[\text{heat}]{\text{white}} 2BN$$

These last two compounds are interesting in that they have the same number of valence electrons in the lattice as solid carbon: $3 + 5 = 4 + 4$. Boron nitride made this way has the structure of graphite with B and N atoms alternating in the C positions. It was a matter of speculation for years whether BN could be made to achieve the diamond lattice. Just after the successful synthesis of diamond, cubic boron nitride was also made at 1800° and 85,000 atm. It turns out to be about as hard as diamond itself. Aluminum nitride has as its only structure the diamond one. All three structures are white (compare graphite).

Nitrogen also reacts at high temperature with most of the transition elements to give "interstitial" nitrides in which the lattice of metal atoms is expanded but holds its structure and the nitrogen atoms go into certain interstices; examples are TiN, NbN, etc. (see Chapter 17).

The element is inert to water, acids, bases, and the halogens, even fluorine. It does react with a few compounds; its reaction with calcium carbide, for example, gives cyanamide (see Chapter 11).

Oxides and Oxyacids

Oxides of nitrogen are known with the oxidation number varying from $+1$ to $+5$, but only three of the corresponding acids exist, $+1$, $+3$, and $+5$.

Dinitrogen monoxide is made by heating ammonium nitrate:

$$NH_4NO_3 \overset{\Delta}{\rightarrow} \overline{N_2O} + \overline{2H_2O}$$

Since too high a temperature causes the reaction to occur explosively, a range of between 200 and 250° is recommended. The compound is a colorless gas (b.p. $-88.6°$) and is known for its anesthetic properties (laughing gas). It is inert toward most chemical reagents at room temperature. When heated, however, it decomposes into nitrogen and oxygen, and therefore it gives at high temperature the reactions expected of a mixture of these gases. For example, it will support combustion:

$$C + 2N_2O \overset{\Delta}{\rightarrow} CO_2 + N_2$$

Another nonsystematic name commonly used for N_2O is nitrous oxide. The gas is quite soluble in water, more than one cc dissolving per cc of water at STP, but the solution is neutral, and there is no reaction between the dinitrogen monoxide and the water. The $+1$ oxyacid, $H_2N_2O_2$, hyponitrous acid, is known, however, and it decomposes into dinitrogen monoxide and water:

$$H_2N_2O_2 \rightarrow \overline{N_2O} + H_2O$$

The situation is the same as in the carbon monoxide-formic acid case, where CO does not behave as the acid anhydride of HCOOH.

Sodium hyponitrite can be made in small yield by the reduction of aqueous sodium nitrate or nitrite with sodium amalgam:

$$2NaNO_3 + 8Na + 4H_2O \rightarrow Na_2N_2O_2 + 8NaOH$$

Neutralization with acetic acid gives an aqueous solution of the undissociated weak acid, from which the insoluble silver salt can be precipitated by addition of silver nitrate. The pure acid is prepared by reacting silver hyponitrite with anhydrous ethereal hydrogen chloride. Silver chloride precipitates, leaving a solution of hyponitrous acid in ether. Crystals of the acid are obtained by evaporating the solvent. The acid is unstable, decomposing often explosively as above, but its salts are reasonably stable when treated carefully. Its main chemical property is its great reducing action:

$$5H_2N_2O_2 + 8KMnO_4 + 12H_2SO_4 \rightarrow$$
$$10HNO_3 + 4K_2SO_4 + 8MnSO_4 + 12H_2O$$

The doubled formula is borne out by many observations. The freezing point depression in water and the existence of acid salts, such as $Ba(HN_2O_2)_2$, as well as the normal salt, BaN_2O_2, may be mentioned.

The $+2$ oxide of nitrogen, NO, nitrogen oxide, is commonly called nitric oxide. It is made commercially in the first step of the Ostwald Process for the manufacture of nitric acid from ammonia by the catalytic gas-phase oxidation of ammonia:

$$4NH_3 + 5O_2 \xrightarrow[Pt]{\Delta} 4NO + 6H_2O$$

In the laboratory it is most conveniently made by the reduction of a nitrite in acid solution by iodide ion or iron(II):

$$2NaNO_2 + 2FeSO_4 + 3H_2SO_4 \rightarrow$$
$$Fe_2(SO_4)_3 + 2NaHSO_4 + 2H_2O + \overline{2NO}$$

Nitrogen oxide is a colorless gas condensing to a blue liquid at $-151.8°$. Since the molecule contains an odd number of electrons, it must be and is paramagnetic. With one unpaired electron, it would be expected to dimerize, at least near the boiling point, as NO_2 does (see below). In fact, it probably does dimerize at low temperature since the solid is diamagnetic, but it has been little studied because of the low boiling point. At room temperature nitrogen oxide reacts instantly with oxygen to form nitrogen dioxide. Actually, an equilibrium is set up which lies far to the right at room temperature:

$$2NO + O_2 \rightleftharpoons 2NO_2 + heat$$

The equilibrium shifts to the left at high temperature, so that at $600°$ there is very little nitrogen dioxide present. That is why NO and not NO_2 is the product of the oxidation of ammonia at high temperature discussed above. In practice, excess oxygen is used in the Ostwald Process, nitrogen dioxide resulting when the product gases are cooled.

The $+4$ oxide of nitrogen, made as above, is a red-brown gas condensing to a red-brown liquid at 21.1°. NO_2 is also an odd-electron molecule, and it is therefore, like NO, paramagnetic. With a boiling point much higher than that of NO, however, the dimerization is appreciable at room temperature. At 25° and 1 atm., the red vapor consists of about 30 per cent nitrogen dioxide and 70 per cent dinitrogen tetroxide, N_2O_4. On heating, the color becomes more intense because of increasing proportion of monomer, until at about 140° dissociation is essentially complete and the gas is black. At still higher temperatures the color lightens because of decomposition into nitrogen oxide and oxygen. Below room temperature the liquid lightens in color until a pale yellow solid is formed at the melting point, $-11.2°$, where dimerization is essentially complete and the compound is diamagnetic.

When nitrogen oxide and nitrogen dioxide are mixed, still another equilibrium is established:

$$NO + NO_2 \rightleftharpoons N_2O_3$$

Very little dinitrogen trioxide is present at room temperature and above, but cooling of the mixture results in a shift toward the formation of dinitrogen trioxide, a blue liquid below 3°C. This compound can be considered the anhydride of nitrous acid, since its solution in aqueous caustic gives nitrites:

$$N_2O_3 + 2OH^- \rightarrow 2NO_2^- + H_2O$$

By this means the nitrites of the strongly basic metals can be prepared. If, however, a strong acid is added to an aqueous solution of a soluble nitrite, the evolution of oxides of nitrogen from the system is observed. This is due to the combination of facts that:

(a) HNO_2 is a weak acid.

$$H_3O^+ + NO_2^- \xrightarrow{\quad\longleftarrow\quad} HNO_2 + H_2O$$

(b) HNO_2 is unstable.

$$2HNO_2 \xrightarrow{\quad\longleftarrow\quad} N_2O_3 + H_2O$$

(c) N_2O_3 is practically completely dissociated at ordinary temperatures.

This reaction of acids on nitrites is usually accompanied by a faint blue flash of color, suggestive of the anhydride.

Since nitrous acid contains nitrogen in an oxidation state intermediate between the highest and lowest, both oxidizing and reducing properties are possible. These are both apparent for nitrous acid, or better a solution of sodium nitrite acidified in the presence of the other reactant, when the results are just what would be expected if nitrous acid had been added to the solution. Reactions illustrative of these properties are:

Reducing

$$2MnO_4^- + 5HNO_2 + H^+ \rightarrow 2Mn^{++} + 5NO_3^- + 3H_2O$$
$$Br_2 + HNO_2 + H_2O \quad \rightarrow NO_3^- + 2Br^- + 3H^+$$

Oxidizing

$$2I^- + 2HNO_2 + 2H^+ \quad \rightarrow I_2 + 2\overline{NO} + 2H_2O$$
$$Fe^{++} + HNO_2 + H^+ \quad \rightarrow Fe^{+++} + \overline{NO} + H_2O$$

When nitrogen dioxide is dissolved in water, a disproportionation reaction takes place:

$$2NO_2 + H_2O \rightarrow HNO_3 + HNO_2$$

The nitrous acid disproportionates also in the presence of the nitric acid:

$$3HNO_2 \rightarrow HNO_3 + H_2O + 2NO\uparrow$$

Since the nitrogen oxide reacts with air to produce more nitrogen dioxide, all of the original nitrogen dioxide can be converted eventually into nitric acid by excess oxygen. This is the basis of the Ostwald Process for making nitric acid. Ammonia is oxidized catalytically to nitrogen oxide by oxygen mixed with steam to make the reaction nonexplosive. Upon cooling, nitrogen oxide reacts with oxygen to become nitrogen dioxide, which is absorbed in water to give nitric acid. Prior to the development of this method, nitric acid was made by reacting sodium nitrate with concentrated sulfuric acid and distilling off the more volatile nitric acid. Some nitric acid is still made by this method. Approximately 1,500,000 tons of nitric acid were produced in the United States in 1951, most of it by the Ostwald Process. Pure HNO_3 is a colorless liquid, but in the presence of light, or reducing agents such as dust, it becomes yellow owing to the presence of NO_2.

The +5 oxide of nitrogen is best made by the dehydration of nitric acid, of which it is the anhydride:

$$2HNO_3 + P_2O_5 \rightarrow N_2O_5 + 2HPO_3$$

Alternatively, dinitrogen tetroxide takes up more oxygen from ozone:

$$N_2O_4 + O_3 \rightarrow N_2O_5 + O_2$$

Dinitrogen pentoxide forms white hygroscopic crystals when pure, subliming at 32.3°. It is stable below 0°, but loses oxygen when warmed to room temperature. If suddenly heated, it explodes. It is a powerful oxidizing agent, and dissolves readily in water to give nitric acid.

Trihalides

Nitrogen forms three trihalides, the fluoride, chloride, and iodide. They are made by the halogenation of ammonia or ammonium salts. For the chloride and iodide the reaction can be carried out in aqueous solution, but the fluoride is best made by the electrolysis of ammonium hydrogen fluoride. The trichloride, a yellow oil, and the triiodide, a black solid usually of the composition $NH_3 \cdot NI_3$, are exceedingly unstable. They are endothermic compounds and explode violently at the slightest provocation. The trifluoride, on the other hand, is a low-boiling, stable gas. It is exothermic and inert to most chemical agents. A number of hydride halides of the type NH_xX_{3-x} also exist.

Oxyhalides

More stable than the trihalides, except NF_3, are the oxyhalides of nitrogen. There are two types; the nitrosyl halides, NOX, with $X = F$, Cl, Br, and the nitryl halides, NO_2X, with $X = F$, Cl. All of the compounds are gases at room temperature and normal pressure. The nitrosyl halides can be prepared by reacting nitrogen oxide with free halogen. The more usual method of preparing nitrosyl fluoride is by fluorination of nitrosyl chloride:

$$NOCl + AgF \rightarrow NOF + AgCl$$

Silver fluoride is an excellent reagent with which to replace a chlorine atom with a fluorine in many compounds. The nitrosyl halides are completely hydrolyzed in water, mostly to nitrous acid and hydrohalic acid:

$$NOX + H_2O \rightarrow HNO_2 + HX$$

Nitryl fluoride is formed, *inter alia*, by the reaction of fluorine with nitrogen oxide:

$$4NO + F_2 \rightarrow 2NO_2F + N_2$$

Nitryl chloride cannot be made using chlorine, but, rather, results from the action of ozone on nitrosyl chloride:

$$NOCl + O_3 \rightarrow NO_2Cl + O_2$$

The nitryl halides are powerful oxidizing agents.

Ammonia

About 18,000,000 tons of ammonia were produced in the United States in 1951, and production goals call for doubling this output. The largest demands for ammonia are in the production of fertilizers and nitric acid.

The Haber Process accounts for most of the synthetic ammonia. By means of catalysts, moderate temperatures, and extremely high pressures, direct synthesis is made economical:

$$N_2 + 3H_2 \leftrightharpoons 2NH_3 + heat$$

There are two other industrial sources of ammonia:

(a) In the production of coke from coal much of the nitrogenous matter appears in the distillate as ammonia. Considerable quantities of ammonia are recovered from coking operations. It is absorbed in sulfuric acid, forming ammonium sulfate. The latter is sold for fertilizer use.

(b) *The Cyanamide Process.* Calcium carbide will react with elementary nitrogen at 1000°C to give calcium cyanamide:

$$CaC_2 + N_2 \xrightarrow{\Delta} CaCN_2 + C$$

It may be used directly as a fertilizer or hydrolyzed with steam to give ammonia:

$$CaCN_2 + 3H_2O \xrightarrow{\Delta} 2NH_3\uparrow + CaCO_3$$

In the laboratory ammonia is made occasionally by two other methods:

(a) Nitrogen is passed over hot magnesium metal. The nitride reacts vigorously with water to give ammonia and magnesium hydroxide. Other metals of equal or greater activity work as well.

(b) Any ammonium salt can be distilled with an excess of alkali to give ammonia:

$$NH_4^+ + OH^- \rightarrow NH_3\uparrow + H_2O$$

Ammonia is very soluble in water. It reacts with moderately strong acids to form salts, most of which are water soluble. In fact the solubilities of ammonium salts are about the same as the solubilities of the corresponding potassium salts.

Dry ammonia is able to react with the more electropositive metals to form amides:

$$2K + 2NH_3 \xrightarrow{cat} 2KNH_2 + H_2\uparrow$$

The reaction is similar to that between potassium and water, except the ammonia reaction is not so violent; in fact, it is very slow in the absence of a catalyst. The amides are strong bases—stronger than hydroxides, since they cannot exist in water:

$$NH_2^- + H_2O \rightarrow NH_3 + OH^-$$

Hydrazine

Hydrazine—N_2H_4 or, better, H_2N—NH_2—is formed when ammonia is reacted with sodium hypochlorite in an aqueous solution containing some dissolved glue or gelatin. The purpose of the latter is not clear, but it is necessary in order to get any kind of a yield at all. One theory holds that the glue deactivates by adsorption traces of metal ions which would otherwise catalyze the decomposition of the hydrazine as it is produced. The proposed mechanism for the reaction is:

$$NH_3 + OCl^- \rightarrow NH_2Cl + OH^-$$
$$NH_2Cl + NH_3 \rightarrow N_2H_4 + HCl$$

The hydrochloric acid is neutralized by the excess alkali as it is formed. Hydrazine is soluble in the aqueous solution. Upon the addition of sulfuric acid to the solution and cooling, hydrazinium sulfate crystallizes from solution. On most bottles the formula of the salt is written $N_2H_4 \cdot H_2SO_4$, yet there is no more reason for this formula than there is for $NH_3 \cdot H_2SO_4$ as a formula for ammonium hydrogen sulfate. The hydrazine molecule has two nitrogen atoms, either of which is almost as good a base as the nitrogen in ammonia. Accordingly, the salt is better represented by the formula $N_2H_5HSO_4$. Hydrazine is a strong reducing agent, being readily oxidized to nitrogen:

$$4Fe^{+++} + N_2H_4 \rightarrow 4Fe^{++} + \overline{N_2} + 4H^+$$

From this point of view, the compound is analogous to hydrogen peroxide in the water system of compounds. Recent commercial processes react urea, $CO(NH_2)_2$, with alkaline hypochlorite to produce hydrazine:

$$CO(NH_2)_2 + NaOCl + 2NaOH \rightarrow$$
$$N_2H_4 + NaCl + Na_2CO_3 + H_2O$$

Hydrazine burns in air, releasing a great deal of heat. It has recently become of considerable interest as a high-energy, low-weight fuel for use in rockets.

Hydrazoic Acid and Azides

The sodium salt of hydrazoic acid, HN_3, is formed when dinitrogen oxide is passed over molten sodium amide at 190°C:

$$2NaNH_2 + N_2O \rightarrow NaN_3 + NaOH + NH_3\uparrow$$

The sodium azide can be crystallized from water solution by way of purification from the sodium hydroxide. The azide ion is a pseudo-halide, that is, an anion that behaves chemically like a halide ion. The free pseudo-halogen, N_6, cannot be made, however. Its silver, lead(II), and copper(I) salts are insoluble. It forms a highly colored complex with iron(III) ion. It is a linear ion with two nitrogen-nitrogen double bonds, and so one way of writing its electron structure is

$$\left[\ :\overset{..}{N}::N::N: \ \right]^{-}$$

involving sixteen electrons, five from each of the three nitrogen atoms and one from the cation in its ionic bonding. Free hydrazoic acid is made by adding dilute sulfuric acid to a solution containing a soluble azide and distilling the free acid. Pure, anhydrous hydrazoic acid is a liquid boiling just above room temperature. In acid strength it is very close to acetic acid. It is a deadly poison and an unpredictable explosive. The acid can act as either a reducing agent or an oxidizing agent. The lead and mercury salts are used as primary detonators, but the alkali and alkaline-earth metal salts are perfectly safe to handle under ordinary conditions.

Hydroxylamine

Hydroxylamine, NH_2OH, may be looked upon as a substituted ammonia, the —OH group replacing —H, or as a substituted water, the —NH_2 group replacing —H. It is formed in a variety of reactions, but two methods of preparation predominate. The first and most efficient is the electrolysis of nitrate in a 50 per cent sulfuric acid solution. With amalgamated lead electrodes at 0°, up to 65 per cent yield of hydroxylammonium sulfate, $(NH_3OH)_2SO_4$, can be obtained in the cathodic reduction. In the second method, alkali nitrite is treated with a bisulfite or sulfur dioxide in nearly neutral, ice-cold solution. The first product is the hydroxylamine-disulfonate ion:

$$NO_2^- + 2HSO_3^- + H^+ \rightarrow HON(SO_3)_2^{--} + H_2O$$

The product may be regarded as a derivative of hydroxylamine in which two hydrogens are replaced by sulfonate groups, —SO_3^-:

hydroxylamine   hydroxylaminedisulfonate

The potassium salt is slightly soluble and can be crystallized. Addition of strong acid and digestion hydrolyzes the hydroxylaminedisulfonate:

$$\text{HO—N} \begin{array}{c} \boxed{SO_3^- \ HO}H \\ \\ \boxed{SO_3^- \ HO}H \end{array} \ + \ + H^+ \rightarrow HONH_3^+ + 2HSO_4^-$$

As was the case for hydrazine, the sulfate can be crystallized from the solution.

TABLE 15.2

Compound	m.p. °C	b.p. °C	Heat of Vaporization	Ionization Constant in Water at 25°*
H_2O	0°	100°	540 cal/g	$K_a = K_b = 1.8 \times 10^{-16}$
NH_3	−78	−33.4	328	$K_b = 1.8 \times 10^{-5}$
NH_2OH	33	58 (at 22 mm)		$K_b = 6.6 \times 10^{-9}$
N_2H_4	1.8	113.5		$K_b = 9.8 \times 10^{-7}$
H_2O_2	−0.89	151	342	$K_a = 2.4 \times 10^{-12}$
HN_3	−80	37		$K_a = 1.8 \times 10^{-5}$

* For $R + H_2O \rightleftharpoons RH^+ + OH^-$, $K_b = \dfrac{[RH^+][OH^-]}{[R]}$. For $HR + H_2O \rightleftharpoons H_3O^+ + R^-$, $K_a = \dfrac{[H_3O^+][R^-]}{[HR]}$. Note that for water, the usual ion product, $K_i = [H_3O^+][OH^-]$, is divided by $[H_2O] = 55.34$ moles/l, to get $K_a = K_b$ for comparison with the other substances listed.

As a base, hydroxylamine is weaker than ammonia. Aqueous solutions of its salts have both oxidizing and reducing properties, the former mostly in basic solution, the latter in acid:

$$2Fe^{++} + NH_2OH + 4OH^- + H_2O \rightarrow 2Fe(OH)_3 + \overline{NH_3}$$
$$4Fe^{+++} + 2NH_3OH^+ \qquad \rightarrow 4Fe^{++} + \overline{N_2O} + 6H^+ + H_2O$$

As with hydrazine, hydroxylamine is extensively employed by organic chemists to form useful derivatives and intermediates.*

A comparison of the various physical properties for a few compounds of hydrogen, nitrogen, and oxygen is given in Table 15.2.

* Hydrazine and hydroxylamine compounds are placed on the organic rather than the inorganic reagent shelves in many laboratories.

Ammonolysis

In the discussions in Chapters 8 and 13 it has been seen that hydrolysis of a compound such as aluminum chloride can be visualized as proceeding via the following mechanism:

$$Al^{+++} + nH_2O \rightarrow Al(H_2O)_n^{+++} \qquad \text{hydration}$$

$$Al(H_2O)_n^{+++} + xH_2O \rightleftharpoons Al(OH)_x(H_2O)_{n-x}^{+3-x}$$
$$+ xH_3O^+ \quad \text{proton transfer}$$

$$Al(OH)_x(H_2O)_{n-x}^{+3-x} \rightleftharpoons \begin{array}{c}\text{aggregated species} \\ \text{in solution}\end{array} \rightleftharpoons$$
$$Al_2O_3 \cdot xH_2O \quad \begin{array}{c}\text{aggregation and} \\ \text{precipitation}\end{array}$$

The hydrolysis can be carried to complete precipitation of the hydrous oxide by the addition of hydroxide ions.

If aluminum chloride is dissolved in anhydrous liquid ammonia, comparable reactions can be used to explain the results:

$$Al^{+++} + nNH_3 \rightarrow Al(NH_3)_n^{+++} \qquad \text{ammoniation}$$

$$Al(NH_3)_n^{+++} + xNH_3 \rightleftharpoons Al(NH_2)_x(NH_3)_{n-x}^{+3-x}$$
$$+ xNH_4^+ \quad \text{proton transfer}$$

$$Al(NH_2)_x(NH_3)_{n-x}^{+3-x} \rightleftharpoons \begin{array}{c}\text{aggregated species} \\ \text{in solution}\end{array} \rightleftharpoons$$
$$AlN \cdot xNH_3 \quad \begin{array}{c}\text{aggregation and} \\ \text{precipitation}\end{array}$$

The ammonolysis can be carried to precipitation of the ammonous nitride by the addition of amide ions. The general phenomenon of solvolysis in protonic solvents then depends on the solvent equilibria of proton transfer between two solvent molecules:

$$2H_2O \rightleftharpoons H_3O^+ + OH^-$$
$$2NH_3 \rightleftharpoons NH_4^+ + NH_2^-$$
$$2HR \rightleftharpoons H_2R^+ + R^-$$

In the water system of compounds, zinc hydroxide is amphoteric:

$$Zn^{++} \cdot aq + 4H_2O \xleftarrow{2H_3O^+} \underline{Zn(OH)_2 \cdot aq} \xrightarrow{2OH^-} Zn(OH)_4^{--} \cdot aq$$
$$aq = \text{water of hydration}$$

Likewise in the ammonia system, zinc amide is amphoteric:

$$Zn^{++}\cdot am + 4NH_4 \overset{2NH_4^+}{\longleftarrow} \underline{Zn(NH_2)_2\cdot am} \overset{2NH_2^-}{\longrightarrow} Zn(NH_2)_4^{--}\cdot am$$

$$am = \text{ammonia of ammoniation}$$

In general, metal amides appear to be more acidic in ammonia than metal hydroxides in water. This is understandable in light of the greater basicity of ammonia, which brings out acid properties more easily. In fact, magnesium amide is amphoteric in ammonia solvent whereas magnesium hydroxide is basic only in water solvent.

THE ACTION OF NITRIC ACID ON METALS

In addition to being a strong acid in water solution, nitric acid is one of the more powerful oxidizing agents. This property makes possible the solution of many metals that would not dissolve by virtue of strong acid action alone. For example, copper is easily soluble in dilute nitric acid, whereas dilute acids such as hydrochloric, sulfuric, and perchloric will not attack copper. When copper is dissolved in nitric acid, at least two reduction products of nitric acid are observed, the relative amounts of each determined by the concentration of acid used. The reaction between copper and relatively concentrated nitric acid is essentially as follows:

$$(1) \quad Cu + 4(H^+NO_3^-) \rightarrow Cu^{++}2NO_3^- + 2\overline{NO_2} + 2H_2O$$

whereas the reaction with dilute (about 3-N) acid is essentially:

$$(2) \quad 3Cu + 8(H^+NO_3^-) \rightarrow 3(Cu^{++}2NO_3^-) + 2\overline{NO} + 4H_2O$$

In neither case is the reduction product all NO_2 or NO, but reaction (1) predominates with concentrated acid, and reaction (2) predominates with more dilute acid.

NO and NO_2 are by no means the only reduction products obtainable from nitric acid. If a more active metal is dissolved, many other reduction products may be detected:

$$Zn + 2NO_3^- + 4H^+ \rightarrow Zn^{++} + 2\overline{NO_2} + 2H_2O$$
$$3Zn + 2NO_3^- + 8H^+ \rightarrow 3Zn^{++} + 2\overline{NO} + 4H_2O$$
$$4Zn + 2NO_3^- + 10H^+ \rightarrow 4Zn^{++} + \overline{N_2O} + 5H_2O$$
$$4Zn + NO_3^- + 10H^+ \rightarrow 4Zn^{++} + NH_4^+ + 3H_2O$$

increasing acid dilution

In general, the more active the metal, the further it is able to carry the reduction; and the more dilute the acid, the lower will be the oxidation number of the reduction product.

Any attempt to explain fully the action of nitric acid on metals leads to some frustration. Even the above tabulation of possibilities is not complete, since no mention is made of nitrous acid as a possible reduction product. It is also known that suitable electrolytic reduction of nitric acid can lead to the formation of hydroxylamine. Furthermore, the possibilities of interreaction among the reduction products and reactions between the reduction products and undecomposed nitric acid add to the confusion. It is also possible that metals do liberate hydrogen from nitric acid, just as they do from the simpler strong acids, although how much of this hydrogen would escape from the solution as molecular hydrogen is questionable, since hydrogen is a reducing agent and nitric acid is certainly an oxidizing agent.

The reactions between metals and nitric acid are complicated further by the passivity of some metals toward the acid. Aluminum and chromium dissolve readily in dilute sulfuric acid but become passive in nitric acid. Passivity has been the subject of much research. Apparently when a metal is passive it is not attacked by an acid that should attack it easily. It is believed that the rapid formation of a closely adhering metal oxide film on the surface of the metal protects the metal from the attack of acid. The protecting effect of the film, probably present on the surface of most metals, is determined by how easily the film is dissolved by the solvent with which it is in contact. Evidently nitric acid is not effective in dissolving the film on the surface of either aluminum or chromium, whereas sulfuric and hydrochloric acids are. The addition of a few drops of hydrofluoric acid to a solution of nitric acid renders the solution capable of dissolving both metals rapidly.

When concentrated nitric acid reacts with tin and antimony, white, insoluble oxides are formed.

$$x\mathrm{H_2O} + \mathrm{Sn} + 4\mathrm{HNO_3} \rightarrow \mathrm{SnO_2 \cdot} x\mathrm{H_2O}\downarrow + 4\overline{\mathrm{NO_2}} + 2\mathrm{H_2O}$$
$$x\mathrm{H_2O} + 2\mathrm{Sb} + 10\mathrm{HNO_3} \rightarrow \mathrm{Sb_2O_5 \cdot} x\mathrm{H_2O}\downarrow + 10\overline{\mathrm{NO_2}} + 5\mathrm{H_2O}$$

A summary of many of the reactions of nitric acid is given in Table 15.3.

TABLE 15.3
Summary of Reactions Between $H^+NO_3^-$ Solutions and Metals

Metal	*Reaction Products*
Cu, Ag	Cu^{++}, Ag^+, plus various reduction products of HNO_3
Pt, Au	No reaction
Zn, Cd, Hg	Zn^{++}, Cd^{++}, Hg^{++}, plus various reduction products of HNO_3
Mn, Fe, Co, Ni	Mn^{++}, Fe^{+++}, Co^{++}, Ni^{++}, plus various reduction products of HNO_3
Al, Cr	Passive
Sn, Sb, W	$SnO_2 \cdot xH_2O$, $Sb_2O_5 \cdot xH_2O$, $WO_3 \cdot xH_2O$ plus $NO_2\uparrow$ conc. acid usually necessary
Pb, Bi	Pb^{++}, Bi^{+++}, plus various reduction products of HNO_3
Be, Mg	Be^{++}, Mg^{++}, plus various reduction products of HNO_3

NITRATES

All known inorganic nitrates are soluble in water. Most of them are more soluble in hot water than cold. As a class of compounds, they are relatively unstable to heat, and at high temperature they are very powerful oxidizing agents. Black powder, a mixture of potassium nitrate, sulfur, and carbon, owes its force to the oxidation of the solid nonmetals to sulfur dioxide and carbon dioxide gases by the saltpeter. Ammonium nitrate decomposes smoothly when carefully heated, as has been seen, but under other conditions it decomposes violently. Several disastrous explosions of large quantities of ammonium nitrate have occurred in recent years.

The nitrate ion is a poor complex former, so that nitrates are widely used to study the chemistry of metal ions in solution without the complication of complex formation, except, of course, with the solvent. Only with metal ions which are very prone to form complexes, such as cobalt, does nitrate coordinate extensively.

Only the nitrates of the most electropositive metals can be melted without decomposition. Even these decompose much above their melting points. Thus, the Ia and IIa metal nitrates lose oxygen when heated:

$$2KNO_3 \xrightarrow{\Delta} 2KNO_2 + \overline{O_2}$$

With less electropositive elements oxides of nitrogen are evolved, and the oxide of the metal stable under the conditions prevailing is formed:

$$2Pb(NO_3)_2 \xrightarrow{\Delta} 2PbO + 4\overline{NO_2} + \overline{O_2}$$
$$Mn(NO_3)_2 \cdot 6H_2O \xrightarrow{\Delta} MnO_2 + 2\overline{NO_2} + 6\overline{H_2O}$$

With the more noble metals, the oxide itself decomposes to the metal and oxygen:

$$2AgNO_3 \xrightarrow{\Delta} 2Ag + 2\overline{NO_2} + \overline{O_2}$$

For these reasons, the anhydrous nitrates of many metals, such as zinc, cannot be prepared from water. The hydrated nitrates come out of aqueous solution and decompose when heated to drive off the water. Recently many anhydrous nitrates, among them those of copper and zinc, have been made by reactions in the N_2O_4 solvent system.

SUGGESTIONS FOR FURTHER READING

E. C. Franklin, *The Nitrogen System of Compounds*, Reinhold, New York, 1935, Chapters I through VII.

D. M. Yost and H. Russell, *Systematic Inorganic Chemistry of the Fifth and Sixth Group Nonmetallic Elements*, Prentice-Hall, New York, 1944, Chapters III and IV.

STUDY QUESTIONS

1. Describe the relationship that exists among NO, N_2O_3, NO_2, and N_2O_4.

2. Indicate, briefly, what happens when:
   (a) a solution of sodium nitrite is acidified.
   (b) ammonium nitrite is heated.
   (c) NO and NO_2 are bubbled into aqueous NaOH.
   (d) potassium nitrate is heated above its melting point.
   (e) steam reacts with calcium cyanamide.
   (f) ammonia is passed over molten sodium.
   (g) potassium amide is put into water.

3. Starting with air, water, and sodium hydroxide, show how the following compounds could be prepared: $NaNO_3$, NH_3, NH_4NO_3, NaN_3, N_2O_4, $NaNH_2$.

4. Divalent tin is amphoteric in liquid ammonia, just as it is in water. Illustrate these facts with appropriate equations to show the parallelism of the HOH and NH_3 systems.

5. When dissolved in water $ZnCl_2$ increases the H_3O^+ concentration of the solution. When dissolved in liquid ammonia $ZnCl_2$ increases the NH_4^+ concentration of the solution. Explain, in detail, the mechanism of the second case.

6. How many milliliters of 0.50 M HCl are required to titrate the ammonia produced from the reaction of excess water with 3.0 grams of magnesium nitride?

7. Write the structural formula for aminetrisulfonic acid.

8. Show how elementary nitrogen is converted into ammonia by two distinct processes. Give equations for the reactions and state the source of all materials.

9. What is a pseudo-halide? Give three examples.

10. Explain the amphoterism of zinc amide in liquid ammonia on the basis of the electronic theory of acids and bases.

11. What happens in the following cases?
    (a) $NaN_3 + AgNO_3$(aqueous)
    (b) $Fe + HNO_3$(dilute)
    (c) $N_2O + H_2O$
    (d) $Na_2N_2O_2 + H_2O$
    (e) $Zn(NO_3)_2 \cdot 6H_2O$ + heat

12. By means of equations and a few words about conditions, show how to carry out the following conversions:
    (a) Make $(NH_3OH)_2SO_4$ from $NaNO_3$.
    (b) Make NOCl from KNO_3.
    (c) Make N_2O_5 from NO.
    (d) Make $H_2N_2O_2$ from N_2.
    (e) Make $AgNO_2$ from any reagents except the product itself.

Chapter 16

Phosphorus, Arsenic, Antimony, and Bismuth

OCCURRENCE AND HISTORY

Phosphorus, arsenic, antimony, and bismuth were among the earliest known elements. Their compounds were known to and used by the ancients. Phosphorus, the most difficult to prepare in elementary form, was the last to be isolated, but that was accomplished by Brand as early as 1669. The element was found to glow in the dark, because of the oxidation of the relatively volatile white variety by moist air, and so it is now named phosphorus (Greek, light bringer).

Phosphorus is the only one of these four elements which never occurs free in nature, although arsenic and antimony rarely exist uncombined. Bismuth, on the other hand, is found as a natural mineral quite frequently. Most of the sources of phosphorus are calcium phosphates containing varying amounts of fluoride or chloride ions. Apatite, $3Ca_3(PO_4)_2 \cdot CaF_2$, and chlorapatite, $Ca_3(PO_4)_2 \cdot CaCl_2$ (which are better written $Ca_5(PO_4)_3F$ and Ca_2PO_4Cl, since their structures are ionic lattices composed of calcium, phosphate, and halide ions) are common "hard" phosphates, hard because they are difficultly soluble in acids. From them "soft" phosphates, more soluble in acids and containing much less halogen, are produced by weathering. Phosphorus is one of the abundant elements in living organisms, occurring mostly as calcium phosphate in

238

bones, teeth, etc. Organophosphorus compounds are also important in many metabolic processes.

Arsenic occurs mainly as the oxide and sulfide, and in many metal sulfide ores, such as arsenical pyrites, FeAsS. Stibnite, Sb_2S_3, is the only important ore of antimony, while bismuth is extracted from oxide and sulfide ores as well as elemental ores.

PREPARATION OF THE ELEMENTS

Phosphorus, arsenic, antimony, and bismuth can be made by reducing the oxides with carbon. For the last three, oxide ores or sulfide ores roasted to the oxides are merely heated with carbon to produce the elements. To prepare phosphorus, the oxide is not isolated as such, but it is replaced by the less volatile silicon dioxide and then reduced as it is evolved, in a one-step high-temperature reaction:

$$Ca_3(PO_4)_2 + 6SiO_2 + 10C \xrightarrow{\Delta} 6CaSiO_3 + 10\overline{CO} + \overline{P_4}$$

The reduction is carried out in an electric arc furnace operating between 1100 and 1500°, one type of which is shown in Fig. 16.1.

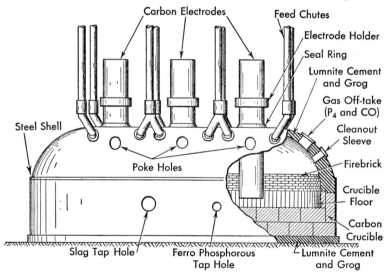

Fig. 16.1. Electric arc furnace for the production of phosphorus. (Courtesy of the Virginia-Carolina Chemical Corporation.)

The gaseous phosphorus is condensed under water to prevent its oxidation, and cast into molds as white phosphorus. It is used mainly in the manufacture of matches.

PHYSICAL PROPERTIES OF THE ELEMENTS

Allotropy is a common feature for these elements. Generally there are two common forms, one a nonmetallic molecular lattice and the other a metal-like lattice. In going down the group, the nonmetallic lattice becomes less stable until for bismuth the metallic state is the only one observed. The general features of the allotropes are compared below.

Non-Metallic Form	*Metal-like Form*
Molecular lattice composed of P_4, As_4, and Sb_4 molecules	Layer lattice going to metallic lattice
White or yellow	Dark colored—red P, gray As, metallic Sb and Bi
More volatile	Less volatile
Less dense	More dense
Soluble CS_2, organic solvents	Insoluble in almost all solvents
Chemically more active	Less reactive

Phosphorus exists in the vapor phase as P_4 molecules which have the structure of a tetrahedron with the phosphorus atoms at the corners:

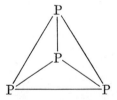

Above 800°, dissociation into P_2 and P molecules becomes appreciable. When the vapor is cooled, it condenses at 280° and 1 atm. to liquid white phosphorus, which freezes at 44° to solid white phosphorus. The other common variety is made by heating molten white phosphorus to about 240° in an inert atmosphere, when it slowly converts to solid red phosphorus. The red modification has a complicated structure in the solid, where no individual molecules exist as such. When heated, it sublimes, the pressure reaching atmospheric at about 420°. It melts in a sealed tube at about 600° under a pressure of about 43 atm. Being much less reactive than the white variety, it does not exhibit the glow phenomenon.

White phosphorus converts to red very slowly at room temperature, so that it usually appears to be yellow. Water-white crystals can be obtained by crystallization from an organic solvent. The white forms of arsenic and antimony are even less stable, and they must be made and kept at low temperature.

There are other modifications of phosphorus, arsenic, and antimony which can be made under various conditions of temperature and pressure. For example, red phosphorus changes to black phosphorus when subjected to a pressure of 35,000 atm. The black variety remains when the pressure is released. It is not known which allotrope is the thermodynamically stable one at room temperature and pressure.

CHEMICAL PROPERTIES AND COMPOUNDS

Oxidation numbers of $+5$ are expected and realized. However, the $+5$ valence tendency is at a maximum stability in phosphorus and progresses to a minimum in bismuth, so much so that $+5$ compounds of bismuth are few indeed. In addition, all four elements form compounds in which they exhibit oxidation number $+3$, and phosphorus has compounds in which all the oxidation numbers from -3 to $+5$ can be assigned to it. The tendency to form -3 compounds is not great, although phosphine, arsine, and stibine are known, as well as phosphides, arsenides, antimonides, and bismuthides of very electropositive metals.

With five valence electrons, it is expected that these elements are electronegative and tend to form covalent compounds rather than ionic compounds in which they would have to lose such a large number of electrons. Such is the case, but the tendency decreases from top to bottom in the group, phosphorus forming only covalent compounds and bismuth forming largely ionic compounds. This group is peculiarly well adapted to illustrate the gradations of properties within groups of elements. Although the electronic configurations are similar, the ionization potentials decrease considerably in going from phosphorus to bismuth. In fact phosphorus is a typical nonmetal and bismuth is a metal. One aspect of this gradation, the transition from acidic oxides to basic oxides, is shown in Table 16.1.

TABLE 16.1
The Common Oxides and Hydroxides of P, As, Sb, and Bi

		P	As	Sb	Bi
Oxides	+3	P_2O_3	As_2O_3	Sb_2O_3	Bi_2O_3
	+5	P_2O_5	As_2O_5	Sb_2O_5	Bi_2O_5 (?)
Hydroxides (or acids)	+1	H_3PO_2	—	—	—
	+3	H_3PO_3	$\left\{ \begin{array}{l} H_3AsO_3 \\ As(OH)_3 \end{array} \right\}$	$\left\{ \begin{array}{l} Sb(OH)_3 \\ H_3SbO_3 \end{array} \right\}$	$Bi(OH)_3$
	+5	H_3PO_4 $H_4P_2O_7$ $(HPO_3)_n$	H_3AsO_4	$Sb_2O_5 \cdot xH_2O$	?

Chemical Reactions of the Elements

White phosphorus is a quite reactive substance, all its reactions being rapid and some violent, whereas the red variety is relatively inert. Generally the reactivity decreases with increasing atomic weight in the series phosphorus, arsenic, antimony, and bismuth. The elements combine with oxygen when heated, phosphorus being the only one which will go to the +5 oxidation state:*

$$4P + 3O_2(\text{limited}) \xrightarrow{\Delta} 2P_2O_3$$
$$4P + 5O_2(\text{excess}) \xrightarrow{\Delta} 2P_2O_5$$
$$4As + 3O_2 \xrightarrow{\Delta} 2As_2O_3, \text{ etc.}$$

Hydrogen, nitrogen, and carbon have no action on these group V elements, but sulfur reacts with them all. White phosphorus combines with explosive violence while red phosphorus and the b-subgroup require heat to react with sulfur. The products are, according to the proportion of sulfur, P_4S_3, P_4S_5, P_4S_7, or P_2S_5; As_2S_3 or As_2S_5; Sb_2S_3 or Sb_2S_5; Bi_2S_3.

Phosphorus, arsenic, antimony, and bismuth all react with all of the halogens to give trihalides. In addition, a number of pentahalides are formed: PF_5, PCl_5, PBr_5; AsF_5; SbF_5, $SbCl_5$. Arsenic

---

* In writing equations involving elementary phosphorus, the formula P_4 will be used to denote white phosphorus only and the formula P to denote all forms.

shows a peculiar reluctance to assume the group valency in the halides, comparable to the behavior of selenium in its oxides and bromine in its oxyacids. These anomalous characteristics of these first long period elements are not understood on a theoretical basis. As expected from its great oxidizing power, bismuth forms no pentahalides.

These elements will gain electrons from active metals to give anions:

$$3Ca + 2P \rightarrow Ca_3P_2$$
$$3Na + Bi \rightarrow Na_3Bi$$

Most of the compounds of bismuth with metals are, however, more suitably classed as alloys.

The elements do not react with oxygen-free water. In fact, white phosphorus is usually stored under water, in which it is insoluble, to protect it from air. They do react with oxidizing acids:

$$P + 5HNO_3(\text{hot, conc.}) \quad \rightarrow H_3PO_4 + 5\overline{NO_2} + H_2O$$
$$As + 5HNO_3(\text{hot, conc.}) \quad \rightarrow H_3AsO_4 + 5\overline{NO_2} + H_2O$$
$$2Sb + 10HNO_3(\text{hot, conc.}) \rightarrow Sb_2O_5 + 5\overline{NO_2} + 5H_2O$$
$$Bi + 4HNO_3(\text{dil.}) \quad \rightarrow Bi(NO_3)_3 + \overline{NO} + 2H_2O$$

In addition, white phosphorus dissolves readily in strong alkali, undergoing a disproportionation to phosphine and hypophosphite:

$$P_4 + 3NaOH + 3H_2O \rightarrow \overline{PH_3} + 3NaH_2PO_2$$

Aqueous alkali have no action on red phosphorus, arsenic, antimony, or bismuth.

+1 Compounds

Phosphorus is the only one of these elements that forms +1 compounds. To prepare hypophosphorous acid, white phosphorus is dissolved in barium hydroxide, evolving phosphine and precipitating the slightly soluble barium hypophosphite. The latter is reacted with dilute sulfuric acid to precipitate the less soluble barium sulfate and leave hypophosphorous acid in solution:

$$\underline{Ba(H_2PO_2)_2} + H_2SO_4 \rightarrow \underline{BaSO_4}\downarrow + 2H_3PO_2$$

The acid is a good reducing agent, easily taking copper(II) salts to metallic copper. It is a monobasic acid of about the same strength as the ortho acids of phosphorus in the +3 and +5 states. This strength is not expected from the empirical formulae, but it is understandable from the generalizations in Chapter 3 and a knowledge of the structure of the three acids:

$$
\begin{array}{ccc}
\overset{\displaystyle H}{\underset{\displaystyle :O:}{\overset{\displaystyle \cdot\cdot}{}}} & \overset{\displaystyle \cdot\cdot}{:O:} & \overset{\displaystyle \cdot\cdot}{:O:} \\[2pt]
H:\overset{\cdot\cdot}{\underset{\cdot\cdot}{O}}:\overset{\cdot\cdot}{\underset{\cdot\cdot}{P}}:\overset{\cdot\cdot}{\underset{\cdot\cdot}{O}}:H & H:\overset{\cdot\cdot}{\underset{\cdot\cdot}{O}}:\overset{\cdot\cdot}{\underset{\cdot\cdot}{P}}:\overset{\cdot\cdot}{\underset{\cdot\cdot}{O}}:H & H:\overset{\cdot\cdot}{\underset{\cdot\cdot}{P}}:\overset{\cdot\cdot}{\underset{\cdot\cdot}{O}}:H \\[2pt]
:\overset{}{\underset{\cdot\cdot}{O}}: & H & H
\end{array}
$$

orthophosphoric acid   orthophosphorous acid   hypophosphorous acid

In each molecule there is one more oxygen atom than ionizable hydrogen atoms. Thus the ionization constants of all three acids are in the range of 10^{-2} to 10^{-3}.

+3 Oxygen Compounds

All four elements form white sesquioxides, all of which exhibit polymorphism. Of the four, only phosphorus(III) oxide is soluble in water, dissolving to give the dibasic phosphorous acid. The acid is a good reducing agent, being oxidized easily to phosphoric acid. It is also thermally unstable, disproportionating when heated:

$$4H_3PO_3 \xrightarrow{200°C} PH_3\uparrow + 3H_3PO_4$$

Here is seen an example of the great stability of pentavalent phosphorus relative to the lower states.

Arsenic sesquioxide is soluble in aqueous sodium hydroxide, forming sodium arsenite. The acidification of arsenite solutions does not give a precipitate of hydrous arsenic(III) oxide. Rather, free arsenious acid is formed which is moderately soluble in water. This may seem peculiar in view of the insolubility of the sesquioxide. Actually, it is the high-temperature form, which is the usual laboratory reagent, that is insoluble. The low-temperature form dissolves to the extent of a few per cent in water, becoming hydrated to arsenious acid. The addition of hydrogen sulfide to an acid solution containing trivalent arsenic gives a yellow precipitate of arsenic(III) sulfide. The precipitate is soluble in basic solution with the formation of thioarsenites and arsenites:

$$As_2S_3 + 6OH^- \rightarrow AsS_3^{---} + AsO_3^{---} + 3H_2O$$

Antimony(III) oxide is more nearly an amphoteric oxide, being soluble in either potassium hydroxide or strong acid solutions, although potassium antimonite is not a very soluble salt. The addition of the base to antimony(III) chloride solution or the addition of acid to potassium antimonite solution precipitates hydrous antimony(III) oxide. As with trivalent arsenic, orange antimony(III) sulfide is insoluble in dilute acid but soluble in sodium sulfide to form thioantimonite.

Trivalent arsenic and antimony are mild reducing agents. Basic or neutral-buffered solutions of either can be oxidized quantitatively to the pentavalent condition by iodine:

$$I_2 + AsO_3^{---} + 2OH^- \rightarrow AsO_4^{---} + 2I^- + H_2O$$

On the other hand, pentavalent arsenic or antimony can be reduced quantitatively to the trivalent condition by iodide in acid solution.

$$2H^+ + 2I^- + H_3AsO_4 \rightarrow I_2 + H_3AsO_3 + H_2O$$

Here is an indication that the $+3$ and $+5$ states of arsenic and antimony are of nearly equal stability.

Bismuth(III) oxide is a basic oxide only. It is soluble in most acids, and many salts can be crystallized from water. Bismuth sulfide is black and insoluble in either acid or basic solution. No thiobismuthites are known.

Trivalent bismuth has practically no reducing properties. Obviously the $+3$ state of bismuth is much more stable than the $+5$ state.

+3 Halides

All sixteen possible trihalides of these elements are known. Their melting points and boiling points are given in Table 16.2. All of the compounds are colorless liquids or gases or white solids except the four red triiodides.

TABLE 16.2
Melting Points and Boiling Points in °C of Trihalides

		F_3	Cl_3	Br_3	I_3
P	b.p.	-101	76	175	dec.
	m.p.	-151	-112	-40	61
As	b.p.	63	130	221	403
	m.p.	-6	-13	31	146
Sb	b.p.	319	220	288	401
	m.p.	292	73	97	167
Bi	b.p.	very high	447	453	—
	m.p.	very high	230	218	439(?)

Obviously the covalent character of the bonding decreases from phosphorus to bismuth, the bismuth halides being more salt-like compounds. All of the trihalides can be prepared by direct synthesis. The chloride, bromide, and iodide of phosphorus are usually made this way. However, a variety of methods have been used to prepare the others. Arsenic trifluoride is prepared conveniently by distilling it from a reaction mixture of fluorspar, arsenic(III) oxide, and excess concentrated sulfuric acid:

$$3CaF_2 + As_2O_3 + 3H_2SO_4 \xrightarrow[\Delta]{} 3CaSO_4 + 3H_2O + 2AsF_3\uparrow$$

Phosphorus trifluoride is prepared from arsenic trifluoride:

$$AsF_3 + PCl_3 \rightarrow AsCl_3 + PF_3$$

The products are separated by fractional distillation.

Since the hydrolysis of the halides of arsenic, antimony, and bismuth is reversible, unlike that of the phosphorus halides, which is irreversible, some of them can be prepared from aqueous solution. Arsenic(III) iodide can be precipitated from an aqueous hydrochloric acid solution of arsenious acid by the addition of potassium iodide. Antimony trichloride is prepared by digesting antimony(III) oxide with concentrated hydrochloric acid, distilling off the excess acid solution, and then distilling the product into a dry receiver.

All of the covalent trihalides have a pyramidal structure with the central atom resting on the halogen atoms which form the base of a pyramid. The phosphorus halides hydrolyze completely. In fact the hydrolysis of phosphorus triiodide and phosphorus tribromide is frequently used to prepare hydrogen iodide and hydrogen bromide:

$$2P + 3X_2 \rightarrow 3PX_3$$
$$PX_3 + 3HOH \rightarrow H_3PO_3 + 3HX\uparrow$$

Local overheating in the reaction is apt to result in the hydrogen halide being contaminated with traces of phosphine, because of the thermal instability of phosphorous acid. Arsenic, antimony, and bismuth halides are successively less hydrolyzed in water. For example, antimony and bismuth trichlorides dissolve in water and, upon dilution, precipitate slightly soluble oxychlorides, SbOCl and BiOCl. These are soluble in excess mineral acid.

Phosphorus forms a number of mixed halides, comparable with those of silicon.

Hydrides

Phosphine can be made by dissolving white phosphorus in strong base or by the action of water or acid on metallic phosphides. Prepared either way, it contains a small amount of diphosphine, P_2H_4. Phosphine is rather unstable, reacting with air instantaneously to give a smoke of phosphoric acid. Pure phosphine is supposed to be stable in air at room temperature. In the absence of air, small amounts of the gas can be collected. It has a vile odor, resembling that of rotten fish, and is very toxic. It has weakly basic properties, weaker than ammonia, forming such compounds as phosphonium iodide, PH_4I. These compounds are unstable and are similar to ammonium compounds in formula only, since they do not ionize but decompose in water. The hydrides of arsenic, antimony, and bismuth are known, but they are even less stable than phosphine. Zinc and hydrochloric acid react with aqueous arsenious acid to liberate arsine:

$$H_3AsO_3 + 3Zn + 6H^+ \rightarrow AsH_3\uparrow + 3Zn^{++} + 3H_2O$$

This reaction is called the Marsh test for arsenic, and, of course, a mixture of arsine and hydrogen is produced. If the gases are passed through a heated tube, the arsine decomposes, depositing a mirror of black arsenic on the walls of the tube.

If the boiling points in degrees absolute of these hydrides are plotted as ordinates against the period number of the central atom as abscissae, a straight line results (see Figure 1.12).

Substituted hydrides of all of the elements in the phosphorus family have been prepared: PH_2CH_3, $PH(CH_3)_2$, $P(CH_3)_3$, $As(CH_3)_3$, etc. They are more stable than the hydrides. Most of them are inflammable liquids, insoluble in water and soluble in organic solvents. As was true in the case of the group IVb elements, P—C, As—C, Sb—C, and Bi—C bonds are more stable than P—H, As—H, Sb—H, and Bi—H bonds respectively.

+5 Oxygen Compounds

Phosphorus burns in excess air to give phosphorus(V) oxide, which readily forms phosphoric acid with water. Salts may be made by neutralization and precipitation. Stronger oxidizing conditions are required to take arsenic and antimony to the +5 state. Usually sesquioxides are boiled with concentrated nitric acid to produce arsenic and antimonic acids:

$$As_2O_3 + 4HNO_3 + H_2O \rightarrow 2H_3AsO_4 + 4\overline{NO_2}$$

Unlike phosphorus, the +5 oxides can be obtained from the acids by thermal dehydration. The free oxide of bismuth in the +5 oxidation state cannot be made, but salts of the acid are known. The only common bismuth(V) compound is sodium bismuthate, made by fusing bismuth(III) oxide with sodium hydroxide under oxidizing conditions:

$$Bi_2O_3 + 2NaOH + O_2 \xrightarrow{\Delta} 2NaBiO_3 + \overline{H_2O}$$

This preparation illustrates some general principles of chemical behavior and preparative technique. First, the higher the valence state of an element, the more acidic its properties. Then, if one wishes to prepare an element in a high oxidation state, it is best to carry out the reaction in basic medium, which then stabilizes the element by reacting with it and driving the oxidation reaction to completion. If sodium bismuthate is acidified, a dark, impure oxide is precipitated which loses oxygen very easily.

Sodium bismuthate is a very powerful oxidizing agent, oxidizing manganese(II) quantitatively to permanganate in cold, dilute nitric acid solution. In oxidizing power $+5$ bismuth is similar to $+4$ lead. The oxidizing power of $+5$ arsenic and antimony is much less, and that of $+5$ phosphorus very slight.

In the vapor state, phosphorus(V) oxide exists as discrete P_4O_{10} molecules, stable well over $1000°$. The structures of the P_4, P_4O_6, and P_4O_{10} molecules form an interesting series. As we have seen, P_4 consists of four phosphorus atoms at the corners of a tetrahedron. P_4O_6 adds to this one oxygen atom along but slightly off of each edge of the tetrahedron. Then P_4O_{10} adds to the P_4O_6 structure an oxygen connected to each of the phosphorus atoms. The structures are shown in Figure 16.2.

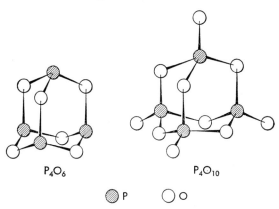

Fig. 16.2.   Structures of P_4O_6 and P_4O_{10}.

In the solid state, phosphorus(V) oxide exists in several polymorphs. When the vapor is rapidly condensed, a crystalline variety composed of discrete P_4O_{10} molecules is formed. The usual laboratory reagent, it is fairly volatile and is the most reactive form. It is metastable, however, and displays an interesting phenomenon on heating. When rapidly heated in a sealed, evacuated tube, it melts to a clear liquid which very soon solidifies to a glass. This behavior is a rare example of a metastable polymorph existing in both solid and liquid states. The amorphous glass is formed by the polymerization of the P_4O_{10} molecules to a linked network of PO_4 tetrahedra. At least two more crystalline modifications, one of which is the stable thermodynamic form at room temperature and pressure, can be made by the prolonged heating of the glass. They are composed of *regular* arrays of PO_4 tetrahedra. These last three forms are much less volatile and reactive than the first. The difference is due to the fact that for the last three to sublime or react, a large network of linked PO_4 groups must be broken up, whereas the first is already broken up into discrete molecules.

With respect to forming a glass, phosphorus(V) oxide resembles silica. The analogy can be carried even further, since many "phosphate glasses" can be produced. For example, if sodium metaphosphate is fused and then cooled rapidly, a clear glassy solid is obtained.

Phosphorus(V) oxide has such an affinity for water that it is a most effective drying agent. Its hydrolysis produces any of the several acids of pentavalent phosphorus. First, metaphosphoric acid, an ill-defined polymeric substance, is formed. Successively the hydrolysis proceeds through the stage of the well-defined pyrophosphoric acid

$$
\begin{array}{ccc}
O & & O \\
\| & & \| \\
HO-P-O-P-OH \\
\| & & \| \\
O & & O \\
| & & | \\
H & & H
\end{array}
$$

to orthophosphoric acid, which is the usual form of the reagent. The thermal dehydration of orthophosphoric acid can go back to metaphosphoric acid, but not all the way to the anhydride. Salts of metaphosphoric and pyrophosphoric acids are more common than the acids themselves. Some of them are used in analytical chemistry.

Orthophosphoric acid is a moderately strong acid in its first ionization:

$$H_3PO_4 + H_2O \rightleftharpoons H_3O^+ + H_2PO_4^-$$

The second and third ionizations are much weaker, the phosphate ion being a strong base (see Chapter 3). Trisodium phosphate is hydrolyzed extensively because of this strong basicity of the phosphate ion:

$$PO_4^{---} + H_2O \rightleftharpoons HPO_4^{--} + OH^-$$

A solution of disodium hydrogen phosphate is nearly neutral, and a solution of sodium dihydrogen phosphate is slightly acid. Excepting the alkali and ammonium salts, most normal metal phosphates are insoluble in water, but the acid phosphates are more soluble. Thus the addition of a strong acid to an insoluble normal phosphate usually results in the solution of the salt to form an acid salt.

$$\underline{Ca_3(PO_4)_2} \rightleftharpoons 3Ca^{++} \quad 2PO_4^{---}$$
$$+$$
$$2H^+$$
$$\Updownarrow$$
$$2HPO_4^-$$

Iron(III) phosphate is insoluble even in acetic acid solution, and iron(III) chloride is therefore used to remove phosphate ion from solutions prior to analysis for other cations. Magnesium ammonium phosphate is slightly soluble in neutral or basic solution, although easily soluble in acid solution. Ignition of this compound yields magnesium pyrophosphate. Either magnesium or phosphate can be determined gravimetrically as this compound.

+5 Halides

The pentafluoride and the pentachloride of antimony have been prepared, as has the pentafluoride of arsenic. The pentafluoride, pentachloride, and pentabromide of phosphorus are well known, decreasing in stability in the order given. All of the pentahalides are covalent compounds. In the presence of excess water they hydrolyze completely:

$$PX_5 + 4H_2O \rightarrow 5HX + H_3PO_4$$

With just a little water the oxyhalides of phosphorus result:

$$PX_5 + H_2O \rightarrow POX_3 + 2HX$$

These compounds are covalent, easily hydrolyzed substances also. No oxyhalides of arsenic(V) or antimony(V) are known.

Phosphorus trifluoride will react with some of the halogens and oxygen as follows:

$$PF_3 + F_2 \rightarrow PF_5$$
$$PF_3 + Cl_2 \rightarrow PF_3Cl_2$$
$$PF_3 + Br_2 \rightarrow PF_3Br_2$$
$$2PF_3 + O_2 \rightarrow 2POF_3$$

The mixed halides are not stable to heat, rearranging when heated to the simple halides:

$$5PF_3Cl_2 \xrightarrow{\Delta} 3PF_5 + 2PCl_5$$

+5 Sulfides

Phosphorus(V) sulfide can only be made by dry methods, since it is completely but slowly decomposed by water to phosphoric acid and hydrogen sulfide. The usual technique is by direct synthesis from heating red phosphorus and sulfur. It is a pale yellow compound, soluble in organic solvents, whose vapor and dissolved species consists of P_4S_{10} molecules. The dimeric molecules are much less stable than the oxygen analogs, so that the vapor density corresponds to a molecular weight of only 208 at 600° (P_4S_{10}, 445). In contrast to phosphorus, the pentasulfides of arsenic and antimony are precipitated by hydrogen sulfide from aqueous solutions, reactions useful in analytical chemistry. Thioarsenates and thioantimonates are also formed in basic solution. The greater stability of As_2S_5 over Sb_2S_5 is shown by the facts that As_2S_5 is insoluble in hot, concentrated hydrochloric acid, while Sb_2S_5 is decomposed by it:

$$Sb_2S_5 + 8HCl \rightarrow 2HSbCl_4 + 2\underline{S} + 3\overline{H_2S}$$

Bismuth(V) is much too powerful an oxidizing agent for the pentasulfide to exist.

A number of sulfur analogs of the phosphorus(V) oxyhalides exist, such as $PSCl_3$, and a mixed oxide-sulfide can be made by heating phosphorus(III) oxide with sulfur:

$$P_2O_3 + 2S \xrightarrow{\Delta} P_2O_3S_2$$

USES

The fertilizer industry is the largest user of phosphorus compounds. Most natural phosphates are not soluble enough to be absorbed readily by plants; they are therefore reacted with sulfuric acid to form "superphosphate of lime":

$$Ca_3(PO_4)_2 + 2H_2SO_4 + 4H_2O \rightarrow Ca(H_2PO_4)_2 + 2CaSO_4 \cdot 2H_2O$$

This reaction is one of the largest uses of sulfuric acid, which indicates the magnitude of the industry.

Elementary phosphorus is used in the manufacture of matches. In the proper proportions, phosphorus reacts with sulfur to form tetraphosphorus trisulfide, P_4S_3. Ordinary friction matches contain this compound, which upon warming by striking, reacts with an oxidizing agent on the head of the match. The heat from the reaction is sufficient to ignite the stem of the match. Safety matches have red phosphorus in the striking surface of the box, which burns when rubbed and ignites the head of the match, made of the easily ignited As_2S_3.

Arsenic and antimony are used in the production of a variety of alloys.

Bismuth's main use is attributable to its low melting point. Upon alloying with other metals even lower-melting metals are obtained. Such alloys are used for automatic fire-protection and safety plugs in heating systems to avoid overheating. An example of a low-melting alloy is Woods Metal, which melts at 71°C and has the approximate composition: Bi, 50 per cent; Pb, 25 per cent; Cd, $12\frac{1}{2}$ per cent; Sn, $12\frac{1}{2}$ per cent.

SUGGESTIONS FOR FURTHER READING

M. E. Weeks, *Discovery of the Elements*, 6th ed., Journal of Chemical Education, Easton, Pa., 1956, Chapters II and III.

D. M. Yost and H. Russell, *Systematic Inorganic Chemistry of the Fifth- and Sixth-Group Nonmetallic Elements*, Chapters V, VI, and VII.

STUDY QUESTIONS

1. Give an acceptable name for each of the following: PH_3, $Zn_2P_2O_7$, NaH_2PO_2, Na_2HPO_3, K_3SbO_3 and K_3AsS_4.

2. Compare the white and red allotropes of phosphorus.

3. Describe the glow phenomenon.

4. Compare the results of adding water to each of the following: PCl_3, $AsCl_3$, $SbCl_3$, and $BiCl_3$.

5. Write balanced equations for each of the following:

(a) Concentrated HCl is added to Na_3SbS_4.

(b) In acid solution $NaBiO_3$ oxidizes Mn^{++} to MnO_4^-.

6. Suggest a means of preparing Na_3AsS_4.

7. Why do you think that it would be impossible to prepare Bi_2S_5?

8. Would you expect antimony(III) to form chloro complexes similar to the chlorostannates? Explain.

9. (a) Which is more basic, $Sb(OH)_3$ or $Bi(OH)_3$?

(b) Which is the better oxidizing agent, H_3PO_4 or H_3SbO_4?

(c) Which hydrolyzes more completely, PCl_3 or $AsCl_3$?

(d) Which is more stable, PH_3 or SbH_3?

(e) Which is the stronger acid, H_3AsO_3 or H_3AsO_4?

(f) Which is more volatile, PF_3 or AsF_3?

10. Show the structural relationship of pyrophosphoric acid to orthophosphoric acid.

11. Starting with $Ca_3(PO_4)_2$, show how to prepare the following: P, P_2O_5, NaH_2PO_2, H_3PO_2, H_3PO_3, H_3PO_4, PCl_3, PH_3, and $Mg_2P_2O_7$.

12. When 8.76 grams of Sb_2O_3 are converted to $KSbO_2$ with excess KOH, 4.78 grams of $KMnO_4$ added to oxidize the antimony from three to five, and the resulting mixture filtered to remove the MnO_2, 10.16 grams of $KSb(OH)_6$ crystals are obtained from the filtrate.

(a) Write equations for each reaction in the preparation.

(b) What is the limiting reagent in the experiment?

(c) What is the theoretical yield of antimonate?

13. Why is natural calcium phosphate reacted with sulfuric acid before it is used as a fertilizer?

14. Do you think it is possible to prepare anhydrous antimony(III) chloride by crystallizing the hydrate from solution and heating the hydrate to drive off the water crystallization?

15. Write balanced equations for the following reactions:

(a) Antimony dissolves in concentrated nitric acid.

(b) Hypophosphorous acid reduces copper(II) sulfate to copper.

(c) Phosphine burns in air.

(d) Magnesium ammonium phosphate is ignited to magnesium pyrophosphate.

16. Draw the electronic structures of P_4, P_4O_6, and P_4O_{10}.

17. On the average, how many oxygen atoms at its corners does a PO_4 tetrahedron share with other tetrahedra in stable solid P_2O_5?

18. What happens in the following cases?
   (a) $P_2S_5 + H_2O$
   (b) Bi + conc HNO_3
   (c) P + KOH(aqueous)
   (d) As_2O_3 + Al + NaOH(aqueous)
   (e) H_3PO_3 + heat

19. By means of equations and a few words about conditions, show how to carry out the following conversions:
   (a) Make Sb_2S_5 from Sb_2O_5.
   (b) Make BiOCl from $KBiO_3$.
   (c) Make PCl_5 from a naturally occurring phosphorus compound.
   (d) Make K_3AsO_4 from As_2O_3.
   (e) Make P_2O_5 from H_3PO_4.

Chapter 17

Vanadium, Niobium, and Tantalum

OCCURRENCE AND HISTORY

Compounds of vanadium, niobium, and tantalum were discovered in 1801 and 1802, but the family relationship was not established for about another thirty years. For example, F. Wohler, in 1831, showed that the element discovered by del Rio of Mexico City in 1801 and named Erythronium, was identical with the element discovered by Sefstrom in 1831 and named vanadium for the Norse goddess Freya, sometimes called Vanadis. Some forty years lapsed after the discovery of tantalum by Gustav Ekeberg and niobium by Charles Hatchett before it was shown that they could be separated and were therefore distinct elements. Tantalum was named by Ekeberg after the Greek god Tantalus (who was at one time submerged in water up to his neck yet never was allowed a drink) since tantalum(V) oxide will not react with strong acids even when supplied in excess. Niobium was named after Niobe, the daughter of Tantalus. In the United States, and to a lesser extent in England, niobium is called columbium. Recently the name "niobium" has been accepted by international convention, and it is hoped, in the interest of uniformity, that "columbium" will cease to be used.

Vanadium, niobium, and tantalum are estimated to exist in 150, 20, and 10 parts per million, respectively, in the lithosphere, the latter two almost always occurring together. The most important ores of niobium and tantalum are the niobates and tantalates, $(Fe,Mn)Me_2O_6$. The former name is applied when the niobium content predominates, and the latter when the tantalum content predominates. The two also occur in several rare-earth minerals. The most important ores of vanadium lie in the Andes Mountains of Peru at 16,000 feet elevation and in the Colorado plateau of the United States. The Peruvian ores are sulfides. The Colorado ores, which are silicates, have been the subject of recent intensive study, since they are closely associated with the uranium-bearing minerals of the region. Trace quantities of vanadium occur widely in conjunction with ores of iron, copper, lead, phosphorus, and chromium. The vanadium can be recovered as a by-product of the manufacture of these elements.

Protactinium was discovered in 1918 among the radioactive elements in pitchblende residues. Its chemical properties were inferred from its position as the fourth member of the Va family and confirmed by experiment. Indeed it was isolated by coprecipitation of its oxide with tantalum oxide. The name protactinium signifies radioactive parent of actinium. The most important isotope of protactinium is that of mass number 231. It is an alpha emitter of half-life 3.48×10^4 years. The question of placing protactinium in group Va or among the actinides (see Chapter 9) is an academic one. Certainly most of its chemistry strongly resembles that of tantalum, although it is known to exhibit lower oxidation states than $+5$. The student is referred to the second reference at the list at the end of the chapter for a review of the chemistry of protactinium and of its proper placement in the periodic table.

PREPARATION OF THE ELEMENTS

Vanadium ore concentrates are roasted with a flux such as NaCl which is suited to convert the vanadium content to water-soluble sodium vanadate, Na_3VO_4. Crude vanadium(V) oxide is precipitated from the water extract of the roast by the addition of acid. V_2O_5 is reduced by a Goldschmidt reaction using a mixture of iron and aluminum as the reducing agent. The metal product is known as ferrovanadium, and the Fe/V content varies in the alloy. Up to 90 per cent vanadium is produced by the aluminothermic process. Since most vanadium is used in the manufacture of steel, little pure vanadium is produced. A few tenths of one per cent vanadium increase the strength and toughness of steel considerably.

Niobium and tantalum ore concentrates are fused with caustic, forming water-soluble niobates and tantalates. Mixed hydrous oxides of niobium and tantalum are precipitated from the water leach by the addition of acid. The oxides are dissolved in hydrofluoric acid containing potassium fluoride, forming potassium pentafluorooxoniobate and potassium heptafluorotantalate:

$$Nb_2O_5 + 6HF + 4KF = 2K_2NbOF_5 + 3H_2O$$
$$Ta_2O_5 + 10HF + 4KF = 2K_2TaF_7 + 5H_2O$$

Advantage is taken of the lesser solubility of K_2TaF_7 to separate the two elements by fractional crystallization. K_2TaF_7 is reduced with sodium, yielding powdered metal. The powder is converted to crystalline bars by compression under a mechanical pressure of about 50 pounds per square inch, at a temperature of 2500°, in a vacuum. Such procedures are generally referred to as powder metallurgical techniques. Under these conditions, most impurities are volatilized. It is also possible to make tantalum by the Kroll reduction of tantalum pentachloride with magnesium, as in the preparation of titanium. Tantalum is produced at the *cathode* in the electrolysis of fused salts containing K_2TaF_7. The mechanism is complex—a simple point of view would be that the TaF_7^{-2} ion would migrate to the anode and deposit metal there—and it is an open question whether the tantalum is the result of a direct electrolytic reduction or not.

Niobium can be made by all of the methods used for tantalum. In addition, it is reported that heating the proper proportions of niobium(V) oxide and niobium carbide gives niobium metal:

$$Nb_2O_5 + 5NbC = 7Nb + 5\overline{CO}$$

All three metals have been made in a high state of purity on a small scale by the deBoer-vanArkel hot-wire method (see Chapter 13).

PHYSICAL PROPERTIES OF THE ELEMENTS

The three elements have melting points near the maximum for their respective periods, which makes tantalum one of the highest melting elements (m.p., 2800°) exceeded only by carbon, tungsten, and rhenium. All are hard, but vanadium much more than niobium and tantalum. Tantalum is the most ductile when pure. They all show excellent tensile strength when work-hardened. The usual large jump in density going from a second-long-row element to its congenor in the third long row is well illustrated in the densities of niobium, 8.4 gm./cc., and tantalum, 16.6 gm./cc. It is seen that tantalum is also one of the most dense elements.

CHEMICAL PROPERTIES AND COMPOUNDS

The electronic configurations of these elements are $(n - 1)d^3ns^2$. Oxidation states of $+2$, $+3$, $+4$, and $+5$ are observed. Compounds of vanadium are known in each state, although $+2$ vanadium compounds are few and easily oxidized. Compounds in which niobium exhibits less than the group oxidation state are rare; tantalum is even more reluctant to assume lower valencies. For example, vanadium(V) is reduced to the $+2$ oxidation state in a Jones Reductor, niobium(V) to the $+3$ (probably complex), while tantalum(V) is untouched.

The effect of the lanthanide contraction is still manifest in this family. Although Nb(V) and Ta(V) ions are as alike in size as Zr(IV) and Hf(IV) are, greater differences between properties of niobium and tantalum compounds are observed. Consequently, the separation of niobium and tantalum, while still a formidable task, is by no means so difficult as the separation of zirconium and hafnium.

Chemical Reactions of the Elements

Vanadium, niobium, and tantalum are more resistant to chemical attack than most other metals. They are inert to air and water at room temperature; they are not dissolved by hot, aqueous alkalies or nonoxidizing acids (except HF). Vanadium is dissolved by nitric acid, but niobium and tantalum are unattacked even by aqua regia:

$$2V + 12H^+ + 10NO_3^- = 2VO_2^+ + 10\overline{NO}_2 + 6H_2O$$

All are attacked by hydrofluoric acid, forming complex fluoroanions. In addition, they are all corroded by fused sodium hydroxide—vanadium most rapidly, tantalum least rapidly.

When heated to a sufficiently high temperature the metals will react with virtually all of the nonmetals:

$$M + O_2 = M_2O_5$$
$$M + X_2 = MX_5$$
$$M + N_2 = MN$$
$$M + C\ \ = MC$$

Like the group IVa elements, at elevated temperatures, vanadium, niobium, and tantalum absorb hydrogen in amounts that vary with the temperature and the pressure of hydrogen over the metal. The resulting substances are brittle, alloy-like solids, of no fixed stoichiometry. Such behavior is in sharp contrast to the Vb elements which form molecular compounds with hydrogen of unvarying stoichiometry, MH_3.

+5 Oxides

V_2O_5 is a dull red, acidic oxide, best prepared by the mild heating of NH_4VO_3. It melts at about 660°. It is soluble to the extent of about 0.1 per cent in water and much more soluble in either strongly basic or strongly acidic solutions. In the strongly basic solutions orthovanadate ions exist:

$$V_2O_5 + 6OH^- = 2VO_4^{---} + 3H_2O$$

Upon reducing the pH of vanadate solutions, a series of condensations occurs, resulting in what are known as isopolyanions, until, at the isoelectric point, vanadium pentoxide precipitates. (For this discussion, the isoelectric point is that ratio of acid added to total V content where the resulting pH is independent of the total concentration of V.) No general agreement on the step-by-step condensation mechanism exists. One group of authors holds that the aggregation to form polyanions is best represented as follows:

$$2VO_4^{---} + 2H^+ \qquad = V_2O_7^{----} + H_2O \text{ divanadate ion}$$
$$2V_2O_7^{----} + 4H^+ \quad = H_2V_4O_{13}^{----} + H_2O \text{ tetravanadate ion}$$
$$5H_2V_4O_{13}^{----} + 8H^+ = 4H_4V_5O_{16}^{---} + H_2O \text{ pentavanadate ion}$$
$$2H_4V_5O_{16}^{---} + 6H^+ = 5V_2O_5 + 7H_2O \text{ isoelectric point, pH} = 2.2$$

Still other authors propose the formation of a trivanadate ion:

$$3VO_4^{---} + 6H^+ = V_3O_9^{---} + 3H_2O$$

The hexavanadate ion, $V_6O_{17}^{----}$, has supporters also. The facts are that condensation precedes precipitation, since polymerized species can be observed *in solution* before precipitation.

It is obvious that only the alkali metal and ammonium ions will form simple vanadates in water solution, since simple vanadate ions exist only at high values of pH, where all polyvalent metal ions form insoluble hydrous oxides.

The vanadate, divanadate, and tetravanadate ions are colorless, but the more highly condensed polyvanadates are yellow to red. Salts of many of the vanadate ions can be crystallized from solution, but the nature of the solute species cannot be inferred from the composition, or even the structure, of the solid, inasmuch as dissolution involves a reaction with the solvent.

The difficulties to be overcome in the precise elucidation of the solute species among which pentavalent vanadium is distributed are many. Not the least of these difficulties is the fact that the vanadium appears to be distributed among a substantial number of species for a given concentration of vanadium, a given pH, and a given temperature. The distribution of the vanadium among the species is certainly a function of these variables, and the kind and number of species is also a function of the same variables. Our knowledge of isopolycation formation is even less precise (see Chapter 8).

Similarly, it is not completely clear how V_2O_5 dissolves in strongly acid solutions. Certainly the solute species are cations containing vanadium. It is presumed that they are VO_2^+ or VO^{+++} ions. It is possible that the ions are multiples of either or both of these cations. Also it is possible that vanadium complex ions are formed with the anion of the acid used to solubilize the V_2O_5. Such acid solutions have a characteristic pale yellow color. No "salts" of the proposed oxyvanadium cations have been isolated. Such cations are sometimes used as the basis for calling vanadium(V) oxide an amphoteric oxid. Acidic solutions of pentavalent vanadium are easily reduced. Mild reducing agents give solutions of tetravalent vanadium compounds, whereas stronger reducing agents effect reduction to V^{+++} and even V^{++} compounds.

As might be expected, the white pentoxides of niobium and tantalum are much weaker acids than V_2O_5. To be sure, they are

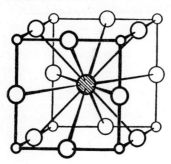

Fig. 17.1. Perovskite-like structure of $NaNbO_3$.

soluble in strongly alkaline solutions, but the nature of the niobate and tantalate ions is still somewhat speculative. It is possible to prepare, by dry methods, pure, solid $NaNbO_3$ (perovskite structure), but this substance contains no discrete NbO_3^+ ions. It is a three dimensional aggregate of Na, Nb, and O ions held together by electrostatic and covalent forces. See Figure 17.1. To the limited extent that the compound is soluble, the crystal structure must be broken up in some way, yielding solute particles. Simply bubbling carbon dioxide into alkaline niobate solutions precipitates hydrous niobium pentoxide:

$$(NbO_3^-)_x + H_2O + CO_2 = \underline{Nb_2O_5 \cdot xH_2O} + CO_3^{--} \text{ or } HCO_3^-$$

The same is true for tantalates.

Nb_2O_5 and Ta_2O_5, when freshly precipitated, are somewhat soluble in very strong hydrochloric acid, but, again, the nature of the solute species is open to some doubt. Acid solutions of Nb(V) can apparently be reduced to Nb(III), as shown by the reducing equivalence of the reduced niobium toward a permanganate titration. Ta(V) solutions have not thus far been reduced. It is to be expected that greater stability of the V state should be observed in going from vanadium to tantalum. This is true also for the reduction of the pentoxides with hydrogen at elevated temperatures. Ta_2O_5 is not reduced by hydrogen; Nb_2O_5 is reduced to NbO_2; V_2O_5 is reduced to V_2O_3 or lower. Both Nb_2O_5 and Ta_2O_5 are high-melting oxides, so high that they can be considered refractories. Like so many refractory oxides, ignited Ta_2O_5 is completely insoluble in all acids save hydrofluoric.

It may be concluded that no simple oxyanion chemistry of the Va metals exists; nor are any simple cationic species of the Va metals in the +5 state known.

Vanadium pentoxide reacts with alcohol on long heating to form esters:

$$V_2O_5 + 6C_2H_5OH = OV(OC_2H_5)_3 + 3H_2O$$

The formula of this ester is sometimes written $(C_2H_5)_3VO_4$. Such a formulation is referred to as an ortho ester, since the highest coordination number of vanadium for oxygen was thought to be 4 at one time. Such esters are liquids at room temperature, and are completely hydrolyzed back to vanadium pentoxide and the alcohol by excess water. The addition of small amounts of water to the ortho esters results in condensation to esters of polyvanadic acids:

$$3(C_2H_5)_3VO_4 + 3H_2O = (C_2H_5)_3V_3O_9 + 6C_2H_5OH$$

The above formation of triethyl trivanadate from the ortho ester is typical. However, as in the case of the formation of the isopolyvanadate ions, a mixture of condensation products is apt to be obtained. Increased degree of aggregation is again accompanied by an increase in color.

+5 Halides

VF_5 is the only pentahalide of vanadium. All four possibilities are known for niobium and tantalum. They must be prepared by direct synthesis or by reaction of a suitable halogenating agent on

	F_5	Cl_5	Br_5	I_5
V	white b.p. 111°	—	—	—
Nb	white m.p. 75° b.p. 229°	yellow m.p. 210° b.p. 254°	red m.p. 268° b.p. 362°	bronze decomposes
Ta	white m.p. 97° b.p. 229°	white m.p. 220° b.p. 239°	yellow m.p. 280° b.p. 349°	black m.p. 496° b.p. 543°

the oxide. All are molecular substances, violently and completely hydrolyzed by water.

In addition, several oxyhalides of vanadium and niobium are known, but none for tantalum. $NbOCl_3$ and $VOCl_3$ are the best known. The first is a white solid, subliming at about 400° and hydrolyzed completely by water. The second is a lemon-yellow liquid, b.p. 127°, and, again, completely hydrolyzed by water.

Lower Oxidation States

A fairly extensive chemistry of vanadium in lower oxidation states exists. V(II) compounds are very easily oxidized. For example V^{++} in acid solution, prepared by electrolytic reduction at a mercury cathode surface, will spontaneously liberate hydrogen from water:

$$V^{++} + H^+ = V^{+++} + \tfrac{1}{2}\overline{H_2}$$

Nevertheless, it has been possible to prepare a red-violet vitriol, $VSO_4 \cdot 7H_2O$.

V(III) compounds are much more stable toward oxidation. A few salts have been prepared, such as green $VCl_3 \cdot 6H_2O$ and violet V(III) alums. In general V^{+++} resembles Al^{+++}, Cr^{+++}, and Fe^{+++}, except that it is slowly oxidized by dissolved oxygen. Anhydrous vanadium trichloride resembles $CrCl_3$ in that it is nonvolatile and will form $V(NH_3)_6Cl_3$ upon reaction with liquid ammonia. However, it is like $FeCl_3$ in that it dissolves quickly in water and the $V(NH_3)_6^{+++}$ ion is rapidly hydrolyzed to the $V \cdot aq^{+++}$ ion.

Dark blue VO_2 behaves as though it were amphoteric, dissolving in either strong bases or strong acids. Oxyanions of V(IV) are called hypovanadates (sometimes vanadites) and appear to be isopolyanions. Acid solutions of V(IV) almost certainly contain the vanadyl ion, VO^{++}. Salts of this blue cation have been crystallized, such as $VOSO_4$ and $K_2SO_4 \cdot 2VOSO_4$.

VCl_4 is a dark red liquid prepared by the chlorination of vanadium or ferrovanadium. It boils at 154°, but slow decomposition to VCl_3 and Cl_2 takes place above the boiling point. The liquid hydrolyzes in water:

$$VCl_4 + H_2O = VO^{++} + 4Cl^- + 2H^+$$

Green vanadyl chloride can be crystallized from the blue solution.

Lower halides of niobium and tantalum, such as $NbCl_3$, $NbCl_4$, $TaCl_3$, and $TaCl_4$, have been prepared by the hot-cold tube reaction.

Complex Compounds

Complex salts of vanadium in all of its oxidation states are known. In fact, a large number of well-defined vanadium complexes have been characterized, in contrast to the confusion which surrounds the "simple" aqueous chemistry of vanadium.

$K_4V(CN)_6 \cdot 3H_2O$ is quite analogous to $K_4Fe(CN)_6 \cdot 3H_2O$, with the caution that solutions containing the hexacyanovanadate(II) ion are much more easily oxidized than those containing hexacyanoferrate(II) ion.

V(III) forms complex anions of the type VA_6^{---} with $A = CN^-$, SCN^-, F^-, and Cl^-. In general, V^{+++} exhibits a coordination number of 6. As has been mentioned, cationic complexes such as $V(NH_3)_6^{+++}$ are also known.

The complex compounds of V(IV) and V(V) are distinguished by the persistence of the V-O linkage in addition to the complexing ligands, such as VOF_4^{--}, $VO(SCN)_4^{--}$, $VO_2(SO_4)^-$, $VOCl_4^-$, $VO_2F_3^{--}$, etc.

In general, the fluoride complexes of vanadium (and of niobium and tantalum also) are the most easily prepared for two reasons:

(1) The fluoro complexes are less soluble.
(2) The fluoro complexes are less easily hydrolyzed.

Certainly the fluoride complexes of niobium and tantalum are the most important compounds of the two elements, since it is by means of such complexes that niobium and tantalum are separated. A number of fluoroniobates and fluorotantalates have been prepared, but, ordinarily, K_2TaF_7 and K_2NbOF_5 result when the freshly precipitated oxides are dissolved in hydrofluoric acid and potassium fluoride. Potassium heptafluorotantalate is considerably less soluble than potassium pentafluorooxyniobate in cold water. K_2NbF_7 can be prepared from anhydrous hydrogen fluoride. The heptafluoroniobate and the heptafluorotantalate are representative of the very small number of AB_7 type structures.

Peroxycompounds

Niobate and tantalate solutions react easily with hydrogen peroxide to form peroxyanions, NbO_8^{-3} and TaO_8^{-3}—yellow and colorless, respectively. Salts such as K_3TaO_8 and K_3NbO_8, and even the free peroxyacids, can be crystallized under suitable conditions. At least three different kinds of peroxyvanadium compounds have been observed. Ordinarily, the addition of H_2O_2 to normal sodium vanadate in mildly basic solution gives a yellow color, typical of the $VO_2(O_2)_2^{---}$ ion. In cold, strongly alkaline solutions, more concentrated H_2O_2 gives a blue color, characteristic of the VO_8^{---} ion. Red-brown peroxyvanadium cations can be made in acid solutions.

Interstitial Compounds

Tantalum powder reacts with finely divided carbon at very high temperatures to form tantalum carbide, TaC, a dark crystalline substance, which melts near 3900°, has a Mohs hardness of between 9 and 10, is as good an electrical conductor as tantalum itself, and is only slightly less dense than tantalum. The carbide is resistant to chemical attack except by hydrofluoric acid. The structure of the carbide is like that of rock-salt. Formally it might be said that carbon is in an oxidation state of -4 and tantalum is in the $+4$ state, but it is actually somewhat superfluous to try to describe the oxidation state of either carbon or tantalum in the compound. Such compounds are referred to as interstitial compounds; that is to say, the forces holding the atoms together are not unlike the forces holding atoms together in a crystal of pure metal. TaB_2 and TaN are substances of the same general type as TaC. Vanadium forms VB, VC, and VN, all of which are isostructural with the NaCl lattice. They exhibit the high melting points and great hardness typical of the class of transition metal-metalloid interstitial phases. Niobium, the IVa, and the VIa elements form similar borides, carbides, and nitrides. Thorium is an exception, forming Th_3N_4 and ThC_2.

The usefulness of these substances lies in their remarkable physical properties and their general resistance to chemical attack.

Polynuclear Complex Halides

About half a century ago a series of very remarkable lower halides of niobium and tantalum was first prepared. $TaBr_5$ was heated to a red heat in an evacuated tube with sodium amalgam. The cooled mass was extracted with hydrobromic acid, leaving much insoluble brown residue, but yielding an intense green solution from which $Ta_6Br_{14}\cdot7H_2O$ was crystallized. A water solution of the crystals behaves as though only two of the fourteen bromine atoms are ionized (that is, only one-seventh of the Br atoms precipitate as AgBr). Also, it has been shown that the rest of the compound behaves as a complex ion, $Ta_6Br_{12}^{++}$. For example, the original green crystals were converted to crystals of $Ta_6Br_{12}(OH)_2\cdot10H_2O$, $Ta_6Br_{12}Cl_4\cdot7H_2O$, and $Ta_6Br_{12}I_2\cdot7H_2O$ by crystallization from solutions of NaOH, HCl, and HI, respectively. Similar compounds, $Nb_6Cl_{12}\cdot7H_2O$ and $Ta_6Cl_{14}\cdot7H_2O$, are known. Recently the structure of the $M_6X_{12}^{++}$ cations has been deduced. About a hundred years ago a compound of the composition $MoCl_2\cdot xH_2O$ was prepared, which subsequently has been shown to exhibit behavior similar to the complex halocations of niobium and tantalum. The compound actually is best represented as $Mo_6Cl_8^{++++}4Cl^-\cdot8H_2O$, since only one-third of the Cl atoms are ionized and conversion to crystals of $Mo_6Cl_8(OH)_4\cdot14H_2O$ is easily accomplished. The $Mo_6Cl_8^{++++}$ cation has been found to consist of a cube formed by the eight Cl atoms at the corners with faces of the cube centered by the six Mo atoms. It is noteworthy that these unusual complex cations result in stabilization of the metal atoms in what are normally considered to be unstable low oxidation states. The interatomic distances are such as to indicate some chemical bonding between neighboring metal atoms within the cation in addition to bonding between metal and halogen. It is considered likely that other transition metal halides of this type will be found.

USES

Next to its use as an alloying element in steel-making, vanadium is most in demand in the form of certain of its oxides for use as catalysts in a variety of industrial processes.

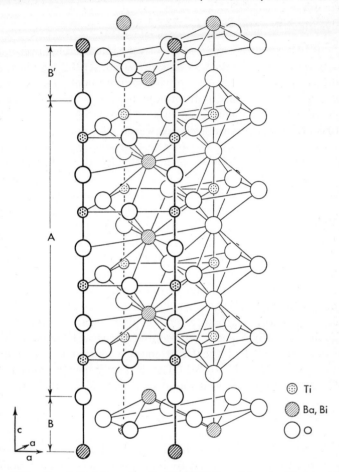

Fig. 17.2. One-half of the unit cell of $BaBi_4Ti_4O_{15}$. A denotes the 4 perovskite layers and B and B' the M_2O_2 layers.

Most uses of tantalum are based on the desirable physical properties and chemical inertness of the metal. Equipment which must be acidproof in the chemical industry is sometimes made of tantalum. Electrolytic capacitors are now also being made with tantalum electrodes. The price for tantalum sheet is about 50 dollars per pound.

Its low work function (the energy required to remove an electron from the surface of the metal) and high melting point lead to the use of niobium in electronic tubes. Some niobium is used as an alloying element in steels and in nonferrous metals. It should be emphasized that niobium and tantalum are classified as very rare metals, produced in very small quantities only.

SUGGESTIONS FOR FURTHER READING

H. Remy, *Treatise on Inorganic Chemistry*, Elsevier, New York, 1956, Vol. II, Chapter 4.

G. T. Seaborg and J. J. Katz, *The Actinide Elements*, McGraw-Hill, New York, 1954, Chapters 5 and 17.

STUDY QUESTIONS

1. What happens in the following cases?
   (a) $V_2O_5 + Fe + Al + heat$
   (b) $Ta_2O_5 + H_2 + heat$
   (c) $VO_4^{---} + H^+$
   (d) $Nb + C + heat$
   (e) $V_2O_5 + CCl_4 + heat$

2. By means of equations and a few words about conditions, show how to carry out the following conversions:
   (a) Make pure Ta from $(Nb, Ta)_2O_5$.
   (b) Make NbO_2 from Nb_2O_5.
   (c) Make $NbCl_5$ from Nb_2O_5.
   (d) Make VCl_4 from a natural vanadium compound.
   (e) Make K_2TaF_7 from Ta.

OCCURRENCE AND HISTORY

Oxygen is the most abundant element of all on the surface of the earth. In fact, the earth's crust may be regarded essentially as close-packed oxygen atoms with the rest of the atoms in the interstices. While the most abundant and a very important element, it is interesting that the true nature of the role of oxygen in combustion processes was not established until late in the eighteenth century. Scheele in Sweden and Priestley in England are credited with independent discoveries of the element. But it was Lavoisier in France who first proposed the concepts of combustion that explained the role of oxygen in many chemical reactions, and, because of this, he is properly known as "father of modern chemistry." His classic experiments proved conclusively that combustion is the chemical reaction between oxygen and the combustible substance.

PREPARATION OF THE ELEMENT

In the laboratory, the thermal decomposition of many compounds is used to prepare small quantities of pure oxygen. Mercury(II) oxide and barium peroxide decompose reversibly to give oxygen:

$$HgO \rightleftharpoons Hg + \tfrac{1}{2}O_2$$
$$BaO_2 \rightleftharpoons BaO + \tfrac{1}{2}O_2$$

In the first case 350°C is the usual temperature, whereas about 700°C is required in the latter.

Pure potassium permanganate yields oxygen when heated above 250°C:

$$2KMnO_4 \rightarrow K_2MnO_4 + MnO_2 + O_2\uparrow$$

However, the reaction between hydrogen peroxide and the permanganate in acid solution yields much more oxygen per gram-atom of manganese:

$$2KMnO_4 + 5H_2O_2 + 4H_2SO_4 \rightarrow$$
$$2KHSO_4 + 2MnSO_4 + 5O_2\uparrow + 8H_2O$$

At high concentrations the reaction proceeds with explosive violence.

Fused potassium nitrate yields oxygen slowly to leave the nitrite. The most familiar preparation is the decomposition of potassium chlorate catalyzed by manganese dioxide:

$$2KClO_3 \xrightarrow[\Delta]{MnO_2} 2KCl + 3O_2\uparrow$$

The commercial production of oxygen uses less costly raw materials. Accordingly, air and water are the usual sources of "large-scale" oxygen. The fractional distillation of liquid air gives oxygen and nitrogen of sufficient purity for most uses. Some oxygen is made by the electrolysis of aqueous solutions, with hydrogen as a by-product. About 20 billion cubic feet of oxygen are produced annually in the United States.

Oxygen has a second gaseous allotropic form, the triatomic ozone, O_3. Ozone is made by the passage of a silent electric discharge—i.e., one which glows but does not spark—through a stream of oxygen. By this method from 5 to 25 per cent of the oxygen can be converted in one pass. The reaction involves the splitting of the O_2 molecules into atoms, which then combine with other oxygen molecules:

$$O_2 \quad \rightarrow 2O$$
$$O + O_2 \rightarrow O_3$$

Oxygen also absorbs ultra-violet light of wave length 1850Å or shorter, splitting into atoms which produce ozone as above. Ozone is also one of the products of many chemical reactions, such as the reaction of fluorine with water and electrolytic processes.

PHYSICAL PROPERTIES OF THE ELEMENT

Oxygen is a colorless, odorless, tasteless gas which is sparingly soluble in water. It is composed of diatomic molecules, O_2, joined by a double bond. A simple electron-dot formula cannot be written for the molecule, however, because of one important experimental fact: the gas is paramagnetic with a magnetic moment corresponding to two unpaired electrons per molecule. That a molecule with an even number of electrons should be paramagnetic puzzled theoreticians for a long time. The answer is provided in the theory of "molecular orbitals." Though the details of this theory are best reserved for more advanced study, the results may nonetheless, be summarized briefly here. The theory begins by assigning the quantized energy levels for the valence electrons to the whole molecule, rather than to the individual atoms. Hence, we have molecular orbitals rather than the atomic orbitals of Chapter 1. In diatomic molecules there are some orbitals which can hold two electrons and others which can hold four. The outermost orbital in the first period will hold four electrons. It is completely empty in the diatomic nitrogen, completely full with two electron pairs in the diamagnetic fluorine, and half-full with two unpaired electrons in the paramagnetic oxygen. It is interesting to note that the S_2 molecule, which occurs only at high temperature in sulfur vapor, is paramagnetic also.

Oxygen condenses at $-183°$ and 1 atm to a blue liquid, which freezes at $-219°$ to a blue solid. The gas at high pressure, the liquid, and the solid exhibit a paramagnetism corresponding to less than two unpaired electrons. This has been explained by assuming the presence of some percentage of dimers, O_4, with all electrons paired, similar to the NO and NO_2 cases. The assumption is supported by spectroscopic and heat capacity data. Some of the physical properties of oxygen are listed in Table 18.1.

Ozone is a blue gas with a characteristic sharp odor. It is a strong absorber of light in the ultra-violet region, beginning at 2900Å. There exists in the upper atmosphere of the earth an ozone layer produced by the action of u.v. from the sun on atmospheric oxygen. Ozone is a much stronger absorber of u.v. than is oxygen, and this ozone layer absorbs much of the u.v. from the sun. Were it not

TABLE 18.1
Some Physical Properties of Oxygen

Melting Point	$-218.71°$
Boiling Point	$-182.97°$
Critical Temperature	$-118.8°$
Critical Pressure	49.71 atm
Critical Density	0.4299 g/cc
Density of Gas at STP	1.429 g/l
Density of Liquid at b.p.	1.1316 g/cc
Density of Solid at $-253°$	1.41 g/cc
Solubility in Water at 0° and 1 atm.	0.049 cc/100 g

there, life would not be possible on earth because of the intensity of strong radiation at the surface. Ozone condenses at $-111.5°$ and 1 atm. to a dark blue liquid and freezes at $-249.6°$ to a dark blue solid. Since ozone is an endothermic compound, it is essentially unstable, and, once the decomposition is started, it can go rapidly. The liquid and solid, being concentrated forms, are especially apt to explode. It has been found recently that the liquid can be kept for some time undecomposed when stored in strictly clean vessels.

The ozone molecule has the three oxygen atoms arranged in an obtuse triangle:

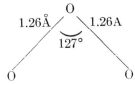

The gas is diamagnetic.

CHEMICAL PROPERTIES AND COMPOUNDS

The octet rule is particularly applicable to oxygen, since it is a second period element. It achieves the octet of electrons in a variety of ways. The simple oxide ion, O^{--}, is found in the oxides of electropositive metals. Two single covalent bonds may be formed, as in water, or one double bond, as in carbon dioxide. A single covalent bond with an additional electron gives rise to the hydroxide ion, OH^-, while three covalent bonds with the loss of an electron result in the hydronium ion, H_3O^+. In numerous solid oxides oxygen has a coordination number greater than 3, but the bonds are always partially covalent and partially ionic.

Because of its great electronegativity, exceeded only by fluorine, oxygen is usually assigned the oxidation number -2 in compounds. Common exceptions are the peroxides—such as Na_2O_2, where -1 is more appropriate—and the superoxides—such as KO_2, where $-\frac{1}{2}$ is the best approximation. In the two uncommon oxygen fluorides, O_2F_2 and OF_2, oxygen must be assigned positive oxidation numbers. The superoxide ion is an oxygen molecule with one additional electron which pairs with one of the two unpaired electrons of O_2 so that superoxides are paramagnetic with a magnetic moment corresponding to one unpaired electron. In the peroxide ion, the second additional electron leads to two pairs of electrons in the outer molecular orbital, isoelectronic with the F_2 molecule, and hence diamagnetism.

Chemical Reactions of the Element

Oxygen is quite a reactive element, although its reaction with most common substances proceeds slowly at room temperature. All of the elements, with the exception of the rare gases, form binary compounds with oxygen. This does not mean that all of the elements will react directly with oxygen. For example, molten silver *dissolves* more oxygen than the solid at the melting point, so that on cooling molten silver in air "blow holes" are formed often as a result of the liberation of the dissolved oxygen; but silver *will not react chemically* with oxygen at ordinary pressures. It is true, nevertheless, that most of the elements will combine with oxygen under some conditions to form oxides directly. The conditions vary greatly and are a function of:

(a) the element concerned—for example, the alkali metals react with oxygen in the air at room temperature instantaneously, whereas copper, silver, and gold are not reactive under these conditions.

(b) the physical state of the element—for example, white phosphorus reacts with oxygen at room temperature, whereas much higher temperatures are necessary for the combustion of red phosphorus. Again, a sheet of lead is inert toward oxygen, but if the lead is prepared as a very finely divided powder and thrown into the air, it ignites instantly; that is, it is possible to prepare pyrophoric lead.

(c) the concentration of oxygen—for example, silver reacts with oxygen at high pressure.

(d) the temperature.

The hydrogen-oxygen reaction is probably the most studied of all chemical reactions, and yet there is by no means general agreement among chemists as to the mechanism of the reaction. When one reactant is present in low concentration, about 1 per cent, the reaction proceeds rapidly but smoothly. At more equal concentrations of the two gases, the reaction proceeds explosively when initiated by heat, an electric spark, a catalyst, or a photochemical process. In the oxyhydrogen torch a stationary explosion is occurring where the velocity of the flame front is matched by the flow of the gases. With this torch, a temperature of about 2800° can be reached, whereas the oxyacetylene torch can become several hundred degrees hotter.

Oxygen also combines with many compounds. Combustion is a familiar reaction. Many reducing agents, such as iron(II) and tin(II) ions, must be protected from air to retain their strength. Many oxidations, particularly those of transition elements in basic fusions, employ oxygen or air:

$$2MnO_2 + 4NaOH + O_2 \xrightarrow{\Delta} 2Na_2MnO_4 + 2\overline{H_2O}$$

Several reagents have been used in the laboratory to remove traces of oxygen from other gases. Depending on circumstances, the following are effective: white phosphorus, alkaline pyrogallol, sodium, hot copper, and solutions of chromium(II) salts.

Ozone is similar to oxygen in chemical properties, except that it is even more active an oxidizing agent. It comes close to atomic oxygen in reactivity. A common test for ozone is its reaction with moist potassium iodide:

$$2KI + \overline{O_3} + H_2O \rightarrow \underline{I_2} + \overline{O_2} + 2KOH$$

This is not a very selective test, however, since many other oxidizing gases—including nitrogen dioxide, chlorine, and hydrogen peroxide—will bring about the same brown color of iodine. Ozone is a powerful enough oxidizing agent to precipitate black silver(II) oxide from neutral solutions of silver nitrate:

$$2AgNO_3 + \overline{O_3} + H_2O \rightarrow 2\underline{AgO} + \overline{O_2} + 2HNO_3$$

Water

The abundance, ease of preparation, and stability of water have made it the standard substance for defining many physical quantities. Among the scales which use physical properties of water are temperature, heat, and volume. Water has in addition some unusual physical properties. The density of the liquid reaches a maximum, defined as 1.00000 g/cc, at 3.98°. The density of the liquid decreases with decreasing temperature to a value of 0.999841 g/cc at 0°. A further expansion takes place upon freezing, so that the density of ice at 0° is 0.917 g/cc. It is unusual for a solid to float in its liquid at the melting point. Because of hydrogen bonding, water has relatively high heats of fusion and vaporization—79.71 and 538.7 cal/g, respectively—making it a useful heat transfer medium. Also, the dielectric constant has the high value of 78.54 at 25°, which is partially responsible for its being a good solvent for ionic compounds.

Chemically, water can act either as an oxidizing or reducing agent. It is reduced by sodium to hydrogen and hydroxide ions and is oxidized by fluorine to oxygen, ozone, fluorides of oxygen, and hydrogen ions.

The hydrogen of natural water contains 0.02 per cent deuterium. When aqueous solutions are electrolyzed, the deuterium content of the evolved hydrogen is less than that of the residual hydrogen, so that by repetitive processes, deuterium oxide of any concentration can be produced. Heavy water has properties slightly different from those of ordinary water: m.p., 3.82°; b.p., 101.4°; density at 25°, 1.1079 g/cc; ion product $(D^+)(OD^-) = 1.6 \times 10^{-15}$. It is of great value for research purposes, enabling the course of specific hydrogen atoms in various processes to be followed.

Hydrogen Peroxide

The only other binary compound of oxygen and hydrogen is hydrogen peroxide. The pure substance is a liquid freezing at $-0.89°C$ and boiling at $151°C$, which is an extrapolated value, since the substance explodes below its normal boiling point. Dilute solutions of hydrogen peroxide are prepared and concentrated by distillation. Barium peroxide in water suspension reacts with carbon dioxide to precipitate barium carbonate, leaving a solution of hydrogen peroxide. Other reagents which have been used to precipitate the barium as an insoluble salt include phosphoric acid, sulfuric acid, fluosilicic acid, and tartaric acid. The electrolysis of cold, saturated solutions of potassium hydrogen sulfate yields potassium peroxydisulfate, which may be hydrolyzed to give dilute solutions of hydrogen peroxide (see Chapter 19). For many years the preparation and handling of concentrated solutions of hydrogen peroxide was considered a hazardous undertaking, since explosions were frequent. In recent years several investigators have shown that pure hydrogen peroxide is hazardous only when handled carelessly. If kept free of dust particles, the pure substance may be stored indefinitely, and concentrated solutions are now available commercially which may be shipped by common carrier under ICC regulations. Many substances catalyze the decomposition of hydrogen peroxide, while a number are known to inhibit the decomposition. Thus, while it is possible to obtain inhibitor-free hydrogen peroxide, most of the commercial peroxide contains inhibitors such as phosphates, acetanilide, and barbituric acid.

On contact with the skin, strong solutions of hydrogen peroxide produce a bleached, seriously burned area. Dilute solutions are used to bleach wool and silk.

Hydrogen peroxide will react as either oxidizing or reducing agent. For example, it will oxidize iodide and iron(II) salts in dilute acid solution. Under the same conditions, it dissolves manganese dioxide via reducing action:

$$2I^- + H_2O_2 + 2H_3O^+ \quad \rightarrow I_2 + 4HOH$$
$$2Fe^{++} + H_2O_2 + 2H_3O^+ \rightarrow 2Fe^{+++} + 4HOH$$
$$\underline{MnO_2 + H_2O_2 + 2H_3O^+ \rightarrow Mn^{++} + O_2\uparrow + 4HOH}$$

In dilute acid solution dichromate is reduced by hydrogen peroxide to trivalent chromium, whereas the latter is oxidized to chromate by peroxide in basic solution.

Hydrogen peroxide reacts with many oxysalts to produce peroxy-type acids or salts. For example, a dilute acid solution of titanium(IV) ion reacts with peroxide to give an intense yellow-orange color:

$$Ti(OH)_2{}^{++} + H_2O_2 + 2H_2O \rightarrow H_2TiO_4 + 2H_3O^+$$

This reaction is used as a sensitive test for the presence of hydrogen peroxide or titanium. Peroxyacids or salts are formed by boron, carbon, nitrogen, phosphorus, sulfur, the transition elements of groups IV, V, and VI, and some of the actinides.

Metal Oxides

The properties of the individual oxides are discussed in the other chapters. It is of some value to attempt a classification of oxides according to position in the periodic table and according to valence number. In general the oxides of the elements of a subgroup increase in basicity from top to bottom of the subgroup. Going from left to right in a period there is a fairly regular increase in the acidity of the oxides of *maximum valence number*, as in Na_2O, MgO, Al_2O_3, SiO_2, P_2O_5, SO_3, and Cl_2O_7. The increase in acidity is associated with the increased electronegative character of the elements. Similarly the increase in acidity is associated with increased covalent bond type.

It is convenient to classify oxides as follows:

  (a) Basic oxides—those that will react with acids to form salts;
  (b) Acidic oxides—those that will react with bases to form salts;
  (c) Amphoteric oxides—those that will react with either bases or acids to form salts;
  (d) Peroxides—compounds containing the —O—O— linkage.

Table 18.2 gives examples of the four types.

TABLE 18.2
Oxide Classification

Basic	Acidic	Amphoteric	Peroxides
K_2O	B_2O_3	BeO	Na_2O_2
MgO	SO_3	SnO	KO_2
CaO	Cl_2O_7	Ga_2O_3	SO_4
La_2O_3	CrO_3	TiO_2	$TiO_3 \cdot xH_2O$
ThO_2	CO_2	Cr_2O_3	

Some oxides exhibit polymorphism; that is, they are capable of crystallizing in two modifications. Sometimes both forms exist at room temperature. In other cases the second modification may be observed only at high temperatures. There are in addition a large number of "mixed" oxides of the metals, which have definite structures and exist only in the solid state. Examples are the spinels, such as $NiCr_2O_4$, perovskites, such as $BaTiO_3$, and garnets, such as $Y_3Fe_5O_{12}$. These oxides often have interesting physical properties. Many of the spinels and garnets are ferromagnetic, while the perovskite structure leads to ferroelectricity, the electrical analog of ferromagnetism. For the structure of these types of oxides see the second reference at the end of the chapter.

Most anhydrous oxides are hygroscopic. Phosphorus pentoxide is so much so that it is an excellent dessicant. Frequently the percentage of a metal in a sample of material is determined by weighing its oxide following ignition. Some of these oxides pick up traces of water while on the balance pan. To be sure, oxides of iron, aluminum, zirconium, etc., are not as hygroscopic as the oxides of phosphorus, sulfur, calcium, etc., but for very careful work they should be weighed in a dry atmosphere. Freshly ignited samples of zirconium and hafnium oxides weighing a few hundred milligrams will absorb as much as a milligram of moisture while on a balance pan under ordinary atmospheric conditions.

Some metal oxides exhibit semiconducting properties similar to those of germanium. The semiconducting properties are due to imperfect stoichiometric ratios making up the crystal lattice. Such substances are called nonstoichiometric or non-Daltonian compounds; that is, substances where the ratios of atoms deviate slightly from Dalton's concepts of stoichiometry. In the case of semiconducting zinc oxide there is a slight excess of zinc ions over oxygen ions. Such a situation can arise when some of the lattice positions that are occupied ideally by oxygen ions are vacant. Since the over-all crystal must be uncharged, the vacant sites are occupied by electrons. Looking at it another way, for every vacant site there must be a neutral zinc atom in the lattice whose valence electrons are said to take the place of the missing oxygen ion. In the case of iron(II) oxide there is an excess of oxygen atoms. Here, the vacant positions correspond to sites occupied by iron(II) ions in the ideal crystal. In order to maintain electrical neutrality in this case, two Fe^{++} ions become two Fe^{+++} ions for each vacant cation site. Nonstoichiometry in ionic crystals is far more common than is generally recognized; however, the deviations from stoichiometry are

so small in most cases as to be outside the range of detection by
ordinary analytical chemical techniques.

SUGGESTIONS FOR FURTHER READING

J. S. Anderson, *Annual Reports to The Chemical Society*, Volume 43,
104 (1946).

A. F. Wells, *Structural Inorganic Chemistry*, 2nd ed., Oxford, 1950, London,
Chapters X and XI.

J. R. Partington, *A Textbook of Inorganic Chemistry*, 6th ed., Macmillan,
London, 1950, Chapters III, X, XVIII, and XIX.

STUDY QUESTIONS

1. Write balanced equations to describe the following:
   (a) H_2O_2 is added to an acid solution of dichromate.
   (b) Ozone reacts with aqueous silver nitrate.

2. Within the classification of peroxides do you think it is possible to
subclassify according to basic or acidic nature?

3. The temperature range over which oxygen will react with mercury is
only about 100 degrees. Would increasing the pressure of the oxygen extend
or shorten this range? Why?

4. $KMnO_4$ sells for about 22 cents per pound, H_2O_2 (35 per cent aqueous
solution) for 21 cents per pound, and sulfuric acid (98 per cent) for about
2 cents per pound. Calculate the cost of the chemicals needed to produce
100 pounds of oxygen by reacting peroxide with permanganate in the
presence of acid.

5. Propose a structural formula for K_2TiO_4.

6. Indicate the products of the following:
   (a) CaO is mixed with water.
   (b) P_2O_5 is mixed with water.
   (c) The products of (a) and (b) are mixed.
   (d) CaO and P_2O_5 are mixed and heated.
   (e) $Fe(NO_3)_2 + O_2 + NaOH$(aqueous).

7. Suggest a way of "annealing out" the imperfections in a non-Daltonian sample of zinc oxide.

8. By means of equations and a few words about conditions, show how
to carry out the following conversions:
   (a) Make H_2O_2 from O_2.
   (b) Make NaOD from D_2O.
   (c) Make O_3 from H_2O.
   (d) Make very pure O_2 from air.
   (e) Make AgO from Ag.

OCCURRENCE AND HISTORY

Since it occurs uncombined in many volcanic regions, sulfur was one of the elements well known to ancient peoples. Its use in medicine is described by early Roman authors. Compounds of sulfur have been used as bleaching agents for centuries, and sulfur matches were used in ancient Rome.

Not only does sulfur occur uncombined, but nature is rich in combined forms of sulfur. Important ores of many metals are sulfides, such as PbS, ZnS, HgS, Sb_2S_3, MoS_2, and CuS. Calcium sulfate, in the form of the 2-hydrate, gypsum, is a common mineral.

PREPARATION OF THE ELEMENT

Inasmuch as the abundant sulfur can be mined in the free state, it is one of the few elements that is cheap and readily available. Elementary sulfur lying at or near the surface of the earth is not abundant enough to supply present demands, and so deeper deposits must be worked. The process for obtaining sulfur from large underground deposits is known as the Frasch Process. The sulfur, which is usually found from 300 to 2000 feet under ground in Louisiana and Texas, is melted by forcing water under pressure at 170 to 180°C through pipes into the sulfur-bearing rock (porous limestone and calcite). Compressed air forces the liquid to the surface through a concentric pipe. See Figure 19.1. Approximately 5 million tons of sulfur were mined in the United States in 1951, and this figure is expected to increase substantially every year. When very pure sulfur is needed, it can be purified by distillation.

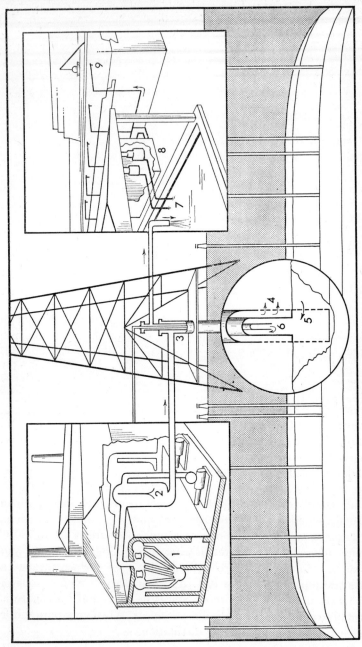

Fig. 19.1. Mining sulphur by the "hot water" process.

PHYSICAL PROPERTIES OF THE ELEMENT

Sulfur exhibits a very complex allotropy in all three phases. There are two common crystalline modifications, orthorhombic and monoclinic sulfur, and an amorphous variety, plastic sulfur. The stable allotrope and usual modification at room temperature and pressure is orthorhombic sulfur, which has a molecular lattice composed of S_8 molecules in puckered rings:

$$S \overset{S}{\underset{S}{\diagup}} \overset{S}{\underset{S}{\diagup}} \overset{S}{\underset{S}{\diagup}} S$$

The true transition temperature of orthorhombic to monoclinic sulfur is 95.6°, but the change is slow even at 100°. When heated rapidly, orthorhombic sulfur melts at 113°, but if maintained at about 100° for several hours, it changes to the monoclinic, which then melts at 118.95°. The structure of monoclinic sulfur is unknown, but it is probably composed of S_8 molecules, like the orthorhombic, since both crystalline forms have molecular weights of 256 in carbon disulfide solution. When cooled to room temperature, the monoclinic allotrope reverts to the orthorhombic in several days. The two crystalline varieties differ only slightly in physical properties. They are both yellow. The density of orthorhombic sulfur is 2.09 g/cc and that of monoclinic 1.96 g/cc. They are both insoluble in water but soluble in organic solvents, monoclinic sulfur being somewhat more soluble below the transition temperature as expected of a metastable variety. The best solvent for sulfur is carbon disulfide, the saturated solution at 25° containing 33 per cent sulfur by weight.

Liquid sulfur at the melting point is a yellow mobile liquid, probably consisting of S_8 molecules. When heated, it darkens in color to a dark red and becomes very viscous in the range 165 to 200°. On further heating to the boiling point, 444.60° (a defined point on the temperature scale), the liquid remains dark in color but becomes mobile once more. The nature of the species in the liquid state is obscure. Undoubtedly the S_8 rings open up above 165° to give a complex variety of molecules. If the liquid is slowly cooled, crystals of monoclinic sulfur form, but rapid cooling produces plastic sulfur, an amorphous allotrope composed of long chains of sulfur atoms. Plastic sulfur slowly reverts to a crystalline modification on standing. It is insoluble in carbon disulfide, although its insolubility is probably due to the fact that it dissolves extremely slowly and not to an inherent property, since it is not the thermodynamically stable form.

The vapor species of sulfur are also complex. The molecules S_8, S_6, S_2, and S are in equilibrium with each other. At low temperature the higher molecular weight species predominate, while dissociation to the lower species takes place as the temperature is raised. As mentioned in the previous chapter, S_2 resembles O_2 in being paramagnetic.

CHEMICAL PROPERTIES AND COMPOUNDS

The difference between the first and second elements of Group VI is considerable. Sulfur readily assumes positive oxidation numbers, while oxygen almost invariably is negative. With the 3d orbitals available for bonding, sulfur can have up to twelve electrons in its valence shell, while oxygen is limited to eight. Sulfur will form chains and the S_8 ring with many S—S bonds, while two oxygen atoms at most will link to each other (compare the reverse trend for the first two elements of Group IV). Sulfur is not so electronegative as oxygen, and its compounds with the electropositive elements are therefore more covalent than those of oxygen.

The common oxidation states of sulfur in its compounds are -2, $+4$, and $+6$. The only monatomic ion is the sulfide, which exists in the sulfides of electropositive metals. In all other compounds, sulfur is covalently bonded to other atoms either in molecules, radicals, or solids. As usual in the nonmetals, there are a number of other sulfur compounds, such as Na_2S_5 and $Na_2S_2O_3$, in which the arbitrariness of the oxidation number concept for covalent compounds becomes highly apparent.

Chemical Reactions of the Element

Sulfur is quite an active element, being about equal in reactivity to oxygen. It burns when heated in air or oxygen to the dioxide (the trioxide is produced only in the presence of a catalyst). With carbon at high temperature carbon disulfide is produced. Sulfur combines very slowly with hydrogen at low temperature, faster at high temperature in the presence of a catalyst. The reaction is reversible:

$$H_2 + S \rightleftharpoons H_2S + heat$$

Up to about 600° the equilibrium lies far to the right, but above that temperature appreciable decomposition of the hydrogen sulfide takes place. The halogens, except iodine, combine with sulfur, the activity of the reaction decreasing with increasing atomic weight of the halogen; a variety of products are formed (see below). Nitrogen is one of the few elements not to combine directly with sulfur, but nitrogen-sulfur binary compounds are known, the most important of which is tetranitrogen tetrasulfide, a volatile yellow solid. It can be made by the action of anhydrous ammonia on sulfur:

$$10S + 4NH_3 \rightarrow N_4S_4 + 6H_2S$$

The product has an interesting structure; it consists of an eight-membered bent ring with alternate sulfur and nitrogen atoms.

All of the metals except gold, platinum, iridium, and tellurium react directly with sulfur. Some metals react at room temperature, but others require heat. Copper and silver sulfides are more stable than the oxides, and they are among the metals that react at room temperature:

$$2Ag + S \rightarrow Ag_2S$$

Sulfur is insoluble in water and acids, even concentrated nitric acid. It dissolves in strong bases with the formation of polysulfides:

$$3Ca(OH)_2 + 12S \rightarrow 2CaS_5 + CaS_2O_3 + 3H_2O$$
$$Na_2S + 4S \rightarrow Na_2S_5$$

Hydrogen Sulfide

Hydrogen sulfide is prepared most easily in the laboratory by the action of hydrochloric acid upon iron(II) sulfide:

$$FeS + 2H^+ \rightarrow Fe^{++} + H_2S\uparrow$$

It is also possible to prepare the substance by direct synthesis near the boiling point of sulfur. The liquid has a normal boiling point of $-60°C$. As a liquid it is not at all like water, having a low dielectric constant and being a poor solvent for salt-like compounds. The greatly diminished amount of hydrogen bonding in going from water to hydrogen sulfide is chiefly responsible for these differences in properties. At room temperature it is a very poisonous, nasty-smelling, colorless gas. It is soluble in water to the extent of about three volumes of gas to one of liquid water. As a solute it behaves as a weak diabasic acid:

$$H_2S \rightleftharpoons H^+ + HS^- \qquad K_1 = 1.15 \times 10^{-7}$$
$$HS^- \rightleftharpoons H^+ + S^{--} \qquad K_2 = 10^{-15}$$

Upon ignition hydrogen sulfide burns in excess air to give water and sulfur dioxide. In a limited amount of air some free sulfur results, since sulfur dioxide reacts with any unburned hydrogen sulfide:

$$2H_2S + SO_2 \rightarrow 2H_2O + 3S$$

Hydrogen sulfide is a reducing agent. Typical of such behavior are its reactions with dilute solutions of iodine, potassium permanganate, and iron(III) nitrate:

$$H_2S + I_2 \rightarrow 2HI + S\downarrow$$
$$5H_2S + 2KMnO_4 + 3H_2SO_4 \rightarrow 5S\downarrow + K_2SO_4 + 2MnSO_4 + 8H_2O$$
$$H_2S + 2Fe(NO_3)_3 \rightarrow S\downarrow + 2Fe(NO_3)_2 + 2HNO_3$$

Metal Sulfides

Most metal sulfides can be prepared by direct synthesis, but the method is rarely used. Rather, they are usually prepared from hydrogen sulfide. Sodium hydrogen sulfide is formed by saturating a solution of sodium hydroxide with hydrogen sulfide. Upon the addition of another equivalent of sodium hydroxide, sodium sulfide 9-hydrate can be crystallized from the solution. As might be expected from the very small K_2 of hydrogen sulfide, solutions of the alkali metal sulfides are hydrolyzed extensively:

$$S^{--} + HOH \rightleftharpoons OH^- + SH^-$$

In fact, the basicity of the sulfide ion is comparable to that of the hydroxide ion. The alkali metal and alkaline earth sulfides and hydrogen sulfides are the only very soluble salts of hydrogen sulfide. The alkaline earth salts are hydrolyzed,

$$2CaS + 2HOH \rightarrow Ca(OH)_2 + Ca(HS)_2$$

and the resulting acid salts are fairly soluble. It is not possible to prepare normal calcium sulfide by the reaction between calcium hydroxide and hydrogen sulfide in water, but the reaction will proceed in the absence of water at about 200°C. It is possible to make the salt also by the reduction of calcium sulfate with charcoal at 800 to 900°C. See Chapter 6.

In light of the very weak acid character of hydrogen sulfide, it might be expected that sulfides of less basic metals could not be made in the presence of water. Indeed, the case of aluminum sulfide, which hydrolyzes completely to hydrous alumina and hydrogen sulfide, would seem to substantiate the point. However, many normal sulfides can be made by bubbling hydrogen sulfide through aqueous solutions of the metal salts. The very small solubilities of most metal sulfides explains this. For example, the sulfides of copper, silver, gold, cadmium, mercury, germanium, tin, lead, arsenic, antimony, bismuth, technetium, and rhenium are so insoluble that these metals can be removed quantitatively from *dilute* acid solution by saturation with hydrogen sulfide:

$$Cu^{++} + H_2S \quad\quad\quad \rightarrow \underline{CuS} + 2H^+$$
$$GeCl_6^{--} + 2H_2S \quad\quad \rightarrow \underline{GeS_2} + 4H^+ + 6Cl^-$$
$$2ReO_4^- + 7H_2S + 2H^+ \rightarrow \underline{Re_2S_7} + 8H_2O$$

While the sulfides of zinc, thallium, manganese, iron, cobalt, and nickel will not precipitate under the same conditions, they do precipitate quantitatively from neutral or basic solution. The gradation in solubilities is of practical use in the analytical separation of the elements. The extreme insolubility of silver sulfide is demonstrated by the ability of elementary silver to displace hydrogen from hydrogen sulfide, even though silver is well below hydrogen in the displacement series. Many compounds containing sulfur are reduced by silver to form silver sulfide. It is little wonder that silver tarnishes so easily.

Most of the insoluble sulfides are highly colored (the white ZnS and GeS_2 are exceptions), whereas the alkali and alkaline-earth sulfides are white. Many of the insoluble sulfides exist in two or more crystalline modifications. The phenomenon is called polymorphism in the case of compounds. Table 19.1 lists some of the

TABLE 19.1
Colors and Solubilities of Some Insoluble Sulfides

Formula	Color as precipitated from solution	Color of natural mineral	Solubility in water (Moles/liter at 25°C)
HgS	black	red	2.1×10^{-23}
CdS	yellow-red	yellow	1.46×10^{-10}
ZnS	white	brown	1.47×10^{-9}
CuS	black	indigo	2.55×10^{-15}
Ag_2S	black	black	2.48×10^{-15}
MoS_2	yellow-brown	black	
As_2S_3	yellow	yellow	
Sb_2S_3	orange	black	8.2×10^{-7}
MnS	pink	black	3×10^{-7}
NiS	black	yellow	4×10^{-10}
PbS	black	black	3.62×10^{-11}

properties of a few of the insoluble sulfides. The values of the solubilities given must not be accepted as exact, since the accuracy with which the solubility of such slightly soluble salts can be determined is not very high.

Thiosalts

A few of the insoluble sulfides are dissolved by aqueous sodium sulfide. The products are called thiosalts, and they are named as though they were derived by substitution of S for O in oxy-salts. For example, the dissolution of arsenic(III) sulfide in sodium sulfide solution can be likened to the solution of arsenic(III) oxide in sodium hydroxide:

$$6NaSH + As_2S_3 \rightarrow 2Na_3AsS_3 + 3H_2S$$
$$6NaOH + As_2O_3 \rightarrow 2Na_3AsO_3 + 3H_2O$$

Many of the thiosalts can be crystallized from solution.

A comparison of the formulas and names of a few oxy- and thio-salts follows:

GeO_3^{--} germanate	GeS_3^{--} thiogermanate
AsO_3^{---} arsenite	AsS_3^{---} thioarsenite
AsO_4^{---} arsenate	AsS_4^{---} thioarsenate
CO_3^{--} carbonate	CS_3^{--} thiocarbonate
SbO_4^{---} antimonate	SbS_4^{---} thioantimonate
SnO_3^{--} stannate	SnS_3^{--} thiostannate

When thiosalts are acidified, the insoluble sulfide reprecipitates and hydrogen sulfide is evolved:

$$2AsS_4^{---} + 6H^+ \rightarrow As_2S_5\downarrow + 3H_2S\uparrow$$

Those sulfides that form soluble thiosalts can be separated from those that do not by digestion in sodium sulfide solution. In the past sulfide solubilities have formed the backbone of many inorganic analytical separations.

Polysulfides

Aqueous solutions of sodium sulfide are able to dissolve free sulfur. The amount of sulfur that can be dissolved per mole of sulfide ion varies slightly with the concentration of the solution, but it is usually possible to dissolve about four atoms of sulfur per sulfide ion. The ratio of sulfur to sodium in the solutions can be varied from 1:2 to a little over 5:2, corresponding to stoichiometry variations between Na_2S and Na_2S_5. The solutes are called polysulfides, and they possess mild oxidizing properties. The sulfur atoms may be thought of as being coordinated to the sulfide ion:

$$\left[\,\ddot{\underset{..}{S}}\, \right]^{--} + \ddot{\underset{..}{S}} \rightarrow \left[\,\ddot{\underset{..}{S}} : \ddot{\underset{..}{S}}\, \right]^{--}$$

It is convenient for purposes of balancing oxidation-reduction equations to consider that the original sulfide ion retains its formal valence number of -2 and that the coordinated sulfur atoms retain formal valence numbers of 0. Alternatively, fractional oxidation numbers can be used if desired.

Solutions of the sodium polysulfides, Na_2S_x, become progressively less hydrolyzed as the value of x increases; the larger the polysulfide anion, the stronger is its corresponding acid. Usually when strong acids are added to the polysulfide solutions, free sulfur is precipitated and hydrogen sulfide is evolved:

$$S_x{}^{--} + 2H^+ \rightarrow (x - 1)S\downarrow + H_2S\uparrow$$

However, when the polysulfide is added very carefully to cold, concentrated hydrochloric acid, a yellow oil separates. The oil consists of the several H_2S_x compounds. The individual hydrogen persulfides are isolated from the oil by fractional distillation under reduced pressure. They are all unstable and decompose easily into sulfur and hydrogen sulfide.

Sulfur Dioxide and the Sulfites

The combustion of free sulfur or the roasting of any metal sulfide in an excess of air produces sulfur dioxide. At one atmosphere pressure the substance is a liquid from $-10°C$ down to $-75.5°C$. It is used extensively as a solvent in preparative chemistry. It is a hygroscopic liquid of low dielectric constant and is not a good solvent for salt-like substances. The heat of vaporization is 95 calories per gram (compare H_2O, 540). The combination of optimum boiling point temperature and favorable heat of vaporization makes the substance useful as a refrigerant in modern industrial refrigerating systems, though, because of its toxicity, it has been replaced by the "freons" in domestic units. The gas is moderately soluble in water, 50 volumes of gas dissolving in one volume of water under ordinary conditions. It dissolves to form the weak, unstable sulfurous acid, which, like carbonic acid, cannot be obtained pure: $\overline{SO_2} + H_2O \rightleftharpoons H_2SO_3$. The acid is considerably stronger than hydrosulfuric acid, and it forms salts with most metallic ions. With the more electropositive elements, such as sodium and potassium, it forms two series of salts, Me_2SO_3 and $MeHSO_3$. Upon the addition of a strong acid to solutions of these salts, free sulfurous acid is formed, which decomposes into sulfur dioxide and water:

$$MeHSO_3 + HCl \rightarrow NaCl + H_2SO_3 \rightarrow NaCl + H_2O + SO_2\uparrow$$

Most of the heavy metal sulfites are water insoluble, but they react in the same manner.

Since in the $+4$ state sulfur is in an intermediate oxidation state, it is capable of reacting as either an oxidizing or a reducing agent. It shows a strong preference to act in the latter fashion, easily reducing iron(III) to iron(II) and permanganate to manganous ion:

$$SO_2 + 2H_2S \rightarrow 3S + 2H_2O$$
$$2Fe^{+++} + SO_2 + H_2O \rightarrow 2Fe^{++} + SO_4^{--} + 4H^+$$

Aqueous sulfur dioxide and its sodium salts are used as bleaching agents in many applications where hypochlorites cannot be used. However, the largest use for sulfite solutions is in the digestion of wood pulp in the paper making industry.

Thiosulfates

Alkaline sulfite solutions will dissolve free sulfur to produce thiosulfates. The most common of these is the photographic fixer, "hypo," $Na_2S_2O_3 \cdot 5H_2O$, which crystallizes readily from solution. The name thiosulfate implies that the ion is derived from the sulfate ion by the substitution of an S for one of the O atoms. Indeed, the structure is

$$\left[\begin{array}{ccc} & \overset{..}{:}\overset{..}{O}: & \\ \cdot : \overset{..}{O}: & S & :\overset{..}{O}: \cdot \\ & \overset{..}{:}\overset{..}{S}: & \end{array} \right]^{--}$$

but it is not possible, as the name might suggest, to make it by replacing an oxygen of the sulfate ion. The thiosulfates are of practical use in photography because of the fact that they form stable complex ions with many cations. A film is fixed by dissolving out the unreacted silver halide:

$$AgX + 2S_2O_3^{--} \rightarrow Ag(S_2O_3)_2^{---} + X^-$$

Free thiosulfuric acid is not known. When dilute acid is added to a solution of sodium thiosulfate, a disproportionation occurs:

$$S_2O_3^{--} + 2H^+ \rightarrow (H_2S_2O_3) \rightarrow S\downarrow + SO_2\uparrow + H_2O$$

If an ion is present that forms an insoluble sulfide, the reaction follows another course:

$$2Sb^{+++} + 3S_2O_3^{--} + 3H_2O \xrightarrow{\Delta} \underline{Sb_2S_3} + 3SO_4^{--} + 6H^+$$

By this means many heavy metal sulfides can be precipitated without resorting to the objectionable hydrogen sulfide.

Polythionates

The thiosulfate ion is oxidized easily, but the products of oxidation vary considerably with the oxidizing agent and the conditions. Vigorous oxidation with hot, concentrated nitric acid or chlorine yields sulfuric acid. Mild oxidation in weakly acid solution with reagents such as iron(III) or iodine gives the tetrathionate ion:

$$2S_2O_3^{--} + I_2 \rightarrow S_4O_6^{--} + 2I^-$$

The iodine-thiosulfate reaction is useful in quantitative analysis, since it is easy to determine the end-point of the reaction using a starch indicator, which gives an intense blue color with iodine. The tetrathionates are typical of salts derived from a series of polythionic acids of the general formula $H_2S_nO_6$ or $HO_3S—S_x—SO_3H$. The structures of the dithionate and the trithionate are given below:

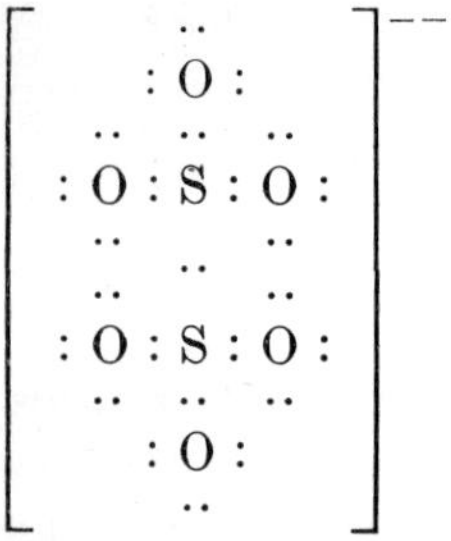

$2Na^+$ or simply

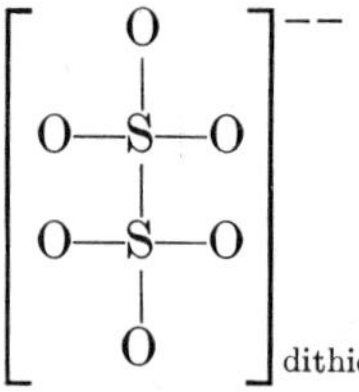

dithionate ion $2Na^+$

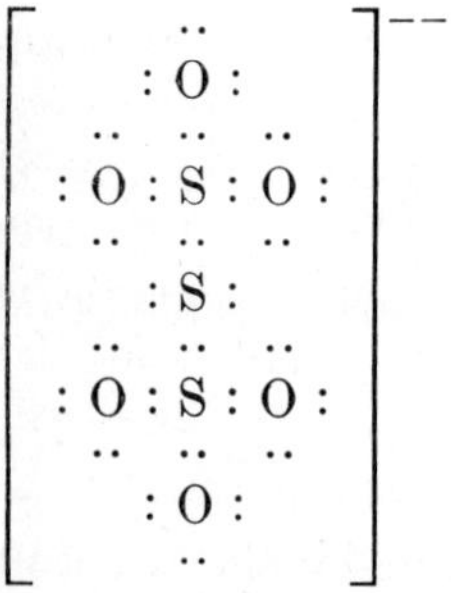

$2Na^+$ or simply

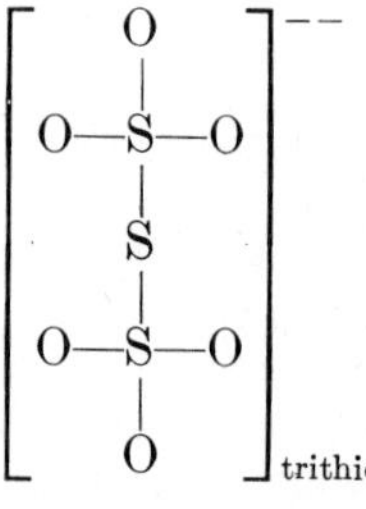

trithionate ion $2Na^+$

The higher polythionates are similar, involving longer chains of sulfur atoms, somewhat reminiscent of the polysulfides. Sodium hexathionate, $Na_2S_6O_6$, is the highest one to be isolated, but there are indications that n may go as high as 10. Dithionic acid and its salts, all of which appear to be soluble in water, are much more stable than the higher polythionates. The latter decompose slowly to sulfur, sulfur dioxide, and sulfate ion. The first and second ionization constants of the polythionic acids must be large, since very few acid salts have been isolated. It is not possible to make $NaHS_3O_6$, for example; only the normal salt has been found.

Sulfuric Acid

Sulfuric acid is produced in larger tonnage than any other synthetic chemical; in 1956 17 million tons were produced in the United States alone. In ton-lots 100 per cent sulfuric acid sells for about one cent per pound.

It is understandable that the production of the compound has been the subject of intense research. It would seem that the oxidation of sulfur dioxide to sulfur trioxide followed by hydration to the acid would be a relatively simple process, since the $+6$ state of sulfur is the more stable. Such is not the case. There are two methods of production now in general use.

(1) *The Contact Process (which accounts for 80 per cent of U.S. production).* This process renders the reaction $2SO_2 + O_2 \rightleftharpoons 2SO_3$ economically feasible. The equilibrium lies far to the right at room temperature and moves to the left with an increase in temperature, but the rate of attaining equilibrium at room temperature is so slow as to be impractical. A moderate increase in temperature ($400°C$), the use of a variety of catalysts (platinum is the best, but oxides of transition metals are also used), and an increase in pressure give satisfactory conversion to sulfur trioxide. Since the gases must be in contact with the solid catalyst, it is called the "contact process." The gases issuing from the reaction chambers consist of sulfur trioxide plus unreacted sulfur dioxide and oxygen. They are passed through concentrated sulfuric acid, which dissolves the sulfur trioxide, forming pyrosulfuric acid, $H_2S_2O_7$, known as "oleum." Adding water to oleum converts the dissolved sulfur

trioxide to sulfuric acid. The sulfur trioxide is not absorbed directly in water because the reaction is violent and difficult to control. By controlling the amount of water added, acid of any desired strength is obtained. The main disadvantage of this process is that impurities in the gases, especially arsenic, which occurs in nature with sulfur, "poison" the catalyst easily.

(2) *The Chamber Process*. Moist air, sulfur dioxide, and oxides of nitrogen are mixed in tremendous lead-lined chambers. The sulfur dioxide is oxidized to the trioxide, which combines with water vapor to form a fog of sulfuric acid. The fog condenses slowly to a liquid in the bottom of the chambers. A simplified explanation is sometimes given:

$$NO_2 + H_2SO_3 \rightarrow NO + H_2SO_4$$
$$2NO + O_2 \quad \rightarrow 2NO_2$$

The nitrogen dioxide involved in the reaction is a homogeneous catalyst, as opposed to the heterogeneous catalyst of the contact process. The oxides of nitrogen are regenerated in the process and used over again, although losses usually require additional oxides of nitrogen in the feed gases. Theoretically acid of any strength might be produced by this process also. However, lead is soluble in sulfuric acid solutions of concentrations greater than 70 per cent. Therefore, using lead chambers, very concentrated acid cannot be produced directly. Of course, the dilute acid can be run off and concentrated by evaporation in a ceramic container.

Sulfur dioxide for sulfuric acid production is made by burning sulfur, by roasting sulfide minerals, and, in some countries, by the reduction of gypsum.

Sulfuric acid has at least two desirable properties, other than its price, which help to explain its use by many large industries.

(1) It is a relatively nonvolatile acid. Since 98 per cent acid boils at 340°C, it can be used to produce the much more volatile hydrogen fluoride and hydrogen chloride and the relatively more volatile nitric acid.

(2) It is an excellent dehydrating agent and is used to remove water from many chemical processes, especially organic reactions, that produce water, and, in order to go to completion, need to have the water removed as it is formed.

Sulfuric acid is a strong acid, the ionization of even its second hydrogen being considerable. Two series of salts can be prepared, typified by sodium sulfate and sodium hydrogen sulfate. The acid sulfates are acids of sufficient strength to liberate carbon dioxide from carbonates:

$$2HSO_4^- + CO_3^{--} \rightarrow 2SO_4^{--} + H_2O + CO_2\uparrow$$

Practically all sulfates are water soluble, the only exceptions being the lead, barium, strontium, calcium, and europium(II) salts. The solubilities of some normal sulfates are listed below:

Salt	Sol. in grams salt per 100 grams H_2O
$BaSO_4$	$0.00024(20°)$
$CaSO_4 \cdot 2H_2O$	$0.208(25°)$
$MgSO_4 \cdot 7H_2O$	$26.8(25°)$
$CdSO_4$	$77.2(25°)$
$Cr_2(SO_4)_3 \cdot 18H_2O$	$120(20°)$
$MnSO_4 \cdot 4H_2O$	$105.3(0°)$
K_2SO_4	$10.75(25°)$
$La_2(SO_4)_3 \cdot 9H_2O$	$2.9(0°)$
Ag_2SO_4	$0.8(25°)$
$NiSO_4 \cdot 7H_2O$	$25.5(15°)$

It is apparent that chromium(III) sulfate is a very soluble salt. However, the anhydrous salt does not dissolve in water, its behavior being similar to the trivalent chromium chlorides (see Chapter 21). Anhydrous iron(III) sulfate is also difficultly soluble in water, whereas the hydrated salt is easily soluble. Like many hydrated sulfates, sodium sulfate 10-hydrate, commonly called Glauber's Salt, shows a sharp discontinuity in the solubility temperature curve at 32.38°C, as shown in Figure 19.2. Above the transition temperature the anhydrous salt is the equilibrium solid phase, and its solubility decreases slightly as the temperature increases. Below the transition temperature the solubility of the decahydrate decreases sharply as the temperature decreases. If a solution that is saturated with respect to the anhydrous salt is cooled below the transition temperature, it is supersaturated with respect to the decahydrate. This system is admirably suited to the demonstration

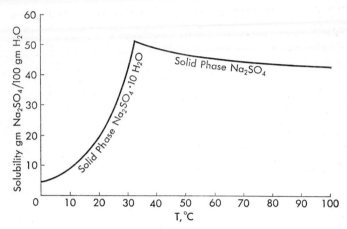

Fig. 19.2. Solubility of Na₂SO₄.

of supersaturation, since a supersaturated solution will remain unprecipitated for years unless nucleated.

The largest single use of sulfuric acid is in the production of fertilizers (see Chapter 16). Large quantities of the acid are used also in the production of other chemicals, petroleum refining, rayon production, and the processing of iron, steel, and nonferrous metals.

Halides and Oxyhalides

In addition to the oxy-acids, oxides, and salts already mentioned, a number of halides and oxyhalides of sulfur are known. They are all volatile, molecular compounds, and, with a few notable exceptions, hydrolyzed instantly and completely on contact with water. The physical properties of the well-known compounds of this type are listed in Table 19.2. It is certain that lower fluorides of sulfur exist, but they have not been as adequately described as the two listed. Similarly, at least one binary compound of sulfur and bromine exists.

Sulfur burns spontaneously in a stream of fluorine gas. Several fluorides can be detected in the product gases, but sulfur hexafluoride is the principal product. The gas is very inert to all chemical reagents, even sodium in the cold. In fact, hot caustic will not hydrolyze the compound. Disulfur decafluoride, a minor product

TABLE 19.2
Halides and Oxyhalides of Sulfur

	Boiling Point in °C	Melting Point in °C	Color
SF_6	Sublimes at -63.7	-50.8 (under pressure)	colorless
S_2F_{10}	29	-92	colorless
SCl_4	decomposes	-31	yellow solid
SCl_2	59 (with dissociation)	-78	red
S_2Cl_2	138	-80	yellow
SOF_2	-43.8	-110	colorless
$SOFCl$	12.2	-140	colorless
$SOCl_2$	75.7	-99.5	colorless
$SOBr_2$	42.5 (at 16 mm)	-52	orange-yellow
SO_2F_2	-55.4	-136.7	colorless
SO_2FCl	7.1	-124.7	colorless
SO_2Cl_2	69	-46	colorless
$S_2O_5Cl_2$	152.5	-37	colorless

of the direct combination separated by fractionation, is resistant to hydrolysis also. The peculiar resistance to attack on the part of SF_6 and S_2F_{10}, even though they are both thermodynamically unstable in the presence of many reagents, is explained by the fact that they are covalently saturated—i.e., sulfur has its maximum number of six covalent bonds, the structure of disulfur decafluoride undoubtedly being F_5S—SF_5. Entering groups then have no way of adding on to the molecule, and a high activation energy results. In addition, the sulfur fluorine bond is a particularly strong one, as is seen below in its relative inertness in SO_2F_2 and HSO_3F. Sulfur hexafluoride has found limited practical use as an insulating gas in high-voltage electrostatic generators, as a result of its high breakdown potential.

The chlorides of sulfur are prepared by direct synthesis. Sulfur tetrachloride dissociates into sulfur dichloride and chlorine below room temperature. Sulfur dichloride dissociates into disulfur dichloride, commonly called "sulfur monochloride," and chlorine at about 100°C. Disulfur dichloride is the easiest to prepare in any reasonable state of purity. Its structure is Cl—S—S—Cl, with the Cl—S—S angle equal to 103°. It hydrolyzes on contact with water to give a mixture of products:

S_2Cl_2 + water → HCl, S, polythionic acids, H_2S, H_2SO_4, and SO_2

Thionyl chloride, $SOCl_2$, is made by reacting sulfur trioxide with disulfur dichloride in the presence of chlorine to convert the by-product sulfur back into disulfur dichloride:

$$SO_3 + S_2Cl_2 \rightarrow SOCl_2 + S + SO_2$$
$$2S + Cl_2 \quad\rightarrow S_2Cl_2$$

Thionyl fluoride and bromide are made from the chloride by replacing the chlorine with AsF_3 and HBr, respectively. A mixture of products, including the mixed oxyhalides, results, and purification by fractionation under anhydrous conditions is necessary. The iodide is not known. The thionyl halides react with water—the fluoride slowly, the chloride and bromide vigorously:

$$O{-}S\begin{matrix} X \\ \\ X \end{matrix} + \begin{matrix} H{-}O{-}H \\ \\ H{-}O{-}H \end{matrix} \rightarrow O{-}S\begin{matrix} OH \\ \\ OH \end{matrix} + 2HX$$

As might be expected, the structures of the compounds are all triangular pyramids with the S at the apex. Recently it has been observed that thionyl chloride will react with metals such as antimony, aluminum, magnesium, iron, tin, bismuth, and mercury in the presence of a catalyst such as aluminum chloride or iron(III) chloride:

$$Sn + 2SOCl_2 \rightarrow SnCl_4 + S{\downarrow} + SO_2$$

It is in addition a good chlorinating agent for many metal oxides:

$$Al_2O_3 + 3SOCl_2 \xrightarrow{\Delta} 2AlCl_3 + 3SO_2$$

Sulfuryl fluoride, SO_2F_2, is prepared by heating dry barium fluosulfonate:

$$Ba(SO_3F)_2 \xrightarrow[\Delta]{} BaSO_4 + SO_2F_2{\uparrow}$$

The chloride results from the direct combination of sulfur dioxide and chlorine:

$$SO_2 + Cl_2 \rightleftharpoons SO_2Cl_2$$

Fluosulfonic acid is prepared by reacting hydrogen fluoride with sulfur trioxide:

$$HF + SO_3 \rightarrow HO—\overset{\overset{\displaystyle O}{|}}{\underset{\underset{\displaystyle O}{|}}{S}}—F$$

Chlorosulfonic acid can be prepared in the same way, but it hydrolyzes very rapidly:

$$HO—\overset{\overset{\displaystyle O}{|}}{\underset{\underset{\displaystyle O}{|}}{S}}—Cl + HOH \rightarrow HO\overset{\overset{\displaystyle O}{|}}{\underset{\underset{\displaystyle O}{|}}{S}}OH + HCl$$

As a result, its salts cannot be prepared in the presence of water. However, the rate of hydrolysis of fluosulfonic acid is slow in all but very dilute solutions, and its salts can be crystallized from solution.

Another indication of the stability of the S—F bond besides the difficulty of hydrolysis of the sulfur-fluorine compounds discussed above is the fact that these compounds do not attack glass, unusual behavior for fluorides.

Pyrosulfuryl chloride, $S_2O_5Cl_2$, is the anhydride of chlorosulfonic acid. Indeed, it has been made by dehydrating the acid with phosphorous pentoxide:

$$Cl—\overset{\overset{\displaystyle O}{|}}{\underset{\underset{\displaystyle O}{|}}{S}}—OH \quad HO—\overset{\overset{\displaystyle O}{|}}{\underset{\underset{\displaystyle O}{|}}{S}}—Cl \xrightarrow{P_2O_5} Cl—\overset{\overset{\displaystyle O}{|}}{\underset{\underset{\displaystyle O}{|}}{S}}—O—\overset{\overset{\displaystyle O}{|}}{\underset{\underset{\displaystyle O}{|}}{S}}—Cl + H_2O$$

Peroxysulfates

If a saturated solution of potassium hydrogen sulfate is electrolyzed, keeping the temperature close to 0°C and using inert electrodes, crystals of potassium perxoydisulfate form at the anode:

$$2HSO_4^- \rightarrow S_2O_8^{--} + 2H^+ + 2e^-$$
$$2K^+ + S_2O_8^{--} \rightarrow \underline{K_2S_2O_8}$$

The salt is slightly soluble in cold water. On digestion in hot acid solution, it is hydrolyzed as follows:

$$
\begin{array}{c}
\underset{\displaystyle O}{\overset{\displaystyle O}{HO-S-O-O}} \;\vert\; \underset{\displaystyle O}{\overset{\displaystyle O}{-S-OH}} \\[2mm]
H \;\vert\; OH \\
\downarrow \\
\underset{\displaystyle O}{\overset{\displaystyle O}{HO-S-}} \;\vert\; O-OH \;+\; \underset{\displaystyle O}{\overset{\displaystyle O}{HO-S-OH}} \\[2mm]
HO \;\vert\; H \\
\downarrow \\
\underset{\displaystyle O}{HO-S-OH} \;+\; H_2O_2
\end{array}
$$

The intermediate stage of hydrolysis, peroxymonosulfuric acid, which can be isolated as such, is commonly called Caro's acid. The final product is hydrogen peroxide. This method is used for the production of the latter.

Potassium peroxydisulfate is an excellent oxidizing agent. In general it is able to oxidize anything that can be oxidized by hydrogen peroxide. But it is also able to oxidize hot, dilute solutions of manganese(II) and chromium(III) to permanganate and chromate, respectively (recall that hydrogen peroxide reduces permanganate). A catalyst of silver nitrate is necessary for these reactions. Nevertheless, it is clear that peroxydisulfate is a much more powerful oxidizing agent than hydrogen peroxide.

SUGGESTIONS FOR FURTHER READING

K. A. Kobe, *Inorganic Process Industries*, Macmillan, New York, 1948, Chapters 6 and 7.

M. E. Weeks, *Discovery of The Elements*, 6th ed., Journal of Chemical Education, Easton, Pa., 1945, Chapter I.

D. M. Yost and H. Russell, *Systematic Inorganic Chemistry*, Prentice-Hall, New York, 1944, Chapters 8 through 11.

STUDY QUESTIONS

1. Calculate the pH of a one-tenth molar solution of NaHS.

2. How would you make Al_2S_3?

3. A solution contains Ca^{++}, Pb^{++}, Zn^{++}, and Sb^{+++}. Suggest a procedure for the separation of the solute cations.

4. Offer an explanation for the apparent difference between the ionization constants of H_2S and H_2S_5.

5. Do you think H_2Se would have a larger or a smaller first ionization constant than H_2S? Explain.

6. Name the following compounds: $Na_3Cu(S_2O_3)_2$, $Na_2S_5O_6$, K_2HgS_2, Na_2S_5.

7. Predict the result of reacting SO_2Cl_2 with anhydrous ammonia.

8. Design an apparatus in which you might expect to prepare thionyl chloride. Show how you would collect samples for use.

9. Write equations to describe: (a) the oxidation of Mn(II) to Mn(VII) in dilute acid solution by $(NH_4)_2S_2O_8$ plus $AgNO_3$ as catalyst; (b) the oxidation of Cr(III) to Cr(VI) in dilute acid solution by $(NH_4)_2S_2O_8$ plus $AgNO_3$ as catalyst.

10. Offer an explanation of why the S—Br bond is so unstable and why compounds containing the S—I bond have not been prepared.

11. Write an equation for the reaction between a dilute acid solution of $KMnO_4$ and SO_2 bubbled through the solution.

12. What happens in the following cases?
    (a) $SbCl_3 + Na_2S_2O_3$(aqueous)
    (b) $SF_6 + H_2O$(heat)
    (c) $BaCl_2 + Ag_2SO_4$(aqueous)
    (d) $Ag + H_2S$
    (e) $Na_2SO_3 + H_2SO_4$

13. By means of equations and a few words about conditions, show how to carry out the following conversions:
    (a) Make H_2SO_4 from Na_2SO_4.
    (b) Make SO_2F_2 from S.
    (c) Make hypo from S.
    (d) Make S from $BaSO_4$.
    (e) Make CaS from a natural sulfur ore.

14. A mixture of 45 g of Na_2SO_4 and 100 g of water is heated to 100° and then cooled to room temperature (23°). Describe what happens during the cooling.

Chapter 20

Selenium, Tellurium, and Polonium

OCCURRENCE AND HISTORY

Tellurium was the first of the elements of group VIb to be discovered. Baron Muller von Reichenstein of Transylvania, a part of contemporary Rumania, recognized it as a new element in 1782; but it was not named until 1798, when the well-known German chemist Martin Klaproth suggested the present name, which means earth. Paul Kitaibel, of Hungary, discovered tellurium independently in 1789.

Selenium was discovered in 1817 by the Swedish chemist Jons Jacob Berzelius, recognized as the outstanding chemist in the world during the first half of the nineteenth century. He derived its name from *selene*, meaning moon, to indicate a relationship between the two elements like that of the moon and the earth.

None other than Mme. Marie Curie discovered element number 84 in 1898, and its name honors her native country, Poland.

Selenium and tellurium are trace elements in every sense of the term. It is estimated that neither makes up as much as a tenth of a part per million of the earth's total crust. However, some soils in the western regions of the United States contain selenium to the extent of several parts per million, with dire results to the cattle which forage there. Since they are so much like sulfur in chemical properties, the important sources of selenium and tellurium are in sulfur-bearing ores. For example, elemental selenium is known to occur in Sicilian sulfur. On the other hand, sulfur from the domes in Louisiana and Texas contains no selenium. Most metal sulfides contain selenium and tellurium in trace amounts as chalcogenides.

The occurrence of polonium will be discussed with the chemistry of the element in a separate section on polonium at the end of this chapter.

PREPARATION OF THE ELEMENTS

Selenium and tellurium are by-products of several large-scale industrial chemical processes; specifically, the electrolytic refining of copper, the roasting of sulfide ores, and the lead-chamber sulfuric acid process. Most selenium and tellurium in North America are extracted from the anode sludges which accumulate in the electrolytic refining of copper. The sludges contain copper, silver, gold, sulfur, selenium, and tellurium, plus minor impurities. Upon digestion with hot, concentrated sulfuric acid, copper and silver are converted to their sulfates, while selenium and tellurium are converted to the dioxides. Selenium dioxide is separated from such a mixture by roasting at 450 to 500°C, whereupon selenium dioxide sublimes. The dioxide is very soluble in water, from which solution it is easily precipitated by sulfur dioxide:

$$SeO_2 + H_2O = H_2SeO_3$$
$$H_2SeO_3 + 2SO_2 + H_2O = Se + 2H_2SO_4$$

Elemental selenium is purified by distillation.

The less volatile tellurium dioxide can be recovered from the roasted sludges by digestion with caustic, which stabilizes the tellurium as water soluble sodium tellurate. (Of course, the more valuable content of the roasted sludges is silver and gold.) Tellurium, like selenium, is easily reduced to the elemental state by the action of sulfur dioxide on a hydrochloric acid solution of the dioxide.

PHYSICAL PROPERTIES OF THE ELEMENTS

Like sulfur, selenium has at least two crystalline modifications. Unlike sulfur, one form is red and nonmetallic-looking, whereas another form is grey and metallic in appearance. When selenium is precipitated from aqueous solution at room temperature, a beautiful red, amorphous solid is obtained. It is converted to crystalline grey selenium by heating. Red selenium is somewhat soluble in carbon disulfide; grey selenium is not. Dissolved in carbon disulfide, selenium exists as Se_8 solute species. Beautiful crystalline red selenium can be obtained by crystallization from carbon disulfide.

Tellurium is typically metallic in appearance. No nonmetallic-looking allotrope is known. Grey tellurium is isomorphous with grey selenium.

TABLE 20.1
Physical Properties of Selenium and Tellurium

	m.p.	b.p.	*density* (room temp.)
red Se	170–80°	—	4.4 gm/cm³
grey Se	220°	684.8°	4.86 gm/cm³
grey Te	449.8°	1390°	6.2 gm/cm³

Liquid selenium is almost black in color, but the vapor is yellow. In the vapor states selenium and tellurium exist as Se_2 and Te_2 molecules.

Neither selenium nor tellurium is a good conductor of electricity, tellurium being much the poorer of the two. However, selenium exhibits a remarkable increase in electrical conductivity upon exposure to light.

Many photoelectric cells employ grey selenium as the light-sensitive element. Tellurium exhibits very poor photoconductivity in comparison with selenium.

CHEMICAL PROPERTIES AND COMPOUNDS

The group VIb elements form a natural family with oxygen and sulfur, sometimes referred to as the chalcogens. The common oxidation states are −2, +4, and +6. The selenides and tellurides (−2 state) of metals are similar to the metal sulfides. The non-metal, acid-forming properties of selenium and tellurium decrease with increasing atomic weight. In this respect the family is like the phosphorus, arsenic, antimony, and bismuth family. Having moved one group farther to the right in the periodic table, and in so doing gone to a more nearly nonmetal electronic structure, it is understandable that the properties of metallicity show up further down in the group. Metallic character is evident in the Te(IV) compounds, which have some saltlike properties. Also, the -2 state of tellurium is less stable than the -2 state of selenium. Thus tetravalent selenium is like S(IV), forming essentially covalent compounds, whereas Te(IV) is more like Sn(IV) or Bi(III).

All soluble compounds of selenium are poisonous.

CHEMICAL REACTIONS OF THE ELEMENTS

Both selenium and tellurium are active elements, combining easily with metals and nonmetals alike. The reactions with the alkali metals proceed violently:

$$Se + 2K = K_2Se$$
$$Te + 2K = K_2Te$$

With other metals the reactions are still vigorously exothermic:

$$2Al + 3Se = Al_2Se_3$$

Neither of the two elements will react spontaneously with oxygen at room temperature. At their melting points, however, they both burn with blue-green flames:

$$Se + O_2 = SeO_2$$
$$Te + O_2 = TeO_2$$

The two elements can be made to combine with hydrogen at a temperature above their melting points, but the conversion to hydrides is *not nearly complete:*

$$Se + H_2 = H_2Se$$
$$Te + H_2 = H_2Te$$

Fluorine reacts with these elements vigorously:

$$Se + 3F_2 = SeF_6$$
$$Te + 3F_2 = TeF_6$$

Reaction with chlorine and bromine are not so vigorous:

$$Se + Cl_2 = Se_2Cl_2 \text{ and } SeCl_4$$
$$Te + Cl_2 = TeCl_2 \text{ and } TeCl_4$$

Little is known about the reactions of iodine with the elements.

Selenium and tellurium are not dissolved by nonoxidizing acids, such as hydrochloric acid and dilute sulfuric acid. Hot, concentrated nitric acid dissolves both elements easily:

$$Se + H_2O + 4HNO_3 = H_2SeO_3 + 4NO_2 + 2H_2O$$
$$Te + 4HNO_3 \qquad = TeO_2 + 4NO_2 + 2H_2O$$

Selenium and tellurium are soluble in aqueous potassium cyanide, forming selenocyanate and tellurocyanate:

$$Se + KCN = KSeCN$$
$$Te + KCN = KTeCN$$

−2 Compounds

Hydrogen selenide and hydrogen telluride can be prepared by much the same methods that are used to prepare hydrogen sulfide. The most satisfactory method seems to be the reaction of the aluminum chalcogenide with water:

$$Al_2Se_3 + 3H_2O = Al_2O_3 + 3H_2Se$$

Direct synthesis, which is not very good even for H_2S, becomes increasingly unsatisfactory as a method of preparation of the hydrides in going from S to Se to Te. H_2Se and H_2Te are increasingly unstable with respect to decomposition into the elements. The two hydrides are gases at room temperature and are soluble in water to the extent of about a tenth of a mole of gas per liter of solution. The smell of H_2Se is, if anything, worse than that of H_2S. Since all soluble selenium compounds are reduced upon ingestion to the −2 state and exhaled partially as H_2Se, the smell of their breath is warning to workers who have been careless in handling selenium compounds.

Hydrogen selenide and hydrogen telluride are even better reducing agents than hydrogen sulfide, both in the free state and dissolved in water. In fact, H_2Te decomposes slowly into tellurium and hydrogen. It is interesting to note the parallel decrease in hydride stability among the group Vb elements. The decomposition rate of hydrogen telluride is not so great that its physical properties cannot be studied conveniently.

TABLE 20.2

Physical Properties of H_2S, H_2Se, and H_2Te

	m.p. °C	b.p. °C
H_2S	-85.5	-60.4
H_2Se	-66	-41
H_2Te	-51	2

The structure of hydrogen selenide is similar to that of hydrogen sulfide, the H—Se—H angle being slightly greater than 90°.

Solutions of the hydrides behave as weak acids:

$$H_2X + H_2O = H_3O^+ + HX^-$$

The ionization constants for H_2Te, H_2Se, and H_2S in the above reaction are 2×10^{-3}, 2×10^{-4}, and 1×10^{-7}, respectively. Salts of two types can be prepared with the alkali metals, Me_2Se and $MeHSe$. The alkali metal selenides, hydrogen selenides, tellurides, and hydrogen tellurides are all white and soluble in water. Polyselenides and polytellurides are known also. The polyvalent metal selenides and tellurides resemble the sulfides with respect to color, solubility, and crystal structure.

Oxides

The most stable oxides of selenium and tellurium are the dioxides. Both compounds are white crystalline solids at room temperature. They are the result of burning the elements themselves or the metal selenides or tellurides:

$$Se + O_2 = SeO_2$$
$$2ZnTe + 3O_2 = 2ZnO + 2TeO_2$$

The elements are converted to the dioxides by digestion with hot, concentrated nitric acid. Selenium dioxide is best purified by sublimation at 300 to 350°C. Tellurium dioxide is by no means as volatile, melting at 452°C. Selenium dioxide is very susceptible to reduction. On standing in a bottle, it can be observed to take on a pink color, which is due to partial reduction to elemental selenium. In fact, selenium dioxide is an excellent oxidizing agent and is used as such in organic oxidations. On the other hand, tellurium dioxide is much more stable. Neither oxide is as easily oxidized to the corresponding trioxide as is sulfur dioxide. Both selenium trioxide and tellurium trioxide are poorly characterized substances. The former is described as a white, hygroscopic solid, resulting from the reaction of ozone upon selenium. The latter is an orange-yellow solid that is prepared by the thermal decomposition of orthotelluric acid:

$$H_6TeO_6 = TeO_3 + 3H_2O$$

SeO_2 is very soluble in water, forming selenious acid:

$$H_2O + SeO_2 = H_2SeO_3$$

TeO_2 is sparingly soluble in water, and is best described as being amphoteric.

Oxyacids

Fairly strong solutions of selenious acid in water can be prepared, the solubility of selenious acid in water being listed as 33 *moles* of acid per liter of water at 30°C. In dilute solution the acid is dibasic with ionization constants $K_1 = 2.4 \times 10^{-3}$ and $K_2 = 4.8 \times 10^{-9}$. Alkali selenites and hydrogen selenites are soluble in water. Most other metal selenites are insoluble in water. Most common reducing agents reduce selenious acid to red selenium. For example, red selenium is produced if sulfur dioxide is bubbled into a selenious acid solution:

$$H_2O + 2SO_2 + H_2SeO_3 = \underline{Se} + 2H_2SO_4$$

Selenites are not quite so easily reduced.

All methods for the preparation of selenic acid use selenious acid or a selenite as the starting material. Long refluxing with concentrated hydrogen peroxide converts selenious acid to selenic acid, which is the most direct method:

$$H_2O_2 + H_2SeO_3 = H_2SeO_4 + H_2O$$

Another, less direct method is the chlorination of an aqueous suspension of silver selenite:

$$Ag_2SeO_3 + H_2O + Cl_2 = 2AgCl + H_2SeO_4$$

Selenic and sulfuric acids are almost identical in their ionizing properties. However, selenic acid is much more easily reduced to selenious acid and to elemental selenium than is sulfuric acid. In concentrating solutions of H_2SeO_4 by evaporation, care must be taken not to heat the solutions in excess of 150°, since the acid begins to lose oxygen above this temperature. It is possible to prepare crystalline $H_2SeO_4 \cdot H_2O$, a white hygroscopic solid, melting at 26°C. Many metal selenates have been prepared. In general, they are just like the corresponding metal sulfates, in most cases being isomorphous. For example, the temperature at which Glauber's Salt ($Na_2SO_4 \cdot 10H_2O$) is in equilibrium with anhydrous sodium sulfate and a saturated solution of the same is 32.38°C; and it is commonly called the transition temperature. The corresponding transition temperature for $Na_2SeO_4 \cdot 10H_2O$ is 30.3°C.

The oxyacids of tellurium bear little resemblance to that of sulfur and selenium; it is here that the more "metallic" nature of tellurium is manifest. Alkali tellurites are prepared by dissolving TeO_2 in strong alkali, followed by crystallizing the salts from solution. The first and second ionization constants of the slightly soluble tellurious acid are about the same as the constants of selenious acid. In addition, though, tellurium dioxide is dissolved by the action of strong acid solutions. From such solutions no well-defined salts can be crystallized. It seems that the tellurium is present in the acid solution as a cationic species (or perhaps as several different kinds of cationic species). On the assumption that it is present as $TeOOH^+$, the first ionization constant as a base is 9×10^{-3}. As was true with selenium, solutions of Te(IV) are easily reduced to elemental tellurium.

The action of concentrated hydrogen peroxide on a suspension of TeO_2 oxidizes the tellurium to the +6 condition, in which it forms white orthotelluric acid, H_6TeO_6. The acid is quite soluble in water, but it has a large temperature coefficient of solubility so that it is easily crystallized from aqueous solutions. The structure of the acid is such that the six OH groups are placed at the corners of a regular octahedron with the Te atom at its center. The acid is dibasic, the first ionization constant being about equal to the second ionization constant of selenious acid, and the second ionization constant being much smaller. Few metal tellurates are soluble in water, but most are soluble in acid solutions, forming the weak soluble telluric acid and the metal salt of the acid used.

Both selenic and telluric acids are reduced to the elements by common reducing agents.

Halides and Oxyhalides

Two fluorides of selenium and two fluorides of tellurium have been adequately characterized. All four compounds are formed by direct synthesis. The ordinary products of the fluorination of the two elements are the colorless gases, SeF_6 and TeF_6. Both substances hydrolyze very slowly in aqueous solutions, but they are less resistant to hydrolytic decomposition than the very stable SF_6:

$$SeF_6 + 4H_2O = H_2SeO_4 + 6HF$$
$$TeF_6 + 6H_2O = H_6TeO_6 + 6HF$$

Colorless selenium tetrafluoride is made by reacting fluorine with selenium under carefully controlled conditions. This compound reacts with many univalent metal fluorides to form complex compounds of the general formula $MeSeF_5$. If these compounds can be shown to contain the SeF_5^- structural unit (and not some polymer thereof) they will be a welcome addition to the very small number of AB_5 type coordination compounds. Ordinarily SeF_4 hydrolyzes to selenious acid and hydrofluoric acid.

Ditellurium decafluoride can be isolated as a product of the fluorination of tellurium under controlled conditions. It is a heavy colorless liquid, even more stable than TeF_6. Hydrolysis is accompanied by disproportionation in this case, since no +5 acid of tellurium is known:

$$Te_2F_{10} + 8H_2O = 10HF + H_6TeO_6 + TeO_2$$

The physical properties of the four compounds are summarized below:

	m.p.	b.p.
SeF_6	-34.6	-46.6
TeF_6	-37.8	-38.9
SeF_4	-9.5	106
Te_2F_{10}	-34	53

As might be expected, the reaction between selenium or tellurium and a halogen is most vigorous by far in the case of fluorine. Chlorine and bromine form chlorides and bromides easily, whereas some doubt surrounds the few iodides of Se and Te that have been proposed. The chlorides and bromides of selenium resemble those of sulfur, although $SeCl_4$ seems to be considerably more stable than SCl_4. The chlorides and bromides of tellurium are rather distinct from the sulfur compounds.

The red liquids Se_2Cl_2 and Se_2Br_2 are the products of reaction between selenium and chlorine or bromine. Both are typical non-metal halides, reacting vigorously with water:

$$2Se_2X_2 + 3H_2O = 4HX + H_2SeO_3 + 3Se$$

Chlorine reacts with Se_2Cl_2 to form white crystalline selenium tetrachloride. The latter substance dissociates upon vaporization into $SeCl_2$ vapor and chlorine. Thus $SeCl_4$ exists only in the solid state, whereas $SeCl_2$ exists only in the gaseous state. Upon condensing $SeCl_2$ and Cl_2, selenium tetrachloride is recovered, so $SeCl_4$ can be sublimed. The selenium bromides exhibit similar behavior.

Tellurium tetrachloride formed as white crystals, appears to be more stable, although otherwise similar to selenium tetrachloride. In the case of tellurium, however, the black solids, $TeCl_2$ and $TeBr_2$, have been prepared. On heating, the former disproportionates to $TeCl_4$ and Te. Reaction with water results in disproportionation also:

$$2TeCl_2 + 2H_2O = Te + TeO_2 + 4HCl$$

The tetrachlorides of selenium and tellurium are unique in that they are not tetrahedral molecules. Evidence indicates that their structures are trigonal bipyramids, with two of the halogens at the apices of the pyramids, the other two at two of the corners of the equatorial triangle, the third corner of the triangle being occupied by the lone pair of unshared electrons:

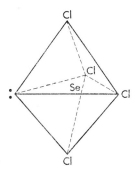

In dilute solution both SeX_4 and TeX_4 hydrolyze completely:

$$SeX_4 + 3H_2O = 4HX + H_2SeO_3$$
$$TeX_4 + 2H_2O = 4HX + TeO_2$$

On the other hand, both SeX_4 and TeX_4 are soluble in concentrated hydrohalic acid to form the complex ions, SeX_6^{--} and TeX_6^{--}. The halotellurates are the more stable. K_2TeBr_6 can be prepared easily by dissolving TeO_2 in concentrated hydrobromic acid and adding potassium bromide, whereupon crystals of potassium hexabromotellurate form. Chlorotellurates are yellow, while the bromotellurates are red. $TeCl_2Br_2$ has been reported recently; presumably a mixed halotellurate complex could also be prepared.

Selenium forms molecular compounds of the formula $SeOX_2$, but $TeOX_2$ compounds of definite stoichiometric composition are unknown. Rather the careful hydrolysis of TeX_4 gives what amounts to basic salts of indefinite composition. Selenium oxyfluoride and selenium oxychloride are colorless liquids while selenium oxybromide is a yellow solid:

	m.p.	b.p.
$SeOF_2$	15	126
$SeOCl_2$	8.5	177
$SeOBr_2$	41.7	dec.

In excess water all three hydrolyze to hydrohalic acid and selenious acid.

POLONIUM

Polonium is the first element in order of atomic number which has no stable isotopes. Twenty-one isotopes of polonium are now known. Only ^{210}Po is of importance, since the others can be obtained only in trace quantities. It has a half-life of 138.4 days and is an alpha-emitter. Formerly it was obtainable only as the last radioactive member of the $4n + 2$ (U-238) series. Now it can be obtained by the neutron irradiation of bismuth:

$$^{209}Bi(n,\gamma)^{210}Bi \xrightarrow[t_{\frac{1}{2}} = 5 \text{ days}]{\beta} {}^{210}Po$$

In a 1 mg sample of ^{210}Po, 10^{13} atoms of polonium are decomposing into lead each minute. The large specific activity of polonium causes self-heating of samples of the element and its compounds. Consequently, weighing cannot be used as a method of assaying the polonium content of a given material. Rather the polonium content of a sample is determined by a measurement of the alpha activity of the sample. The atmosphere surrounding a sample containing polonium glows as a consequence of the intense ionizing radiation from the sample. Although the short range of alpha particles is not sufficient to represent a hazard to workers in the vicinity, the danger of ingesting trace quantities is so great that all experiments on polonium are carried out in protective boxes, the materials being manipulated through gloves. Compounds of polonium decompose continuously, since the activity is certainly sufficient to rupture chemical bonds. Thus the determination of the physical and chemical properties of polonium compounds is a very difficult task.

Hydrogen polonide is known to exist, and a number of metal polonides have been identified. In general, they resemble the tellurium compounds.

Polonium tetrachloride is a yellow solid, soluble in hydrochloric acid solution, from which solution yellow cesium hexachloropolonate(IV) crystals are obtained on the addition of cesium chloride. Again it is observed that polonium compounds resemble the corresponding tellurium compounds.

NONPROTIC SOLVENTS

Most nonaqueous solvents are likened to water, particularly when the solvent dissociation can be said to involve proton transfer. A number of solvents that contain no hydrogen have been used with some frequency. Sulfur dioxide and selenium oxychloride are two such solvents. The latter is a somewhat better solvent for salts, having a dielectric constant of 46 at 20°C. Although the conductivity of the pure solvent is quite low, a dilute solution of potassium chloride in selenium oxychloride can be electrolyzed. Chlorine is liberated at the anode, diselenium dichloride is formed at the cathode. Metals such as copper, magnesium, zinc, and iron dissolve in selenium oxychloride:

$$Mg + SeOCl_2 = MgCl_2 + Se_2Cl_2 + SeO_2$$

The rate of attack of the solvent on the metal is increased by dissolving a little tin(IV) chloride in the solvent. The above phenomena involving selenium oxychloride as a solvent can be explained by assuming a solvent ionization:

$$SeOCl_2 = SeOCl^+ + Cl^- \quad \text{actually } SeOCl(SeOCl_2)_x^+$$

like $\quad HOH = H^+ + OH^- \quad \text{actually } H_3O^+$

and $\quad Mg + 2SeOCl^+ = Mg^{++} + [2SeOCl]$

$$[6SeOCl] = Se_2Cl_2 + 2SeO_2 + 2SeOCl_2$$

like $\quad Mg = Mg^{++} + [2H]$

$$[2H] = H_2$$

The increased rate upon adding tin(IV) chloride is explained by the action of $SnCl_4$, which removes Cl^- from the solvent equilibrium. To keep the solvent equilibrium constant, the solvent must ionize a little more, producing more $SeOCl^+$, the active species:

$$2SeOCl_2 \leftrightarrows 2SeOCl^+ + 2Cl^-$$
$$+$$
$$SnCl_4$$
$$\updownarrow$$
$$SnCl_6^{--}$$

USES

The world production of selenium is estimated to be 1.5×10^6 pounds per year. Tellurium is produced in quantities somewhat less than half this figure.

The most important uses of selenium are in the manufacture of photocells and rectifiers. Considerable quantities of selenium dioxide are used as oxidation agent in organic chemical synthesis. Elemental selenium is used sometimes as an additive to glass, for the purpose of adding a red color. Minor amounts of other compounds of selenium have been used as rubber additives, for the treatment of dandruff, and as insecticides.

Tellurium is used to a limited extent as an alloying metal. In the early days of radio communication, crystals of tellurium were popular in the crystal receivers. Diethyltellurium has been proposed as a possible anti-knock additive to gasolines.

SUGGESTIONS FOR FURTHER READING

K. W. Bagnall, "The Chemistry of Polonium," *Quarterly Reviews*, Vol. 11, pp. 20–48.

W. C. Fernelius, ed., *Inorganic Syntheses*, McGraw-Hill, New York, Vol. II, 1946, pp. 183–190.

G. B. L. Smith, "Selenium Oxychloride as a Solvent," *Chemical Reviews*, Vol. 23, pp. 165–185 (1938).

D. M. Yost and H. Russell, *Systematic Inorganic Chemistry*, Prentice-Hall, New York, 1944, Chapters 8, 9, and 10.

STUDY QUESTIONS

1. What happens in the following cases?
   (a) $SeF_6 + KF$
   (b) $H_2Te + Te$
   (c) Se + hot, conc HCl
   (d) $Te_2F_{10} + H_2O$
   (e) Se + hot, conc HNO_3

2. By means of equations and a few words about conditions, show how to carry out the following conversions:
   (a) Make SeF_6 from SeO_2.
   (b) Make TeO_3 from TeO_2.
   (c) Make H_2Po from Po.
   (d) Make H_2SeO_4 from Se.
   (e) Make Rb_2TeBr_6 from Te.

3. Write balanced equations for the following reactions: (a) the action of concentrated H_2O_2 on TeO_2; (b) the reduction of selenious acid by tin(II) chloride.

4. Discuss the reaction of magnesium with a solution of tin(IV) chloride in selenium oxychloride solvent from the point of view of the Lewis acid-base concept.

Chapter 21

Chromium, Molybdenum and Tungsten

OCCURRENCE AND HISTORY

In the late eighteenth century compounds of these elements were recognized, but the metals themselves were not isolated until well into the nineteenth century. This was due in no small part to the difficulty experienced in reducing the elements from their compounds. Furthermore, the very high melting points of all three metals make the task of obtaining them in a "metallic-looking" form difficult.

Ores of these elements are not too abundant, and they occur in widely scattered regions. The principal ore of chromium is chromite, $FeO \cdot Cr_2O_3$, a spinel.* Molybdenum occurs chiefly as molybdenite, MoS_2, and tungsten ores of importance are wolframite, $FeWO_4$, scheelite, $CaWO_4$, and hubnerite, $MnWO_4$.

PREPARATION OF THE METALS

Most of the metallic chromium that is produced is not pure, but alloyed with iron. The commercial product is called ferrochromium and is made by the high temperature reduction of chromite with carbon:

$$FeO \cdot Cr_2O_3 + 4C \xrightarrow{\Delta} Fe + 2Cr + 4CO\uparrow$$

* The spinels are mixed oxides of the general formula, AB_2O_4, after the prototype mineral, $MgAl_2O_4$.

Inasmuch as a principal use of chromium is as an alloying constituent in steels, the presence of this iron impurity is unobjectionable. If pure chromium is desired, one of two processes is used:

(1) *Goldschmidt reduction.* The reduction of purified chromium(III) oxide with aluminum is practical if a small amount of potassium dichromate is added to increase the heat of the reaction (see Chapter 8).

(2) *Electroplating.* Chromium is conveniently plated on to a surface of copper from solutions containing chromium(III) salts, chromates, and sulfuric acid.

To produce molybdenum from the ore, molybdenite is roasted to obtain the trioxide. The latter can be reduced with carbon at high temperatures.

Most tungsten ores are insoluble tungstates. They must be fused with alkali to give the more soluble sodium tungstate. Upon the acidification of a solution of sodium tungstate, tungstic acid is precipitated, which yields the trioxide upon dehydration. This oxide can be reduced with carbon also, but only with difficulty. Furthermore, the metal forms as a powder, since the temperature of the process is well below the melting point of tungsten. To obtain the high purity tungsten used for incandescent lamp filaments, pure tungsten(VI) oxide is reduced with hydrogen.

PHYSICAL PROPERTIES OF THE ELEMENTS

The physical properties of these metals are quite remarkable, as may be seen from Table 21.1.

TABLE 21.1
Physical Properties of Chromium, Molybdenum, and Tungsten

Element	Melting Point	Density
Chromium	1615°C	7.1 g/cc
Molybdenum	2625	10.2
Tungsten	3370	19.3

The very high melting points, combined with the fact that all of the metals are very inert to most chemical reagents, makes them useful materials of construction. Tungsten, for example, is used to make filaments for light bulbs, because it can be heated to a very high temperature in an oxygen-free atmosphere without melting. In addition, all of these metals are very strong and fairly ductile when pure. Tungsten has amazing tensile strength.

The combination of strength, ductility, resistance to chemical action, and high melting point makes these metals valuable alloying constituents of steel. Chrome, moly, and tungsten steels offer an impressive variety of properties, suitable to many special fabrication problems. The student is referred to The American Society for Metals Handbook for detailed consideration of the properties of alloy steels.

CHEMICAL PROPERTIES AND COMPOUNDS

Chromium, molybdenum, and tungsten have six valence electrons in two quantum levels: Cr, $3d^54s$; Mo, $4d^55s$; W, $5d^46s^2$. This is in contrast to the elements of group VIb, where all of the valence electrons are in one quantum level. When elements have a large number of valence electrons distributed between two quantum levels, they show metallic properties; but when there are a large number of valence electrons in one quantum level only, they show nonmetallic properties. In either case, varied valence patterns are the rule. Opposite from the trend in the b-subgroup, however, the lower oxidation states are more stable for chromium than for molybdenum and tungsten; chromium commonly exhibits $+2$, $+3$, and $+6$, with $+3$ the most stable, while molybdenum and tungsten commonly show $+2$, $+3$, $+4$, $+5$, and $+6$, with $+6$ the most stable for both.

The effect of the lanthanide contraction is still evident in subgroup VIa, but it is diminished over that in Va. As a result, molybdenum is much more like tungsten than chromium, but the resemblance is not so great as that between niobium and tantalum. The acidity of the trioxides falls off rapidly from chromium to tungsten. There is a tendency to form condensed acids and salts in this subgroup: a little for chromium and a great deal for molybdenum and tungsten. There is a great inclination towards complex ion formation in the subgroup.

Chemical Reactions of the Elements

Chromium, molybdenum, and tungsten might be expected to be quite electropositive. Indeed, chromium is quite high up in the E.M.F. Series. All three metals are so resistant to chemical attack, however, that measurements of their standard electrode potentials are extremely difficult. They are inert to most reagents except at high temperature. Chromium does dissolve slowly in dilute hydrochloric and sulfuric acids, while molybdenum and tungsten are unattacked:

$$Cr + 2H^+ \rightarrow Cr^{++} + \overline{H_2}$$

The chromium(II) ion produced is a powerful reducing agent, so that it is easily oxidized to chromium(III). This reaction with acids is an indication of decreasing reactivity with increasing atomic number in the subgroup. In nitric acid the metals become passive, presumably due to an oxide film which protects the surface underneath. After exposure to nitric acid, chromium remains passive and will not then dissolve in hydrochloric acid. The passivity can be removed by touching the metal with zinc under dilute sulfuric acid.

Fluorine attacks all three elements in the cold, taking chromium to poorly defined fluorides higher than the trifluoride, and molybdenum and tungsten to the hexafluorides. When heated very hot in oxygen, they burn—chromium to the sesquioxide, and molybdenum and tungsten to the trioxides. By evaporating amalgams, however, they can be made pyrophoric, an indication of their innate reactivity. At high temperatures, they also react with nitrogen, the other halogens, sulfur, carbon, water, etc. At no temperature do they react with or absorb appreciable amounts of hydrogen.

+6 Oxy-acids

All three elements show acidic properties in the +6 valence state. The ores of the metals can be fused with alkali plus an oxidizing agent to yield the sodium salt of the hexavalent acid:

$$4FeO \cdot Cr_2O_3 + 8Na_2CO_3 + 7O_2 \xrightarrow{\Delta} 8Na_2CrO_4 + 2Fe_2O_3 + 8CO_2\uparrow$$

The resulting melt, if leached with water and filtered to remove the insoluble iron oxide, gives a yellow solution of sodium chromate.

Similar procedures may be used to prepare the corresponding molybdate and tungstate. The alkali chromates, molybdates, and tungstates are quite soluble in water, but most of the other metal salts are insoluble. The molybdate and tungstate ions are colorless and their salts are white. The chromate ion is yellow and most of its salts are yellow. A few of the basic salts of heavy metals are orange to red. For example, lead chromate is yellow whereas basic chromates of lead can be formed which are orange and red in color. The normal chromate is sold as "chrome yellow" in the pigment trade. $PbO \cdot PbCrO_4$ is called "chrome-red," and a pigment known as "molybdenum orange" contains chromates, molybdates, and sulfates of lead.

It is possible to prepare the trioxides of the three elements by acidification of salts, but the conditions vary. To prepare chromium(VI) oxide, concentrated sulfuric acid is added to a cooled solution of sodium chromate.* Red crystals of the oxide form on standing. The crystals cannot be filtered using filter paper, since the oxide is a powerful oxidizing agent and will decompose paper.

Chromium(VI) oxide is very soluble in water, forming a solution of chromic acid. It is not necessary to use concentrated acid to precipitate the less soluble trioxides of molybdenum and tungsten. White "molybdic acid," $MoO_3 \cdot xH_2O$, precipitates from solution when an equivalent of nitric acid is added rapidly to a hot solution of sodium molybdate. White tungsten(VI) oxide can be prepared the same way, but if the precipitation is done from hot solution, a yellow oxide is formed, $WO_3 \cdot H_2O$. It has been established that the white variety is a hydrous oxide and that the yellow one is a true hydrate, according to the vapor-pressure-isotherm criterion. Anhydrous molybdenum(VI) oxide, which is white, and tungsten(VI) oxide, which is yellow, are practically insoluble in water. However, freshly precipitated molybdenum(VI) oxide is moderately soluble in water and very soluble in basic solutions and concentrated solutions of hydrochloric or sulfuric acids. To the extent that it dissolves in water, it behaves as an acid. Hydrous or hydrated tungsten(VI) oxide is soluble only in basic solutions to form tungstates.

---

* Such a solution is referred to frequently as "cleaning solution." Glassware is cleaned very effectively by immersion in warm cleaning solution followed by thorough rinsing in water.

Potassium chromate is a good oxidizing agent, and it is used frequently as such in volumetric analysis. Most reducing agents reduce the chromium to the trivalent condition. In fact, the $+3$ state is the most stable valence state of chromium. The lower valence states of molybdenum and tungsten are less stable. In fact, the $+6$ state is the most stable for both elements, and molybdates and tungstates are very poor oxidizing agents.

Isopoly Acids

The addition of dilute sulfuric acid to a yellow solution of potassium chromate changes the color of the solution to orange. The color change is due to the aggregation (sometimes called condensation) of the chromate ions:

$$\begin{bmatrix} & O & \\ & \| & \\ O-&Cr&-O \\ & \| & \\ & O & \end{bmatrix}^{--} + \begin{bmatrix} & O & \\ & \| & \\ O-&Cr&-O \\ & \| & \\ & O & \end{bmatrix}^{--} + 2H^+ \rightarrow$$

$$\begin{bmatrix} & O & & O & \\ & \| & & \| & \\ O-&Cr&-O-&Cr&-O \\ & \| & & \| & \\ & O & & O & \end{bmatrix}^{--} + H_2O$$

Potassium dichromate is made by just such a procedure. The process is reversed by the addition of potassium hydroxide to the orange dichromate solution. While the dichromate ion is unique in that it is so easily made, it is typical of a number of isopoly anions. An isopoly (Greek *iso*, same; *poly*, many) acid radical is one formed by the polymerization of two or more radicals of the same simple acid. Higher isopoly salts of chromium are known, such as potassium trichromate, $K_2Cr_3O_{10}$, but they are of less importance. Many of the insoluble metal chromates are soluble in acids because of the formation of the dichromate ion, since practically all dichromates are soluble:

$$2MeCrO_4 + 2H^+ \rightarrow 2Me^{++} + Cr_2O_7^{--} + H_2O$$

Isopoly salt formation is less well understood in the molybdate and tungstate systems. For example, molybdenum(VI) oxide is soluble in a solution of sodium molybdate. The resulting solution is supposed to contain various polymolybdate ions. Careful addition of acid to a molybdate solution produces condensation also. The nature of the species produced when a solution of sodium molybdate is acidified is not yet settled. The following condensation scheme has been proposed as the pH of a molybdate solution is lowered:

$$MoO_4{}^{--} \overset{6}{\rightleftharpoons} Mo_3O_{11}{}^{-4} \overset{4.5}{\rightleftharpoons} Mo_6O_{21}{}^{-6} \overset{2}{\rightleftharpoons} Mo_{12}O_{41}{}^{-10} \overset{1}{\rightleftharpoons}$$
$$Mo_{24}O_{78}{}^{-12} \overset{<1}{\rightleftharpoons} MoO_3 \cdot xH_2O\downarrow$$

Approximate pH values are indicated over the equilibrium arrows. The omission of the dimolybdate has been questioned. Recently evidence has been obtained which indicates that little, if any, trimolybdate and hexamolybdate are formed during the aggregation process. An alternate scheme suggests:

$$MoO_4{}^{--} \rightleftharpoons Mo_7O_{24}{}^{-6} \rightleftharpoons Mo_8O_{26}{}^{-4} \rightleftharpoons MoO_3 \cdot xH_2O\downarrow$$

Actually, when acid is added to a sodium molybdate solution, there is an abrupt lowering of the pH, followed by a slow increase in pH as polymerization proceeds back to some steady value less than that of the original molybdate solution. Eventually the addition of enough acid precipitates hydrous molybdenum(VI) oxide.

Heteropoly Acids

When molybdenum(VI) oxide is digested in a solution of phosphoric acid for several hours, most of the oxide dissolves, giving a yellow solution of 12-molybdophosphoric acid. Although the acid is very soluble in water, it can be crystallized as a yellow hydrate, $H_3PO_4 \cdot 12MoO_3 \cdot xH_2O$. The slight solubility of the ammonium salt of the acid is used in the quantitative determination of small amounts of phosphate ion. Such acids are called heteropoly, since the anion is composed of more than one central atom of two different elements. A number of heteropoly acids and salts have been prepared; for example, $H_4SiO_4 \cdot 12WO_3$ or $H_4SiW_{12}O_{40}$, $(NH_4)_6TeO_6 \cdot 6MoO_3 \cdot 7H_2O$ or $(NH_4)_6TeMo_6O_{24} \cdot 7H_2O$, $H_3PO_4 \cdot 12WO_3$ or $H_3PW_{12}O_{40}$. The structure of the heteropoly and isopoly acids has presented interesting problems. In a few cases the structures have been established, and others may be inferred. For example, in the 6-molybdotellurate ion, the Te atom is the central atom surrounded octahedrally by six O atoms. Each of these O atoms occupies also one corner of an MoO_6 octahedron. It is interesting that molybdenum is surrounded tetrahedrally by oxygens in normal molybdate ions, but that upon condensation the coordination number of molybdenum for oxygen changes to six. This appears to be true for isopoly as well as hetero-poly condensation.

Trivalent Chromium

Hydrogen sulfide, potassium iodide, iron(II) sulfate, sodium thio-sulfate, sodium nitrite, sulfur dioxide, and tin(II) chloride are only a few of the reducing agents that will reduce potassium dichromate to trivalent chromium:

$$6KI + K_2Cr_2O_7 + 7H_2SO_4 \rightarrow 3I_2 + Cr_2(SO_4)_3 + 4K_2SO_4 + 7H_2O$$

Most natural sources of chromium contain the element in its tri-valent condition. Ignited chromium(III) oxide is a green refractory substance that is inert to most chemical reagents at room tem-perature. Freshly precipitated hydrous chromium(III) oxide is amphoteric:

$$CrO_3^{---} + H_2O \overset{OH^-}{\longleftarrow} \underline{Cr_2O_3 \cdot xH_2O} \overset{H^+}{\rightarrow} Cr^{+++} + H_2O$$

Solutions of chromites are deep green in color, while solutions of hydrated chromium(III) salts are green or violet. The halides, nitrate, sulfate, and perchlorate are soluble in water. It is possible to obtain highly hydrated crystals of the salts from the solutions.

Chromite solutions are basic by hydrolysis:

$$CrO_3^{---} + H_2O \leftrightharpoons HCrO_3^{--} + OH^-$$

Solutions containing chromium(III) ion are acidic by hydrolysis:

$$Cr(OH_2)_6^{+++} + H_2O \leftrightharpoons Cr(OH)(OH_2)_5^{++} + H_3O^+$$

A solution of sodium chromite is oxidized to the yellow chromate by hydrogen peroxide, and, if the peroxide is strong enough, peroxysalts are formed:

$$3HO_2^- + 2CrO_3^{---} + H_2O \rightarrow 2CrO_4^{--} + 5OH^-$$

Remarkably enough, in dilute acid solution chromate is reduced to the trivalent condition by hydrogen peroxide:

$$10H^+ + 3H_2O_2 + 2CrO_4^{--} \rightarrow 2Cr^{+++} + 8H_2O + 3O_2\uparrow$$

It is also possible to prepare peroxychromates from hydrogen peroxide and chromate in acid solution, if they are extracted from the water solution quickly enough. Under ordinary conditions in dilute aqueous solution they are not observed.

Three different forms of chromium(III) chloride 6-hydrate are known. From a solution of the violet form, silver nitrate precipitates all three chloride ions, indicating that the structure is $Cr(OH_2)_6^{+++}3Cl^-$. From the green form, silver nitrate precipitates only two of the three chlorides, and only one of the three chlorides is ionized in the dark green form, indicating that their structures are $CrCl(OH_2)_5^{++}2Cl^-\cdot H_2O$ and $CrCl_2(OH_2)_4^+Cl^-\cdot 2H_2O$. This phenomenon is known as ionization (or coordination) isomerism, and the three forms are isomers. $Cr(NH_3)_6^{+++}Co(C_2O_4)_3^{---}$ and $Co(NH_3)_6^{+++}Cr(C_2O_4)_3^{---}$ represent another example of coordination isomerism (see Chapter 25).

It is not possible to make anhydrous chromium(III) chloride by ordinary thermal dehydration of the hydrated salt, since hydrolysis occurs. If, however, the dark green form of the hydrate is heated in an atmosphere of carbon tetrachloride, beautiful violet crystals of chromium(III) chloride are obtained. The crystals do not dissolve at all in water unless a trace of a chromium(II) salt is present. Then the crystals dissolve easily. Anhydrous chromium(III) chloride reacts with liquid ammonia, and from the resulting precipitate it is possible to get yellow crystals of hexamminechromium(III) chloride. Other salts of the hexamminechromium(III) ion can be prepared from this one by metathesis in water solution. However, it is impossible to form the ammonia complex in the presence of water. Indeed, the addition of strong aqueous ammonia to a solution of hydrated chromium(III) ion only precipitates the hydrous oxide. It is remarkable that the complex ion persists in water when it cannot be formed in the presence of water. The explanation lies in the slow rate at which the hexammine ion is decomposed by water. It must be recognized that the rate at which complex ions can be substituted is sometimes more important than their equilibrium stability. Here is an example of a complex which is unstable in the presence of water, but which decomposes so slowly that it can undergo numerous metathetical reactions unchanged. Many complex compounds of trivalent chromium are known in addition to ammines—Cr(III), Co(III), and Pt(IV) are the greatest complex formers of all ions. The trioxalato complex is one of the more stable. The potassium salt, $K_3Cr(C_2O_4)_3$, is soluble in water. The addition of base to a solution of the complex does not precipitate hydrous chromium(III) oxide.

Divalent Chromium

The hydrated chromium(II) ion is a bright blue. It can be made by reducing a hydrochloric acid solution of chromium(III) chloride with zinc. The dichloride is soluble in water and is very easily oxidized back to the trivalent condition. In the presence of a catalyst it will liberate hydrogen from acids:

$$2Cr^{++} + 2H^+ \rightarrow 2Cr^{+++} + H_2\uparrow$$

The most readily obtained chromium(II) compound is the deep-red acetate, easily made by precipitation, since it is sparingly soluble in cold water. It is a good starting material for other salts, since it reacts with strong acids.

Oxygen oxidizes Cr(II) to the trivalent state; even the dry acetate absorbs oxygen from the air. Chromium(II) chloride solutions are used to remove oxygen from gases when necessary:

$$4H^+ + 4Cr^{++} + O_2 \rightarrow 4Cr^{+++} + 2H_2O$$

As might be expected, it is difficult to keep solutions of divalent chromium. They do, however, find use as reducing agents to some extent.

Anhydrous chromium(II) chloride is white. It can be made by reducing anhydrous chromium(II) chloride with hydrogen at a red heat:

$$2CrCl_3 + H_2 \underset{\Delta}{\rightarrow} 2CrCl_2 + 2HCl\uparrow$$

Unlike the trichloride, it is easily soluble in water.

Lower Oxidation States of Molybdenum and Tungsten

The lower oxidation states of molybdenum and tungsten are of less importance than those of chromium. It is possible to reduce molybdenum and tungsten to the $+5$, $+4$, and $+3$ states in water solution, but for the most part the reduced species are complex ions. For example, potassium octacyanomolybdate(IV) 2-hydrate is a yellow crystalline solid, stable in air and soluble in water. Even the strongest oxidizing agents, such as potassium permanganate and cerium(IV) sulfate oxidize it to potassium octacyanomolybdate(V) only. Tungsten forms the same complexes.

Complexes such as K_3MoCl_6 and $K_3W_2Cl_9$ can be made in which the apparent oxidation number of the central atoms is $+3$. The molybdenum salt is made by electrolyzing a solution of molybdenum(VI) oxide dissolved in strong hydrochloric acid. The tungsten complex is also prepared by electrolytic reduction; it has an interesting structure and might well be called an isopoly anion. In the $W_2Cl_9^{---}$ ion each W is surrounded by six Cl atoms in such a way that the two octahedra share a face. The result is a remarkably short W-W distance in the ion.

The reduction of weakly acidic solutions of tungstates and molybdates can lead to substances called blues because of their uses in the dye industry. For example, tin(II) chloride reduces an acid solution of sodium molybdate to give an intensely blue solution. The oxidation state of molybdenum in molybdenum blue is not definite, but it is somewhere between $+5$ and $+6$. It is possible to precipitate the blue substance from solution with strong hydrochloric acid.

Halides

Chromium forms no binary halides in the sexavalent state. Two $+6$ oxyhalides are known, chromyl fluoride and chromyl chloride. Both of these substances hydrolyze rapidly, and they are similar to the sulfuryl halides:

$$2CrO_2X_2 + 3H_2O \rightarrow H_2Cr_2O_7 + 4HX$$

The fluoride is prepared by distillation from a mixture of concentrated sulfuric acid, fluorspar, and a chromate in a platinum still:

$$3H_2SO_4 + CaF_2 + K_2CrO_4 \rightarrow$$
$$CrO_2F_2\uparrow + CaSO_4 + 2KHSO_4 + 2H_2O$$

The dark red liquid chloride can be obtained in a similar way, substituting sodium chloride for fluorspar. In the latter case, glass apparatus can be used.

The only common binary halides of chromium are the $+2$ and $+3$ compounds. An example of each type has been discussed. Molybdenum and tungsten, on the other hand, form halides in a variety of oxidation states. All of the following have been prepared:

MoF_6	WF_6 WCl_6 WBr_6
$MoCl_5$	WCl_5 WBr_5
$MoCl_4$	WCl_4 WI_4
MoF_3 $MoCl_3$ $MoBr_3$	
$MoCl_2$ $MoBr_2$	WCl_2 WBr_2 WI_2

In addition oxyhalides of the type MeO_2X_2 and $MeOX_4$ are known. The hexahalides are prepared usually by direct synthesis. They are volatile, covalent compounds, completely decomposed by water. The pentahalides are like the hexahalides. The lower halides are more difficult to make and to keep. While most of them are hydrolyzed extensively, the tendency towards complex ion formation makes it possible to prevent hydrolysis by much the same means used in the case of group IVb halides. For example, tungsten(V) chloride is decomposed by pure water to an insoluble oxide, but it dissolves in cyanide solutions to form a stable complex:

$$WCl_5 + 8CN^- \rightarrow W(CN)_8{}^{---} + 5Cl^-$$

Similarly, molybdenum(III) chloride, which hydrolyzes partially in water, forms a soluble, stable complex in the presence of excess chloride ion:

$$MoCl_3 + 3Cl^- \rightarrow MoCl_6{}^{---}$$

SUGGESTIONS FOR FURTHER READING

D. H. Killeffer and A. Linz, *Molybdenum Compounds*, Interscience, New York, 1952.

K. C. Li and C. Y. Wang, *Tungsten*, 2nd ed., Reinhold, New York, 1947.

Metals Handbook, 1948 ed., American Society for Metals, Cleveland, Ohio, pp. 458–462, 468–473, 482–484.

M. E. Weeks, *Discovery of the Elements*, 6th ed., Journal of Chemical Education, Easton, Pa., 1956, Chapter 9.

STUDY QUESTIONS

1. Suggest a detailed procedure for the preparation of $CrCl_2 \cdot xH_2O$, including all of the precautions necessary to prevent oxidation of the product.

2. Look up and draw the structure of a spinel.

3. Suggest a reason why it would be difficult to make an alloy of cadmium and tungsten.

4. What are the important properties imparted to steel by alloying with chromium? Molybdenum? Tungsten?

5. Predict the result of adding a dilute acid solution of $K_2Cr_2O_7$ to a dilute solution of K_3MoCl_6.

6. What happens when sodium hydroxide solution is added to excess molybdenum(VI) oxide?

7. Name four reducing agents that will reduce chromium from 6 to 3 in acid solution. Write an equation for each of the four reactions.

8. Propose a structure for the eight coordination complexes of Mo and W.

9. $MoCl_5$ is said to be soluble in sulfuric acid solution. What are the species present in solution?

10. What do you think is the formula for the anionic species present in chromite solutions? Defend your answer.

11. Write an equation showing how the yellow precipitate is formed when a slightly acid solution of $(NH_4)_2MoO_4$ is added to a solution containing a small amount of phosphate ion.

12. Do you think Mo would cost more per pound as the pure metal or as ferromolybdenum? Take into account the fact that you would have to buy more of the alloy to get the same total weight of Mo. How did you arrive at your answer?

13. What happens when an insoluble salt such as $PbMoO_4$ is digested with aqueous NaOH?

14. When $Pb(NO_3)_2$ is added to a solution of $K_2Cr_2O_7$, $PbCrO_4$ precipitates. Do you think that a pH change accompanies the precipitation? Why, or why not?

15. Draw a picture of the $W_2Cl_9^{---}$ ion.

16. What happens in the following cases?

    (a) $K_2MoO_4 + H_2SO_4$(aqueous)

(b) $Mo + Cl_2 \xrightarrow{250°C}$

(c) $Cr(H_2O)_6Cl_3 + NH_3$(aqueous)

(d) $K_2Cr_2O_7 + NaNO_3$

(e) $WO_3 + H_3PO_4$(aqueous)

17. By means of equations and a few words about conditions, show how to carry out the following conversions:

(a) Make $Cr(C_2H_3O_2)_2$ from Cr_2O_3.

(b) Make Na_2MoO_4 from molybdenite.

(c) Make CrO_3 from Cr.

(d) Make $K_3W_2Cl_9$ from WO_3.

(e) Make $Cr_2O_2Cl_2$ from a natural chromium ore.

Chapter 22

Fluorine, Chlorine, Bromine, Iodine, and Astatine

OCCURRENCE AND HISTORY

In 1774 chlorine was first prepared in the free state by K. W. Scheele, a Swedish chemist. During the ensuing hundred years bromine and iodine were prepared, and in 1886 Moissan added to the list by preparing free fluorine. Compounds of the elements had been recognized much earlier than their preparation. For example, fluorspar, CaF_2, has long been used to etch glass. Common salt had also been used as a condiment for centuries.

Fluorine also occurs as cryolite, Na_3AlF_6. Chlorine occurs in sea water as halide ion, as does bromine to a much smaller extent. It is estimated that the average iodine content in sea water is less than 0.1 parts per million. Iodine appears to be concentrated in oil-well brines, in certain forms of seaweed on the coast of Great Britain and Japan, and in the form of iodates in the Chilean nitrate deposits.

Astatine does not occur in nature except in minute amounts in the radium and thorium series. It was discovered in 1940 by Corson, Mackenzie, and Segrè as a product of the cyclotron bombardment of bismuth by alpha-particles:

$$^{209}_{83}Bi + ^{4}_{2}He \rightarrow ^{211}_{85}At + 2^{1}_{0}n$$

The ^{211}At isotope has a half-life of 7.5 hours, and the longest lived isotope, ^{210}At, has $t_{\frac{1}{2}} = 8.3$ hr. The discoverers named the new element after the Greek word for unstable. Since the element is prepared only in minute amounts and decays so rapidly, studies of its chemistry are limited to tracer concentrations; present knowledge indicates that it resembles iodine closely. It is volatile when heated, and advantage of this fact is taken in separating it from the bismuth target of the cyclotron. It is soluble in benzene and carbon tetrachloride, but not in aqueous alkali. It can be reduced to the -1 state, where it forms insoluble silver and thallium(I) salts. It can be oxidized to positive oxidation states.

PREPARATION OF THE ELEMENTS

The only satisfactory method for the preparation of fluorine is the electrolysis of a solution of potassium fluoride in anhydrous hydrogen fluoride. Hydrogen fluoride is like water in that it is a very poor conductor of electricity when pure. In the case of water, the addition of an electrolyte provides ions to carry the electric current and allow the electrode reactions to take place at a reasonable rate. Similarly, the addition of potassium hydrogen fluoride makes possible the electrolysis of hydrogen fluoride:

$$(x + 2)HF \leftrightharpoons H(HF)_x{}^+ + HF_2{}^-$$
$$2H(HF)_x{}^+ + 2\ominus \rightarrow 2xHF + H_2\uparrow$$
$$2HF_2{}^- \qquad\qquad \rightarrow 2HF + F_2\uparrow + 2\ominus$$

The process is difficult to carry out because of the extreme activity of fluorine and the very corrosive action of hydrogen fluoride. The usual electrolyte is of the composition KF·1-3HF. The higher the ratio of hydrogen fluoride to potassium fluoride, the lower the melting point of the electrolyte. Cells of platinum (used in the original preparation and on a laboratory scale only), steel, or copper may be used. Many anodes have been tried, but carbon anodes appear to be the most efficient. Sheet steel is used as the cathode. The anode and cathode compartments must be separated by means of a diaphragm, since hydrogen and fluorine recombine explosively at all temperatures and any concentrations. Because of the extreme reactivity of fluorine, it has only recently been made available in cylinders as an industrial chemical.

Chlorine is one of the most important chemicals in the world. Annual U.S. production was estimated at 2.5 million tons in 1951. The original method of preparation (Scheele) has long since been superseded by more economical processes. The reaction

$$MnO_2 + 4HCl \rightarrow MnCl_2 + 2H_2O + Cl_2\uparrow$$

is still used in the laboratory and was used for a considerable time on the continent of Europe as an industrial source of chlorine, particularly when large amounts of hydrogen chloride were available as a by-product of the LeBlanc soda process. It was known then as the Weldon Process. The manganese chloride was reoxidized to manganese dioxide by oxygen in the presence of excess lime. At the present time most of the commercial chlorine is manufactured by electrolyzing brine solutions (see Chapter 4).

The demand for chlorine has increased to the point where at least two other more costly processes are used. One of these is a revival of the old Deacon Process, in which hydrogen chloride is catalytically oxidized to chlorine by oxygen at a temperature of 450°C. Copper(I) chloride is the catalyst. The mechanism has been described as being:

$$4CuCl + 4HCl + O_2 \rightarrow 4CuCl_2 + 2H_2O$$
$$2CuCl_2 \xrightarrow{\Delta} 2CuCl + Cl_2$$

In organic chlorination plants sizeable amounts of by-product hydrogen chloride result and are converted to chlorine by the Deacon Process.

In the second process nitric acid and sodium chloride react to form chlorine and nitrosyl chloride in accordance with the following equation:

$$3NaCl + 4HNO_3 \rightarrow 3NaNO_3 + NOCl + Cl_2 + 2H_2O$$

The by-product nitrosyl chloride is converted to nitric and hydrochloric acids by reaction with oxygen and water.

Bromine is produced in large quantities from sea water by chlorination, which liberates free bromine:

$$Cl_2 + 2Br^- \rightarrow Br_2 + 2Cl^-$$

The percentage of the bromide liberated as bromine is a function of the pH of the water, so acid is added to lower the pH of the natural sea water in order to get the maximum yield. Bromine is concentrated by blowing air through the water and passing the vapors into a solution of soda ash, in which the bromine dissolves. It may be liberated again, in much higher concentration, by acidifying this solution. About 2000 tons of bromine were produced in the United States in 1950.

Much iodine is prepared by reducing the naturally occurring iodate with sodium bisulfite:

$$2IO_3^- + 5SO_3^- \rightarrow \underline{I_2} + 5SO_4^{--} + H_2O + 3H^+$$

Two other processes are used to extract iodine from its natural sources:

(1) Oil well brine solutions containing the iodine as I^- are reacted with silver nitrate and iron(III) chloride. Silver iodide is precipitated and is coagulated by the hydrous iron oxide, which is the result of hydrolysis of the iron chloride. Acid dissolves the hydrous oxide, leaving a sludge of silver iodide. An active metal such as iron will reduce the silver, leaving iodide in solution, from which it may be liberated by means of a suitable oxidizing agent. The silver, of course, is recovered.

(2) Brine solutions containing at least 60 p.p.m. of iodine may be worked for iodine using a process similar to that used to recover bromine from sea water. A solution containing iodide of 30 to 70 p.p.m. is reacted with sodium nitrite and acid to liberate iodine. Activated charcoal adsorbs iodine from this very dilute solution, concentrating the iodine. Sodium hydroxide dissolves the adsorbed iodine to form sodium iodide and iodate. Free iodine is liberated again from this more concentrated solution by acidifying. The use of this process has been discontinued in recent years, due to the greatly increased competition within the iodine market.

In late 1953 the market quotations for the halogens were as follows: for bromine, 20 cents per pound in tank lots and up to 34 cents per pound in small lots; for chlorine, 7 cents per pound; for iodine, two dollars and 50 cents per pound.

PHYSICAL PROPERTIES OF THE ELEMENTS

It is unusual to find a family of elements with so few stable isotopes. Only one stable isotope of fluorine and one of iodine are known. Only two each are known for chlorine and bromine.

Table 22.1 lists a few of the physical properties of the halogens.

TABLE 22.1
Physical Properties of the Halogens

	b.p. °C	m.p. °C	color at room temperature
Fluorine	−187	−223	pale yellow
Chlorine	−34	−101	greenish yellow
Bromine	59	−7	red-brown
Iodine	185	114	black with metallic luster (violet vapor)

Plotting the boiling points in °K of the halogens against the boiling points of the next rare gases, a fairly straight line is obtained (Figure 22.1). Notice that hydrogen falls on the line, which makes it a member of the family in this respect. It is well to point out the

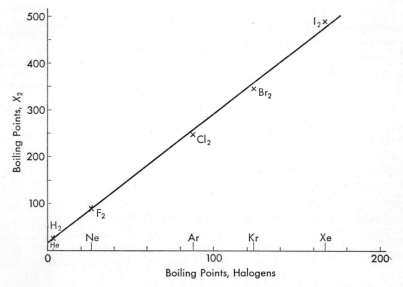

Fig. 22.1. Boiling points of the Malogens vs. those of the next rare gases.

similarities between hydrogen and the halogens, since all too often hydrogen is likened to the alkali metals.

Chlorine and bromine are soluble in water, with which they react, whereas iodine is insoluble (see below under reactions of the elements). Fluorine reacts with all common solvents, but the other halogens are soluble in most organic solvents, such as carbon tetrachloride, benzene, alcohol, etc. Chlorine and bromine do not change color on dissolving, but iodine forms solutions of different colors— violet when dissolved as the molecule, as in carbon tetrachloride and carbon disulfide; and red to brown when dissolution is accompanied by tight solvation, as in benzene and alcohol.

CHEMICAL PROPERTIES AND COMPOUNDS

With the outer electron structure ns^2np^5, the halogens can acquire the stable inert-gas configuration by gaining one electron. Thus, these elements are quite electronegative and form uninegative ions, with, as expected, a decreasing tendency with increasing atomic number in the group. Being the most electronegative of all the elements, fluorine exhibits the oxidation number -1 in all compounds. The other halogens show positive oxidation numbers, of which the odd numbers are more common and more stable than the even. The group maximum of $+7$ is achieved by chlorine and iodine only; all attempts to prepare perbromates have failed. This peculiarity of the first long period elements is a well known but little understood fact; compare the series: PCl_5, no VCl_5 nor $AsCl_5$, $NbCl_5$ and $SbCl_5$; SO_3 easily made, SeO_3 made only quite impure with difficulty, TeO_3 easy to make relatively pure; $HClO_4$, no $HBrO_4$, HIO_4 or, more commonly, H_5IO_6. In the $+7$ compounds the order of stability is $Cl > I$; in the $+5$, $I > Br > Cl$; in the $+1$, $Cl > Br > I$.

Fluorine is in many ways a unique element in this series. It is the least well known of the halogens, excepting of course astatine, because of the difficulty of preparing the element and handling its compounds. Fluorine brings out the extremes of behavior in other elements. When fluorides are ionic, they are remarkably ionic. The difference in fusibility and volatility of the aluminum and titanium halides has been discussed in Chapter 1; those of tin, mercury, bismuth, etc., follow a similar pattern. On the other hand, in covalent compounds the small polarizability of fluorine leads to small inter-molecular forces and consequently high volatility; compare at STP the gaseous SiF_4 with the liquid $SiCl_4$. Fluorine tends to bring out the highest oxidation number and the maximum covalency in other elements, as in AgF_2, SiF_6^{--}, SF_6, IF_7, etc. The structures and solubilities of fluorides are usually quite different from the other halogens. Whereas many metal chlorides, bromides, and iodides have layer- or chain-structures in the solid state, with a great deal of covalent bonding, fluorides, when ionic, tend to have three-dimensional arrays, with a stacking based primarily on size considerations. In this and other respects, fluorides resemble oxides considerably; for example, many difluorides and dioxides have the same structures.

Chemical Reactions of the Elements

The halogens are all active elements, with decreasing reactivity in going down the group. In fact, fluorine is chemically the most reactive substance known. The reactions of the halogens with the rest of the elements have been taken up in the other chapters. The replacement reactions of the halogens should be familiar to the reader from freshman chemistry:

$$F_2 + 2Cl^- \rightarrow 2F^- + Cl_2$$
$$Cl_2 + 2Br^- \rightarrow 2Cl^- + Br_2$$
$$Br_2 + 2I^- \rightarrow 2Br^- + I_2$$

These reactions are not as simple as depicted by the above equations, since they undoubtedly involve the formation of interhalogens and polyhalide ions (see below).

Paper, rubber, household gas, and flesh ignite spontaneously in a fluorine atmosphere. Even glass, heated to a red heat, burns in fluorine although at room temperature it is not attacked. Practically all of the metals and most of the nommetals react vigorously with fluorine, forming fluorides. It is possible to store the gas at moderate pressures in stainless steel and monel containers. This is not to say that fluorine does not react with these alloys; rather, they form a protective coating of metal fluoride which adheres closely to the surface of the bulk of the metal, protecting it from further attack. A new polymeric material has been developed that reacts with neither fluorine nor hydrogen fluoride. It is called "teflon," and is a polymer of tetrafluoroethylene. It is possible to see through thin layers of the substance. However, the material will not withstand either high temperatures or high pressures.

Chlorine is a very reactive element also, but it is much less dangerous than fluorine. Finely powdered metals ignite spontaneously and sometimes explosively in chlorine. Most of the nonmetals react with chlorine also. Liquid chlorine is stored in steel cylinders almost with impunity. Even here, though, corrosion of valves is a hazard.

Bromine and iodine are less reactive than chlorine, but both are capable of inflicting severe burns on the skin. In particular, bromine is usually more dangerous than chlorine because it's being a liquid permits a high contact concentration.

The reactions of the halogens with water, acids, and bases are complicated. Fluorine reacts completely with water to give hydrogen fluoride, oxygen, hydrogen peroxide, ozone, and oxygen fluorides. Chlorine and bromine are somewhat soluble in water, dissolving to the extent of about 0.1 mole per liter at STP. Iodine is about 1000 times less soluble at $0°$, with a sharply rising solubility as the temperature increases. In addition to simply dissolving, however, the halogens undergo at least three reactions with aqueous media:

$$(1) \quad X_2 + H_2O \; \rightleftharpoons HX + HOX$$
$$(2) \quad 3X_2 + 3H_2O \rightleftharpoons 5HX + HXO_3$$
$$(3) \quad X_2 + H_2O \; \rightleftharpoons 2HX + O_2$$

The extent to which each reaction goes depends on the halogen involved, the temperature, and the pH. Reaction (3) takes place rapidly for fluorine, slowly for chlorine, and hardly at all for bromine and iodine. Reaction (1) is the main reaction for chlorine at room temperature, a minor one for bromine, and a very minor one for iodine. Reaction (2) is the converse of (1) at room temperature and the principal reaction for all three at the boiling point. The reactions are further complicated for iodine, and somewhat for bromine, by the formation of polyhalides. As expected by mass-action, the above equilibria are driven to the right by bases and to the left by acids, so that the halogens are quite soluble in basic solution but not acid.

Reaction (3) lies far to the left for hydriodic acid under ordinary conditions, so that HI solutions form copious deposits of iodine when left exposed to air and light, which speed up the reaction, for a long time.

The halogens react with each other to form interhalogens and with halide ions to form polyhalide ions. The former are discussed in a later section of this chapter. A feature characteristic of the nonmetals is shown by the halogens in forming the latter. The polyhalides, also called the perhalides, are uninegative ions composed of a central atom (always Br or I except in the unstable Cl_3^-) to which are attached ligands of other halogen atoms (the higher polyiodides have recently been shown to be composed of branched chains, with one iodine at the apex). They are made by reaction between halogen or interhalogen and a halide ion. The most familiar example is the triiodide ion; iodine forms the most numerous and stable polyhalides. Iodine is much more soluble in aqueous potassium iodide than in water alone, due to the formation of this brown ion. Representative preparations are:

$$I_2 + I^- \quad \rightarrow I_3^-$$
$$I_2 + I_3^- \quad \rightarrow I_5^-, \text{ up to } I_9^-$$
$$ICl_3 + Cl^- \rightarrow ICl_4^-$$

Table 22.2 lists the known polyhalide ions.

The trichloride is quite unstable and exists in solution only; its formation is shown by the solubility of chlorine in hydrochloric acid.

TABLE 22.2
Polyhalide Ions

Triatomic	Penta-atomic	Hepta-atomic	Nona-atomic
Cl_3^- (solution only)	Br_5^- (solution only)	I_7^-	I_9^-
Br_3^-	I_5^-	IF_6^-	
I_3^-	BrF_4^-		
Br_2Cl^-	ICl_4^-		
$BrCl_2^-$	ICl_3F^-		
ICl_2^-	I_4Br^-		
IBr_2^-	I_4Cl^-		
I_2Cl^-			
I_2Br^-			
$IBrCl^-$			
$IBrF^-$			

Salts of the polyhalides can only be obtained when the cation is large, such as KI_3, $Ni(NH_3)_6(I_7)_2$, and salts of various organic bases. On heating, the solid polyhalides decompose to give a simple halide containing the more electronegative halogen:

$$KICl_4 \xrightarrow{\Delta} KCl + \overline{ICl_3}$$

The structures of the trihalides are linear, while the tetrachloro-iodate(III) ion has the four chlorines arranged in a square with the iodine in the center. A few compounds are known with empirical formulas, $Me^I I_4$, but since they are diamagnetic, they probably contain equal amounts of I_3^- and I_5^- and not the odd-electron I_4^- ion.

Hydrogen Halides

The hydrogen halides are the most important compounds of the halogens. They may be prepared by direct synthesis:

$$H_2 + X_2 \rightarrow 2HX$$

Hydrogen fluoride, however, is never prepared this way intentionally, since fluorine and hydrogen combine explosively under all conditions. Rather, it is prepared by distilling the gas from a mixture of fluorspar and concentrated sulfuric acid:

$$CaF_2 + H_2SO_4 \rightarrow CaSO_4 + 2HF\uparrow$$

The gas is condensed and marketed as the pure liquid in cylinders, or it is dissolved in water and sold as an aqueous acid. Hydrogen and chlorine combine vigorously and can be detonated under suitable conditions. It is more economical to react concentrated sulfuric acid and salt and catch the gaseous hydrogen chloride in water:

$$H_2SO_4 + NaCl \rightarrow NaHSO_4 + HCl\uparrow$$

Bromine and iodine react more slowly with hydrogen. Nevertheless, the reactions can be catalyzed, and direct synthesis is used as a source of the gaseous halides, trapping out the unreacted halogen. Hydrogen bromide and hydrogen iodide are made frequently by the hydrolysis of a phosphorus trihalide:

$$PX_3 + 3HOH \rightarrow H_3PO_3 + 3HX\uparrow$$

The phosphorus tribromide or triiodide is usually generated *in situ* from a mixture of red phosphorus and free halogen. Dilute solutions of hydroiodic acid are prepared by passing hydrogen sulfide into a suspension of iodine in water:

$$H_2S + I_2 \rightarrow 2HI + S\downarrow$$

The anhydrous hydrogen halides are all colorless gases, but hydrogen fluoride barely makes it, boiling at 19°C. It was shown in Chapter 1 that hydrogen fluoride has abnormal physical properties. Compounds of the other three halogens usually resemble each other, with differences in degree only. All of the hydrogen halides, including the fluoride, are enormously soluble in water; but the chloride, bromide, and iodide are strong acids, while hydrogen fluoride is relatively weak. In 0.1 molar solution the percentage ionization of hydrogen fluoride is about 10 per cent, whereas the apparent dissociation of the other three is between 90 and 95 per cent. Yet hydrofluoric acid burns are much more severe than burns from the other aqueous acids. Also, wax or plastic containers must be used for hydrofluoric acid, since it reacts with glass. The others may be stored in glass. The dielectric constant of anhydrous liquid hydrogen fluoride is 66. The other liquids have dielectric constants less than 10. Consequently, hydrogen fluoride—but not the others—has some potentialities as an ionizing solvent similar to water.

There is a fairly regular increase in the reducing power of the hydrogen halides. Hydrogen fluoride has no chemical reducing power. Hydrochloric acid is oxidized by strong oxidizing agents such as manganese dioxide, potassium permanganate, lead dioxide, etc. Hydrobromic acid requires less powerful reagents, and iodine is liberated from hydroiodic acid by iron(III) chloride.

Halides of the Elements

Second only to the oxides, the halides are the most important class of compounds. The halides vary in their properties from the ionic, high-melting, conducting compounds, such as sodium chloride, to the covalent, volatile, nonconducting compounds, such as molybdenum hexafluoride (b.p. 35°C). The variations can be classified according to the oxidation state of the element in the compound:

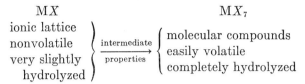

$$MX \qquad\qquad\qquad MX_7$$

MX		MX$_7$
ionic lattice		molecular compounds
nonvolatile	intermediate properties →	easily volatile
very slightly		completely hydrolyzed
hydrolyzed		

In other chapters the methods of preparation and the properties of specific halides have been discussed. There are four general preparative techniques:

(1) *Direct Synthesis.* This method is used extensively for the trihalides and higher polyhalides. It is about the most practical for most metal iodides and bromides and all nonmetal halides.

(2) *Dehydration of Hydrated Salts.* Any halide that can be crystallized from aqueous solution as a hydrate can be dehydrated under suitable conditions. Of course, there are many halides that hydrolyze so completely as to exclude this as a possibility. By and large this method is most used for the di- and trihalides.

(3) *Decomposition of Oxides.* This method is more frequently used to make bromides and chlorides of tetra- and pentavalent metals from the oxides. It is described in Chapter 13.

(4) *Displacement Reactions.* Most metal fluorides are prepared by displacement from the more available chlorides or oxides. There are a number of special techniques applicable to the preparation of unusual halides. One such technique is the hot-cold tube described in Chapter 13.

A few halides can be crystallized or precipitated directly from aqueous solution: the chlorides, bromides, and iodides of the alkali metals, silver, lead, mercury(I), copper(I), and thallium(I), and many fluorides, such as manganese fluoride and lithium fluoride. In addition, many mixed halides may be made this way, such as $KNiF_3$, $Na_5Al_3F_{14}$, $K_3W_2Cl_9$, etc.

The tetra- and higher halides are so extensively hydrolyzed by water that measurements of their solubilities are not significant. For example, silicon tetrachloride does not dissolve in water to give simple $Si(OH_2)_x^{++++}$ and Cl^- ions. It was shown in Chapter 12 that silicon tetrachloride reacts with water to give four moles of hydrochloric acid per mole of silicon tetrachloride, and the silicon precipitates as hydrous silicic acid.

Most chlorides, bromides, and iodides are soluble in water. Notable exceptions are tabulated on pages 119–120. Excepting the alkali salts, relatively few fluorides are soluble, and those that are form the least soluble chlorides, bromides, and iodides. For example, silver fluoride is one of the few really soluble fluorides.

Oxygen Compounds of the Halogens

Table 22.3 lists the known oxides and oxyacids of the halogens.

TABLE 22.3
Oxides and Oxyacids of the Halogens

	F	Cl	Br	I
Oxides	OF_2 O_2F_2	Cl_2O ClO_2 ClO_3 Cl_2O_7	Br_2O BrO_2 Br_3O_8	I_2O_4 I_4O_9 I_2O_5
Acids	—	$HClO$ $HClO_2$ $HClO_3$ $HClO_4$	$HBrO$ $HBrO_3$	HIO HIO_3 $HIO_4(H_5IO_6)$

Few of the free acids can be prepared, but salts are known for all those listed except the quite unstable hypobromous and hypoiodous acids. Most of the oxides are unstable and difficult to prepare; chlorine dioxide, which sometimes replaces chlorine in bleaching and water purification, is the only one of use outside of research laboratories. Fluorine forms no oxyacids.

Oxyacids of Chlorine

Hypochlorous acid is formed when chlorine is passed into water (see above). The pure acid cannot be isolated; it exists in solution only. Its salts are more stable than the free acid, and a few can be isolated, such as those of sodium and calcium. Solutions of hypochlorites are used as bleaching agents. Their action results from their oxidizing power; hypochlorites will oxidize chromium(III) to chromate and lead(II) to lead dioxide:

$$Cr_2O_3 \cdot xH_2O + 3ClO^- + 4OH^- \rightarrow 2CrO_4^{--} + 3Cl^- + (2 + x)H_2O$$
$$2Pb^{++} + 2ClO^- + 4OH^- \rightarrow \underline{2PbO_2} + 2Cl^- + 2H_2O$$

When chlorine is passed into hot caustic, hypochlorite is formed first until the base is neutralized. The hypochlorous acid then formed oxidizes the hypochlorite to chlorate, a series of reactions which may be formally represented as follows:

$$Cl_2 + 2OH^- \rightarrow ClO^- + Cl^- + H_2O \qquad (1)$$
$$\text{then } ClO^- + 2HClO \rightarrow ClO_3^- + 2Cl^- + 2H^+ \qquad (2)$$
$$\text{and } H^+ + ClO^- \rightarrow HClO \qquad (3)$$

For an over-all reaction

$$3Cl_2 + 6OH^- \rightarrow$$
$$ClO_3^- + 5Cl^- + 3H_2O \qquad [3 \times (1)] + (2) + [2 \times (3)]$$

Chloric acid itself is made from its salts, usually by adding sulfuric acid to a barium chlorate solution and filtering. It is a strong acid, but it cannot be isolated in the pure state, since it decomposes to perchloric acid when concentrated. Chloric acid is a powerful oxidizing agent, as shown by the fact that it will take manganese(II) ion to manganese dioxide in strong nitric acid solution:

$$5Mn^{++} + 2ClO_3^- + 4H_2O \rightarrow \underline{5MnO_2} + \overline{Cl_2} + 8H^+$$

Most chlorates are white soluble salts; the most common one is potassium chlorate because it is not so soluble and is therefore easily obtained as a crystalline solid. The salt decomposes thermally near 400°C in the absence of a catalyst:

$$4KClO_3 \xrightarrow{\Delta} 3KClO_4 + KCl$$

The catalyzed reaction into oxygen and potassium chloride is better known, but it occurs at an inconsequential rate, along with formation of the perchlorate at 400° in the uncatalyzed reaction.

Aqueous solutions of perchloric acid are prepared by oxidizing a solution of ammonium perchlorate with nitric and hydrochloric acids, a complicated reaction roughly represented by the over-all equation:

$$34NH_4ClO_4 + 36HNO_3 + 8HCl \rightarrow$$
$$34HClO_4 + 4Cl_2\uparrow + 35N_2O\uparrow + 73H_2O$$

The dilute solutions are concentrated and freed of volatile impurities and excess reagents by evaporating to a boiling point of 200°C. The acid is further purified by distilling in a partial vacuum. The distillate approximates the composition $HClO_4 \cdot 2H_2O$, or 72 per cent $HClO_4$. The pure acid, although a violent explosive, can be made by distillation under reduced pressure from potassium perchlorate and concentrated sulfuric acid (this is a reaction to be undertaken only with extreme caution).

Perchloric acid is a very strong acid. When hot and concentrated, it is both a good dehydrating agent and a good oxidizing agent, but in dilute solutions it has very weak oxidizing properties.

Practically all metal perchlorates are soluble in water, the group Ia and ammonium salts being only slightly soluble in cold water but moderately soluble in hot water. This is unusual, since most acids form insoluble salts with at least a small number of the metals. In addition, many of the metal perchlorates are soluble in a variety of organic solvents. This is most unusual for salts. The perchlorate ion has less tendency to form coordination complexes than most acid radicals. All of these properties make perchloric acid an exceedingly useful and versatile compound.

Many perchlorates have such an affinity for water that they are useful dehydrating agents. Magnesium perchlorate, for example, is as good a drying agent as phosphorus pentoxide. It has a further advantage that it can be regenerated *in situ* by heating and pumping off the water. Organic matter must, however, be kept away from it because of its strong oxidizing power. The heavy metal perchlorates are dangerous to handle; serious accidents have been caused by the detonation of silver and lead perchlorates.

Chlorine dioxide can be made by the careful addition of concentrated sulfuric acid to potassium chlorate (another dangerous reaction). The yellow gas comes off with oxygen and small amounts of chlorine:

$$4KClO_3 + 2H_2SO_4 \rightarrow 4\overline{ClO_2} + \overline{O_2} + 2K_2SO_4 + 2H_2O$$

Chlorine dioxide reacts with water containing alkali to form chlorites and chlorates:

$$2ClO_2 + 2NaOH \rightarrow NaClO_2 + NaClO_3$$

Chlorous acid and the chlorites are not very stable. It is impossible to keep a solution of the acid longer than an hour or so without appreciable decomposition:

$$8HClO_2 \rightarrow 6\overline{ClO_2} + \overline{Cl_2} + 4H_2O$$

The salts, which are more stable, are used to some extent as oxidizing agents. When dry, however, they detonate upon shock.

It is difficult to compare the oxidizing power of the four oxyacids of chlorine under ordinary conditions, because kinetic as well as thermodynamic considerations determine the course of the reaction. The oxidation potentials *under standard conditions* fall steadily from HClO to HClO₄, but they are of little help in practical situations. When hot and concentrated, perchloric acid is probably the best oxidizer, but in dilute solution neither the acid nor its salts are good oxidizing agents. Hypochlorites, chlorites, and chlorates are good oxidizing agents under most conditions.

Oxyacids of Bromine

Hypobromous acid is much less stable than hypochlorous. It is impossible to obtain even a dilute solution of the free acid, since its decomposition product, bromic acid, is always present. In addition, no salts of hypobromous acid are known.

Bromates are made by the oxidation of bromine, either by chlorine or by the bromine itself:

$$Br_2 + 5Cl_2 + 12KOH \rightarrow 2KBrO_3 + 10KCl + 6H_2O$$
$$3Br_2 + 6KOH \rightarrow KBrO_3 + 5KBr + 3H_2O$$

The sparingly soluble white potassium bromate is crystallized by concentrating and cooling. As for chloric acid, solutions of bromic acid can be made from the barium salt and sulfuric acid. The free acid exists in solution only, decomposing when concentrated. Bromic acid and bromates are good oxidizing agents, although not so strong as the chlorine compounds. The stability of the +5 acids of the halogens is $HClO_3 < HBrO_3 < HIO_3$, as shown by the reaction:

$$6HClO_3 + 5HI \rightarrow 5HIO_3 + 3Cl_2 + 3H_2O$$

Perbromic acid and perbromates are not known.

Oxyacids of Iodine

Hypoiodous acid and hypoiodites are even less stable than the bromine compounds. Iodic acid and iodates are made like and behave like the chlorine and bromine analogs, with a few differences. In the case of iodine, the free iodic acid can be isolated by careful concentration as a colorless hygroscopic solid. The dehydration can even be carried as far as the anhydride, I_2O_5. The acid in concentrated solution has a tendency to polymerize, giving rise to salts such as $KH_2I_3O_9$.

Periodic acid is the formal analog of perchloric acid, but in many ways it is quite different. Iodine extends its coordination number to six, so that the usual form is orthoperiodic acid (sometimes called paraperiodic acid), H_5IO_6. The periodates are much less soluble than the perchlorates.

Periodates can be made in many ways, usually by starting with iodate:

$$NaIO_3 + K_2S_2O_8 + 4NaOH \rightarrow Na_3H_2IO_6 + K_2SO_4$$
$$+ Na_2SO_4 + H_2O$$
$$NaIO_3 + Cl_2 + 4NaOH \quad \rightarrow Na_3H_2IO_6 + 2NaCl + H_2O$$

The metaperiodate can be obtained by reacting sodium ortho-periodate with nitric acid:

$$Na_3H_2IO_6 + 2HNO_3 \rightarrow NaIO_4 + 2NaNO_3 + 2H_2O$$

Upon concentration, the colorless metaperiodate crystallizes first. The free ortho-acid can be made from the barium salt and sulfuric or nitric acid (barium nitrate is insoluble in concentrated nitric acid). It is a colorless hygroscopic solid, which when heated *in vacuo* goes to paraperiodic acid, $H_4I_2O_9$, and eventually to the meta-acid, HIO_4.

Periodic acid is not so strong an acid as perchloric (recall the rules about acid strength in Chapter 3). Its salts are mostly di- or tribasic: $Na_2H_3IO_6$, $Na_3H_2IO_6$, etc. It is a stronger oxidizing agent, especially in dilute solution, than perchloric acid, and it is not explosive.

INTERHALOGEN COMPOUNDS

Each halogen will react with each of the other halogens. In addition, more than one binary compound exists for several pairs of the halogens. The known compounds are listed with some physical properties in Table 22.4. Generally, the interhalogen compounds resemble the free halogens with respect to color, physical properties, and reactivity. For example, iodine monochloride can cause serious skin burns and also attacks rubber.

TABLE 22.4
Interhalogen Compounds

ClF	m.p. $-156°$	BrCl m.p. $-66°$	IBr m.p. $36°$
	b.p. $-101°$	b.p. $5°$	b.p. $116°$
BrF	m.p. $-33°$	ICl m.p. $27°$	
		b.p. $97°$	
ClF$_3$	m.p. $-83°$		
BrF$_3$	m.p. $9°$	ICl$_3$ dissociates easily	
	b.p. $127°$		
BrF$_5$	m.p. $-61°$		
	b.p. $40°$		
IF$_5$	m.p. $8°$		
	b.p. $97°$		
IF$_7$	subl. $4°$		

All of the interhalogen compounds are made by synthesis from the elements. Iodine monochloride is made easily by trapping liquid chlorine in a cooled flask and adding the stoichiometric amount of solid iodine. The product is purified by freezing out iodine monochloride at the convenient temperature of 27°C. Suitable choice of reaction vessels is the major consideration in making the fluorides. Bromine trifluoride has become an important substitute for fluorine itself in many chemical reactions. To be sure, it is a hazardous chemical, detonating on contact with organic matter, but, being a liquid, it is easier to handle and store than fluorine itself. It is about as effective as fluorine in the preparation of metal fluorides.

The interhalogen compounds react with water, but the vigor of the reaction varies. In the hydrolysis the less electronegative halogen usually behaves as if it has a positive oxidation number, going to the corresponding oxyacid or its decomposition products, while the lighter halogen goes to hydrohalic acid. Most of the fluorides react violently, sometimes explosively, to give many products. Iodine heptafluoride is an exception in that it hydrolyzes quietly:

$$IF_7 + 6HOH \rightarrow H_5IO_6 + 7HF$$

Iodine monochloride dissolves in water without hydrolysis if excess chloride ions are present:

$$ICl + Cl^- \rightarrow ICl_2^-$$

However, in the absence of the complexing agent the compound hydrolyzes:

$$
\begin{array}{lll}
ICl + H_2O & \rightarrow HIO + HCl & (1) \\
3HIO & \rightarrow HIO_3 + 2HI & (2) \\
HIO_3 + 5HI & \rightarrow 3I_2 + 3H_2O & (3)
\end{array}
$$

$$5ICl + 3H_2O \rightarrow HIO_3 + 2I_2 + 5HCl \qquad \dfrac{15(1) + 5(2) + 2(3)}{3}.$$

USES

Fluorine is used largely in the production of organic fluorine compounds, such as the freons and fluorinated polyethylene. The most important fluorine chemical is hydrofluoric acid, which is used to etch glass and in the petroleum industry.

The heaviest consumers of chlorine are bleaching and water purification facilities. Of course, large quantities of the element are used in the production of other chemicals.

Most of the world's supply of bromine is consumed in the manufacture of lead tetraethyl and ethylene dibromide to remove the lead from the cylinder of engines. Photosensitive emulsions are made of silver bromide.

Iodine and its compounds are used mainly in medicine and the chemical industry.

SUGGESTIONS FOR FURTHER READING

N. V. Sidgwick, *The Chemical Elements and Their Compounds*, Oxford, London, 1950, Group VIIb.

M. E. Weeks, *Discovery of the Elements*, 6th ed., Journal of Chemical Education, Easton, Pa., 1956, Chapter 27.

A. F. Wells, "Structural Inorganic Chemistry," 2nd ed., Oxford, London, 1950, Chaps. VIII and IX.

STUDY QUESTIONS

1. What happens when cold brine solution is electrolyzed and the products, excepting hydrogen, are permitted to mix in the solution?

2. What happens when hot brine solution is electrolyzed and the products, excepting hydrogen, are permitted to mix in the solution?

3. Look up the cost of nitric acid and salt in the current issues of *Chemical and Engineering News* and compute the cost of the raw materials needed to make one pound of chlorine by the acid process.

4. Write an equation for the solution of bromine in sodium bicarbonate.

5. Compare the reactivity of $CsCl$, $BaCl_2$, $LaCl_3$, $HfCl_4$, $TaCl_5$, WCl_6, and IF_7 toward water.

6. Predict the products of reacting ClO_3 with water.

7. Predict the products of reacting I_2O_4 with water.

8. Write the equation for the oxidation of Mn^{++} to $HMnO_4$ by potassium periodate.

9. What are the products of the electrolysis of a solution of sodium bromide which is stirred vigorously during the electrolysis?

10. Write the equation for the oxidation of Mn^{++} to MnO_2 by $KClO_3$ in nitric acid solution.

11. Estimate the ionization constants of $HClO$, $HClO_2$, $HClO_3$, $HClO_4$, and H_5IO_6.

12. What happens in the following cases?
    (a) $I_2 + Cl_2$
    (b) $BaClO_3 + H_2SO_4$(dilute)
    (c) $BaClO_3 + H_2SO_4$(conc.)
    (d) $P + Br_2 + H_2O$
    (e) $IF_5 + H_2O$

13. By means of equations and a few words about conditions, show how to carry out the following conversions:
    (a) Make $KClO_3$ from a natural chlorine compound.
    (b) Make F_2 from fluorspar.
    (c) Make H_5IO_6 from I_2.
    (d) Make KI_3 from KI.
    (e) Make $CuCl_2$ from $CuCl_2 \cdot 2H_2O$.

Chapter 23

Manganese, Technetium, and Rhenium

OCCURRENCE AND HISTORY

Although three times as abundant as chlorine, manganese is not nearly so available, since it is spread out thinly in the earth's silicate crust. Occasional concentrated deposits of pyrolusite, impure manganese dioxide, are the principal sources of commercial manganese. Compounds of manganese have been used for many centuries, particularly pyrolusite as a coloring agent in the glass and ceramic industries. Large amounts of the dioxide impart a beautiful violet color to glass, while small quantities clear it of greens and yellows to make it more brilliant.

Rhenium is less abundant than manganese by a factor of a million. Its discovery in 1925 by Noddack, Tacke, and Berg, who named it after the German Rhine, is an excellent example of a practical use of periodicity. Since searches in manganese ores had failed to reveal the missing elements 43 and 75, Noddack and Tacke searched in sulfide and oxide ores of the heavy elements, using predicted chemical properties to separate the unknown elements, and generalizations about abundance to determine the extent of concentration. Rhenium was first isolated from columbite after prolonged concentration. Through Moseley's technique of x-ray analysis, Berg identified it. Later is was found in greater abundance in molybdenite, and its chief source today are the residues of the manufacture of molybdenum. Noddack, Tacke, and Berg thought that they had also discovered element 43, but their claim is now known to be wrong.

In 1938 there were four missing elements in the body of the periodic table: 43, 61, 85, and 87. Since then they have all been made artificially and some discovered in minute amounts in natural sources. Element 43 was first recognized in 1939 by Perrier and Segrè of Italy among the radioactive products in an old molybdenum deflector plate from the 37-inch Berkeley cyclotron. They called it "technetium," the artificial element. It is produced in relatively high yield in the fission of uranium, and gram quantities have been isolated at Oak Ridge from the old slugs of nuclear reactors. Diligent searches of natural ores have failed to reveal any natural technetium. All of its isotopes are radioactive, and the longest lived, ^{99}Tc, has a half-life of 10^6 years, just short enough for any that was present at the formation of the earth to have disappeared by now.

PREPARATION OF THE ELEMENTS

Like the elements of group VIa, pure manganese is not easily prepared by reduction of the oxide with carbon, because the metal forms a carbide so easily. Nevertheless, most of the manganese metal is prepared by this method, using mixed oxides of iron and manganese and yielding an alloy of the two metals, ferromanganese. The iron and carbon impurities are unobjectionable, since the largest use of the manganese is as an alloying constituent in steels.

Pure manganese metal is more easily prepared by reduction of the oxide Mn_3O_4 with aluminum (thermite process). The pure metal melts at 1260°C and is quite electropositive. It "rusts" easily and is of little use as a structural material.

The preparation of rhenium and technetium metals is accomplished on a laboratory scale by reduction of potassium perrhenate and pertechnate or any of the oxides with hydrogen:

$$Re_2O_7 + 7H_2 \xrightarrow[\Delta]{} 2Re + 7H_2O\uparrow$$

The reduction is carried out well below the melting points of the metals, so a fine powder is obtained. Rhenium has been made in coherent form by the de Boer-van Arkel process on the chloride (see Chapter 13).

PHYSICAL PROPERTIES OF THE ELEMENTS

Manganese, technetium, and rhenium are silvery metals which tarnish easily. They are near the maximum in melting points and densities in their respective periods. This makes rhenium the second highest melting metal after tungsten and one of the densest (see Table 1.1).

Manganese forms many alloys with other metals; its use in hardening steel has been mentioned. An interesting series is the Heusler alloys, composed of manganese, aluminum, and copper; many other elements may also replace the other two. Although these alloys do not contain any ferromagnetic constituents, they are strongly ferromagnetic. Apparently a band of electrons in the metallic bonds of the alloy similar to that of iron, cobalt, and nickel can be synthesized by combining metals which do not have the correct electron structure for ferromagnetism themselves.

CHEMICAL PROPERTIES AND COMPOUNDS

The known oxidation states of manganese, technetium, and rhenium—the common ones underlined and the rare ones in parentheses—are listed below:

$$
\begin{array}{llllllll}
\text{Mn:} & 0 & (+1) & \underline{+2} & +3 & +4 & +6 & +7 \\
\text{Tc:} & 0 & & & & +4 & & \underline{+7} \\
\text{Re:} & (-1) & 0 & (+1) & (+2) & +3 & \underline{+4} & +5 & +6 & \underline{+7}
\end{array}
$$

The usual tendency in the a-subgroups of increasing stability for the upper oxidation states with increasing atomic number is evident here (the -1 state for rhenium is at present anomalous). In the higher oxidation states manganese is a good oxidizing agent and rhenium a poor one, while rhenium in the lower oxidation states is a good reducing agent and manganese a poor one. In the few compounds that have been investigated, technetium resembles rhenium much more than it does manganese, although some differences are noted. The only point of similarity of group VIIa with the halogens is in the $+7$ oxidation state; perchlorates, permanganates, and perrhenates generally have comparable solubilities, and perrhenate forms mesoperrhenates with excess base the same way as periodate forms mesoperiodates.

The increasing stability of the upper oxidation states and the increasing tendency toward covalent bond formation of rhenium, and presumably of technetium, over manganese result in more complex compounds for the heavier elements. Rhenium forms a wide variety of complexes, especially in the $+3$, $+4$, and $+5$ oxidation states, while manganese has a smaller number in the $+2$, $+3$, and $+4$. The only simple cation formed by these metals is the $+2$ manganese ion. The half-full 3d shell confers a particular stability upon it.

Chemical Reactions of the Elements

Manganese is an ignoble metal, more reactive than the metals around it in the periodic table. It tarnishes readily in moist air, unlike massive rhenium, which remains unchanged, although powdered rhenium can be pyrophoric. When the metals are heated in excess air or oxygen, manganese takes up varying amounts of oxygen, depending on conditions, to give mixtures of compounds between MnO and Mn_3O_4, while technetium and rhenium go all the way to the heptoxides:

$$4Tc + 7O_2 \xrightarrow{\Delta} 2\overline{Tc_2O_7}$$

No hydrides of the elements are known, and only poorly defined carbides and nitrides have been described. The metals react with hot sulfur:

$$Mn + S \xrightarrow{\Delta} MnS$$
$$Re + 2S \xrightarrow{\Delta} ReS_2$$

In the reactions with the halogens, the variation in stability of various valences of these elements is clearly illustrated. The active fluorine will convert manganese to the trifluoride, while the other halogens give dihalides only. Rhenium with an excess of the halogens under suitable conditions gives the highest halide in each case: the hexafluoride, pentachloride, tribromide, and no iodide. Technetium does not react with chlorine, apparently becoming coated with a nonvolatile protective coating.

Manganese releases hydrogen from water, slowly in the cold, rapidly when heated or acidfied:

$$Mn + 2H^+ \rightarrow Mn^{++} + \overline{H_2}$$

Water and ordinary acids have no action on rhenium. Under oxidizing conditions it is converted to perrhenate:

$$Re + 7HNO_3 \qquad\qquad \rightarrow HReO_4 + 7\overline{NO_2} + 3H_2O$$
$$2Re + 7H_2O_2 + 2NH_3 \rightarrow 2NH_4ReO_4 + 6H_2O$$

None of the metals is attacked appreciably by base.

+6 and +7 Manganese

When manganese dioxide is fused with caustic in the presence of an oxidizing agent (even air will do), potassium manganate is formed:

$$O_2 + 2MnO_2 + 4KOH \xrightarrow{\Delta} 2K_2MnO_4 + 2H_2O$$

The green salt is soluble in water, but it is stable only in the presence of excess base. If the green solution is neutralized, a disproportionation occurs:

$$3MnO_4^{--} + 4H^+ \rightarrow 2MnO_4^- + MnO_2{\downarrow} + 2H_2O$$

Brown-black, insoluble manganese dioxide and deep purple potassium permanganate are the products. Potassium manganate can also be oxidized to permanganate by anodic oxidation. It is possible to oxidize manganese dioxide directly to permanganate in acid solution with such powerful oxidizing agents as lead dioxide, bismuth dioxide, and potassium periodate. Permanganic acid cannot be isolated, but in solution it behaves as a strong acid. Practically all of its salts are soluble in water, the most common being potassium permanganate. The isolation of crystals of the latter is difficult, since they cannot be filtered on paper. Dust and traces of organic matter, as well as paper, will reduce permanganate to manganese dioxide. The permanganate ion, then, is a powerful oxidizing agent and is reduced by mild reducing agents such as iron(II) salts, bromide ion, and hydrogen sulfide. In an acid solution the manganese is reduced to the +2 state, whereas in a neutral or basic solution it is reduced to the dioxide only. The bacteriacidal action of potassium permanganate is based upon its oxidizing potency.

The anhydride of permanganic acid, Mn_2O_7, can be isolated (a dangerous procedure) by adding potassium permanganate to cold concentrated sulfuric acid, when it separates as a dark red oil. Manganese heptoxide is an extremely unstable compound, losing oxygen at $0°$ and exploding just above that temperature. It is quite a powerful oxidizing agent.

+4 Manganese

The only common compound of tetravalent manganese is the dioxide. It is a black solid that occurs naturally. It can be prepared by the reduction of a higher state of manganese or by oxidation from a lower state. The thermal decomposition of manganese nitrate gives the purest dioxide, but even this product falls below a 2:1 oxygen to manganese ratio:

$$Mn(NO_3)_2 \xrightarrow{\Delta} MnO_2 + 2NO_2\uparrow$$

Care must be exercised to avoid overheating, since manganese dioxide loses oxygen on heating to higher temperatures, going to Mn_2O_3, and Mn_3O_4, and MnO.

Usually manganese dioxide behaves as an oxidizing agent. It reacts with hydrochloric acid to give chlorine:

$$MnO_2 + 4HCl \rightarrow MnCl_2 + Cl_2\uparrow + H_2O$$

Dilute acid solutions of many reducing agents dissolve the dioxide:

$$2FeSO_4 + 2H_2SO_4 + MnO_2 \rightarrow Fe_2(SO_4)_3 + MnSO_4 + 2H_2O$$
$$H_2C_2O_4 + H_2SO_4 + MnO_2 \rightarrow MnSO_4 + 2CO_2\uparrow + 2H_2O$$
$$H_2O_2 + H_2SO_4 + MnO_2 \rightarrow MnSO_4 + O_2\uparrow + 2H_2O$$

In basic solution potassium permanganate and manganese dioxide react to form potassium manganate:

$$4KOH + MnO_2 + 2KMnO_4 \rightarrow 3K_2MnO_4 + 2H_2O$$

A few other tetravalent manganese compounds can be made. As expected, the most stable compounds are complexes, of which the fluoro derivative is the most well defined. When concentrated hydrofluoric acid is added to a manganate, hexafluoromanganate(IV) is formed in a disproportionation reaction:

$$3K_2MnO_4 + 8HF \rightarrow K_2MnF_6 + 2KMnO_4 + 4H_2O + 2KF$$

The complex can be obtained as golden-yellow crystals; it is easily hydrolyzed to manganese dioxide.

+3 Manganese

The +3 oxidation state of manganese is limited to a few simple compounds and numerous complex compounds. The Mn^{++}-Mn^{+++} couple has a standard potential of about 1.5^v in acid solution, which makes the Mn^{+++} ion a powerful oxidizing agent unable to exist in water in any appreciable concentration. Thus, most compounds of trivalent manganese are either insoluble or complex. The hydrous sesquioxide can be made by the oxidation of manganese(II) salts in nearly neutral solution by air or chlorine. It is an insoluble dark brown compound which upon gentle dehydration goes to the oxide hydroxide $MnOOH$. The anhydrous sequioxide is obtained as a black powder when manganese oxides are heated to red heat in pure oxygen. The oxide and oxide-hydroxide occur naturally as the minerals braunite and manganite, respectively.

Chemically the sesquioxide is basic only. The most common simple compound is the acetate, made by heating solid manganese(II) nitrate 2-hydrate with acetic anhydride. In this reaction the liberated nitric acid acts as the oxidizing agent:

$$Mn(NO_3)_2 \cdot 2H_2O + 3(CH_3CO)_2O \xrightarrow{\Delta}$$
$$Mn(OCOCH_3)_3 + \overline{NO_2} + HNO_3 + 3CH_3COOH$$

The acetate is a black solid, often used to synthesize other manganese(III) compounds.

Another simple salt is manganese(III) sulfate, made by heating manganese dioxide with concentrated sulfuric acid:

$$4MnO_2 + 6H_2SO_4 \xrightarrow{\Delta} 2Mn_2(SO_4)_3 + \overline{O_2} + 6H_2O$$

The dark green compound is hydrolyzed by water with the precipitation of hydrous manganese(III) oxide. Mixed sulfates in the alum class also occur, the easiest to prepare being the cesium salt, $CsMn(SO_4)_2 \cdot 12H_2O$.

As examples of complexes of $+3$ manganese may be mentioned the acetylacetonate, $Mn(C_5H_7O_2)_3$, the cyanides, $K_3Mn(CN)_6$, the oxalates, $K_3Mn(C_2O_4)_3 \cdot 3H_2O$, and the halides, K_3MnF_6 and K_2MnCl_5. The cyano compound illustrates the greater stability of trivalent manganese over divalent in complexes. When potassium cyanide is added to a manganese(II) salt, the hexacyanomanganate(II) ion is formed:

$$Mn^{++} + 6CN^- \rightarrow Mn(CN)_6^{----}$$

The deep blue potassium salt crystallizes from solution. Merely bubbling air through a solution of the divalent complex oxidizes it to hexacyanomanganate(III):

$$4Mn(CN)_6^{----} + O_2 + 2H_2O \rightarrow 4Mn(CN)_6^{---} + 4OH^-$$

The potassium salt of the latter complex is more soluble, but it can be obtained as red crystals by the addition of alcohol to the solution. Hexacyanomanganate(III) can also be made directly by the addition of potassium cyanide to manganese(III) acetate.

When manganese oxides are ignited in air at red heat, the phase in equilibrium with 0.2 atm. of oxygen is predominantly trimanganese tetroxide, Mn_3O_4. The red-brown compound, which occurs naturally as hausmanite, is a mixed $+2$ and $+3$ oxide.

$+2$ Manganese

This is the only oxidation state in which simple hydrated cations of manganese are known. The chloride, bromide, iodide, nitrate, sulfate, and perchlorate salts are quite soluble in water. They crystallize from water as hydrated pale pink crystals. The normal carbonate, fluoride, phosphate, and sulfide salts are insoluble. However, they are dissolved by acids to form soluble acid salts. In general, the chemistry of simple divalent manganese salts is similar to that of magnesium salts. The hydrated manganese(II) ion is pale pink, which passes unnoticed in dilute solution but which is more evident in concentrated solutions. While manganese(II) salts are quite stable, freshly precipitated hydrous manganese(II) oxide is oxidized slowly on contact with air to the sesquioxide. In the presence of strong hydrochloric acid solutions of manganese(II) chloride can be oxidized to a dark brown complex ion, $MnCl_4^-$.

+1 Manganese

The +1 oxidation state is rare indeed for manganese. Potassium hexacyanomanganate(I) can be isolated as colorless crystals by the reduction of hexacyanomanganate(II) with aluminum powder. It is easily oxidized, releasing hydrogen from boiling water.

Rhenium

Since the discovery of rhenium in 1924, its chemistry has been studied by a few investigators, mostly at universities. The main lines of its behavior have been described, but rhenium is one of the most complicated of the chemical elements, and the detailed knowledge of it remains to be acquired (the same can be said of the platinum metals). From what is known so far, the expected generalization is borne out that rhenium is to manganese as tungsten is to chromium.

The most stable oxidation state of rhenium, at least in oxygen-containing compounds, is the heptavalent. The yellow heptoxide, which can be made by direct synthesis, sublimes undecomposed at about 300°; compare Mn_2O_7. Rhenium(VII) oxide is very soluble in water, dissolving to form the strong perrhenic acid, $HReO_4$. Upon evaporation, a solution of the acid loses water continuously, going to the acid anhydride without the intermediate formation of the pure acid as a chemical individual. Many salts of perrhenic acid exist, as for perchloric. The perrhenates are generally less soluble than the permanganates: for example, $KMnO_4$ is soluble at 20° to the extent of 6.38 g/100 ml of water; $KReO_4$, 1.21 g/100 ml; $NaMnO_4$ is so soluble that it cannot be isolated; $NaReO_4$, 25g/100 ml. These differences are even more striking on a mole basis. The most insoluble perrhenate, one suitable for the quantitative determination of rhenium, is the tetraphenylarsonium salt, $(C_6H_5)_4AsReO_4$.

Potassium perrhenate is not a good oxidizing agent. When heated, it melts at about 500° and distills undecomposed at about 1300°; compare $KMnO_4$ and $KClO_4$, which lose oxygen at about 200 and 400°, respectively. Hydrogen sulfide, which reduces permanganate to manganese(II), precipitates black rhenium(VII) sulfide quantitatively from an acid solution of perrhenate:

$$2ReO_4^- + 7H_2S + 2H^+ \rightarrow \underline{Re_2S_7} + 8H_2O$$

Few compounds of +6 rhenium are known because of the tendency of rhenium(VI) to disproportionate to rhenium(VII) and rhenium(IV). The trioxide forms when rhenium burns in limited oxygen, but it is better made by the reduction of rhenium(VII) oxide with dioxane or carbon monoxide:

$$Re_2O_7 + CO \xrightarrow{\Delta} 2ReO_3 + CO_2$$

Rhenium(VI) oxide is a red solid with metallic luster which is unattacked by water and most reagents without oxidizing or reducing properties. When heated to 400° in a vacuum, it disproportionates:

$$3ReO_3 \xrightarrow{\Delta} Re_2O_7 + ReO_2$$

In spite of many efforts, rhenium has not been made to take the group oxidation number with fluorine, the highest fluoride obtained being the hexafluoride. Rhenium hexafluoride is a volatile compound which is extremely reactive. A few rhenates, oxyhalides, and complexes of hexavalent rhenium have been described, but they are unstable and little known.

The highest chloride of rhenium is the pentachloride, prepared by direct synthesis or the action of carbon tetrachloride on the heptoxide in a sealed tube:

$$Re_2O_7 + 7CCl_4 \xrightarrow{\Delta} 2ReCl_5 + 7COCl_2 + 2Cl_2$$

It is a dark green unstable solid, losing chlorine when heated and disproportionating with most reagents. A few hyporhenates and complexes of pentavalent rhenium have been described.

The next most stable oxidation state for rhenium after the +7 is the +4. The insoluble black dioxide is relatively inert, like manganese dioxide. It is formed when rhenium is burned in limited oxygen or by reduction of higher valent compounds. A black disulfide is also made by direct synthesis. The only well established tetrahalide is the fluoride, a green, low-melting, nonvolatile compound made by hydrogen reduction of the hexafluoride:

$$ReF_6 + H_2 \rightarrow ReF_4 + 2HF$$

The most stable compounds of tetravalent rhenium are complex, particularly the halides, made by the reduction of perrhenate in the presence of halide; for example:

$$2KReO_4 + 16HCl + 6KI \rightarrow 2K_2ReCl_6 + 3I_2 + 4KCl + 8H_2O$$

In the trivalent state rhenium is becoming unstable and forms only a few compounds. The red trichloride, made by the thermal decomposition of the pentachloride, is a surprisingly inert compound, probably because it is dimerized like many other trihalides:

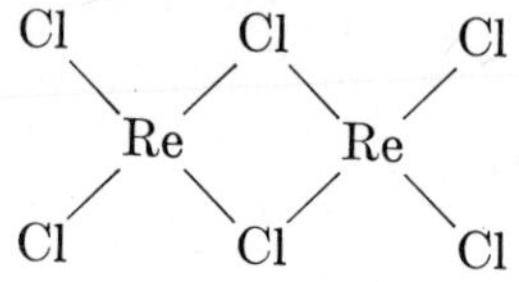

It gives a red solution in water which gives no precipitate with silver nitrate. When the solution is made basic, the black hydrated sesquioxide precipitates, which is very easily oxidized by air. A tribromide is also known, the highest bromide of rhenium. When alkali halides are added to solutions of the rhenium trihalides, a series of complexes, $MeReX_4$, can be isolated.

The lower oxidation states of rhenium are quite unstable. In one respect, however, rhenium has unique behavior for a transition metal; it will gain an electron to attain a negative oxidation state. When perrhenate solution is passed through a Jones reductor (a column of amalgamated zinc beads), the reduced solution requires eight equivalents of oxidizing agent to take the rhenium back to perrhenate. The inescapable conclusion is that the rhenium has an oxidation state of -1. Attempts have been made to isolate solid rhenides, but the solution decomposes when concentrated. A few impure solids have been made containing rhenide, but the composition and nature of the species which contains the uninegative rhenium remains in doubt.

Technetium

Insofar as it has been studied, technetium has been found to resemble rhenium rather closely. The most stable oxidation states are the $+7$ and $+4$. As expected, pertechnate is a little better oxidizing agent than perrhenate, but not nearly so good as permanganate. Most of the differences between technetium and rhenium are of degree, with a few differences of kind known at present. The highest chloride of technetium is the tetrachloride, a red compound made by the sealed tube reaction of Tc_2O_7 with CCl_4. When compared to the behavior of the elements near Tc and Re in the periodic table, this reduced affinity of technetium for chlorine is not surprising on an empirical basis, as can be seen by considering the highest known anhydrous chlorides in this region:

$$NbCl_5 \qquad MoCl_5 \qquad TcCl_4 \qquad RuCl_3$$
$$TaCl_5 \qquad WCl_6 \qquad ReCl_5 \qquad OsCl_4$$

The affinity for chlorine definitely falls off in going up as well as across the periodic table. The fluorides of these metals follow a similar pattern. No theoretical explanation has been given for this general phenomenon.

Another way in which technetium differs from rhenium is that it does not form technide, as rhenium forms rhenide, when passed through a Jones reductor.

USES

The principal use of manganese is as the metal as an alloying agent to harden steel. The use of pyrolusite in the glass and ceramic industries has also been mentioned. Another important application of manganese is in dry cells, where the dioxide forms one of the active anode chemicals. The essential parts of a dry cell are shown in Figure 23.1. It consists of a zinc metal outer case which serves as the container as well as the cathode. The anode consists of a paste of MnO_2, NH_4Cl, powdered graphite to reduce the resistance, and an inert filler to hold the water, all in contact with a graphite rod which acts as a conductor to lead in electrons. When supplying current at a slow rate to an outside source, the cell behaves as follows. At the cathode the zinc metal gives up electrons to the external circuit and goes into solution as the ion:

$$Zn \rightarrow Zn^{++} + 2e^- \text{ cathode}$$

The zinc ions diffuse into the anode paste. The anode extracts electrons from the external circuit, which reduce the manganese to the

+3 oxidation state, in which it precipitates a mixed oxide with the zinc ions:

$$2MnO_2 + Zn^{++} + 2e^- \rightarrow 2ZnO \cdot Mn_2O_3 \text{ anode}$$

The product is identical with the natural mineral hetaerolite, which is structurally related to hausmanite, Mn_3O_4, a zinc ion replacing

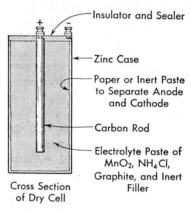

Fig. 23.1.   Cross section of dry cell.

the manganese(II) ion. The voltage generated by these two reactions is about 1.5v. If the cell is rapidly discharged, reactions other than those above occur, building up other products in the cell. These side-products generate back-E.M.F.'s which reduce the voltage of the cell. Such a cell is called polarized. Unless completely discharged, it will recover its original voltage on standing.

Potassium permanganate finds use as a bleaching agent, in the chemistry laboratory as an oxidizing agent, and in medicine.

The scarcity of rhenium has precluded any commercial use so far.

SUGGESTIONS FOR FURTHER READING

J. G. F. Druce, *Rhenium*, Cambridge, London, 1948.

J. C. Hackney, "Technetium—Element 43," *Journal of Chemical Education*, Vol. 28, p. 186 (1951).

K. J. Mysels, "Textbook Errors V: The Reaction of the Leclanche Dry Cell," *Journal of Chemical Education*, Vol. 32, p. 638 (1955).

N. V. Sidgwick, *The Chemical Elements and their Compounds*, Oxford, London, 1950, pp. 1262–1316.

M. E. Weeks, *Discovery of the Elements*, 6th ed., Journal of Chemical Education, Easton, Pa., 1956, Chapters 5, 30, and 31.

STUDY QUESTIONS

1. What happens in the following cases?
    (a) $MnO_2 + H_2O_2 + acid$
    (b) $KMnO_4 + Na_2S_2O_3 + H_2SO_4$ (aqueous)
    (c) $NH_4ReO_4 + H_2$ (heat)
    (d) $KMnO_4 + H_2S + H^+$
    (e) $Tc + NaOH$

2. By means of equations and a few words about conditions, show how to carry out the following conversions:
    (a) Make $KMnO_4$, from pyrolusite.
    (b) Make $TcCl_4$ from $KTcO_4$.
    (c) Make $MnSO_4$ from $KMnO_4$.
    (d) Make K_2ReI_6 from Re.
    (e) Make cesium manganese(III) alum from $MnSO_4 \cdot H_2O$.

3. An unknown compound contains potassium, technetium, and chlorine. After dissolving 0.1400 g in alkaline hydrogen peroxide and boiling, the solution is acidified with nitric acid. In a potentiometric titration with 0.1 N silver nitrate 20 ml are required to reach the end-point. The silver chloride is filtered off and 0.2731 g of tetraphenylarsonium pertechnate precipitated. Write the empirical formula for the compound.

4. Potassium permanganate is soluble in water at 25° to the extent of 7.64g per 100g of water. The density of the saturated solution is 1.046g/ml. Calculate the molarity and molality of the solution. What is its normality towards oxalic acid?

Chapter 24

Iron, Cobalt, and Nickel

OCCURRENCE AND HISTORY

Metallic iron has been used by man for at least 5000 years. The extraction of iron from its ores and the conversion of iron into structural steel is one of the most important bases of modern civilization. Iron is fourth in order of abundance of the elements in the earth's crust and the second most abundant metal, making up nearly 5 per cent of the matter that is available to man. Only insignificant amounts of iron occur as the element, yet practically all soils and rocks contain compounds of iron. Iron mineral bodies of economic importance are magnetite, Fe_3O_4 (sometimes called black oxide of iron); hematite, Fe_2O_3; limonite, $Fe_2O_3 \cdot 1.5H_2O$; and siderite, $FeCO_3$. Good grade ores as mined in the Great Lakes region of the U.S. contain about 50 per cent Fe, between 5 and 20 per cent SiO_2, 1 to 5 per cent H_2O, and varying amounts of phosphorus and manganese. Some African ores contain as much as 65 per cent Fe.

By comparison with iron, cobalt and nickel are rare metals, constituting about 23 and 80 ppm. of the earth's crust, respectively. Treated ores of cobalt were used extensively in the sixteenth century to color glass, but the element was first isolated by Georg Brandt of Vestmanland, Sweden, during the period 1735–1739. In like manner, compounds of nickel were used to color glass green long before the isolation of the metal in 1751 by the Swedish chemist A. F. Cronstedt. The names cobalt and nickel both mean demon, and are so named because of the trouble that their ores gave miners who were looking for something else.

The rich ores of iron are nowhere to be duplicated in the cases of cobalt and nickel. The former is found in conjunction with copper or nickel, or both, as the sulfide or arsenide. The only important deposit of nickel in North America lies in Ontario; it consists of low grade sulfides of copper and nickel containing only 2.5 per cent of nickel and copper combined.

PREPARATION OF THE ELEMENTS

Pure iron is prepared on a small scale only by the electrolysis of chloride or sulfate solutions of iron(II), and by the reduction of any oxide of iron with hydrogen at red heat.

The commercial production of iron is a complicated metallurgical process that has been evolved over many centuries. In essence, it involves the reduction of iron oxides by hot carbon monoxide and carbon. The reaction is carried out on a grand scale, and naturally pure reactants are not used. The smelting of the ore, which is usually preroasted to remove sulfur, moisture, and to powder the ore, is carried out in a blast furnace. This is a large furnace, up to 100 ft. high and 25 ft. in diameter, lined with refractory bricks. Into the top are fed ore, coke, and limestone, which fall through progressively hotter zones. Near the bottom blasts of hot air come in from stoves which have been previously heated by having the exit gases burn in them. The arrangement is shown schematically in Figure 24.1.

The principal reactions in the blast furnace are as follows:

(1) coke burning $\quad 2C + O_2 \qquad\qquad \rightarrow 2CO + \text{heat}$

(2) reduction of ore $\quad Fe_2O_3 + 3CO \xrightarrow{\Delta} 2Fe + 3CO_2$

(3) slag formation $\quad CaCO_3 \xrightarrow{\Delta} CaO + CO_2$

$\qquad\qquad\qquad\quad CaO + SiO_2 + Al_2O_3 \rightarrow \text{liquid}$

The molten iron drops to the bottom or hearth of the blast furnace along with the molten slag which floats on it. The liquids are periodically tapped from the hearth. The furnace operates twenty-four hours a day and can produce up to 1500 tons of iron metal in that time. For every ton of iron, one-half ton of slag is produced. The iron made in this way is still quite impure and is called pig iron. It contains a few per cent of carbon, with some manganese, phosphorus, sulfur, and silicon. Some of it is molded as such, when it is

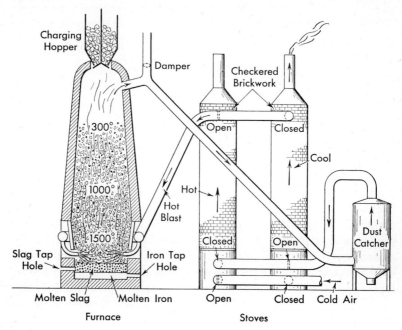

Fig. 24.1. Blast furnace.

called cast-iron and is more or less brittle, depending on heat treatment. Most pig iron, however, is used to make steel, in a process which consists of purification, heat treatment, and combination with additives. Steel contains from a few tenths (soft steel) up to 1.5 per cent (hard steel) of combined carbon, mostly as cementite, Fe_3C, with the previously mentioned impurities reduced to small amounts, and perhaps other alloying metals for special purposes. Steel is less brittle than pig iron. It can be "tempered"—that is, after it has been hardened by heating and sudden cooling, reheating or tempering at a given temperature results in the desired degree of hardness plus toughness.

Cobalt ores are dissolved in order to separate cobalt from its companion elements by chemical means. Ultimately, the cobalt is precipitated from solution as the hydrous oxide, which is dried and reduced in hydrogen to the metal.

Nickel sulfide is separated from the sulfides of copper and iron with which it occurs by physical means such as flotation. The separated nickel sulfide is roasted to the oxide, which is in turn reduced to the metal. The metal is purified electrolytically or by the Mond carbonyl process (see Chapter 11). Nickel carbonyl, made by reacting the metal with carbon monoxide at 60°, is decomposed back to a fine powder of pure metal and CO by heating to about 200°:

$$Ni(CO)_4 \xrightarrow{\Delta} Ni + 4CO$$

PHYSICAL PROPERTIES OF THE ELEMENTS

Iron, cobalt, and nickel melt at nearly the same temperature, all within 50° of 1500°, and they have nearly the same densities. The three metals are ferromagnetic; that is, they are strongly attracted to a magnet and exhibit remanence or remain magnetized after the external field is removed. The latter property leads to their ability to form permanent magnets. Iron is the most strongly magnetic, cobalt next, and nickel about one-third the intensity of iron. The metals lose their ferromagnetism and become ordinary paramagnets at elevated temperatures, called their Curie points: Fe, about 766°, Co about 1100°, and Ni about 360°.

These elements exhibit allotropy, each showing two solid phases. The relationship of the phases in iron is somewhat peculiar. The low temperature phase, α-iron which is body-centered cubic (b.c.c.), is stable up to about 906°, when γ-iron, which is cubic close packed or face-centered cubic (f.c.c.), becomes the stable phase. (The term β-iron for the b.c.c. form between the Curie point and 906° has generally been discontinued because a structural change is not involved in the magnetic transition.) Then at about 1400° the b.c.c. phase, now called δ-iron, becomes again stable to the melting point:

$$\alpha\text{-Fe (b.c.c.)} \xrightarrow{906°} \gamma\text{-Fe (f.c.c.)} \xrightarrow{1400°} \delta\text{-Fe (b.c.c.)} \xrightarrow{1535°} \text{liquid}$$

For cobalt a modified hexagonal close packed (h.c.p.) structure is the stable low temperature form, while a f.c.c. structure obtains at high temperature. For nickel the reverse is true—f.c.c. at low temperature, h.c.p. at high.

Pure iron is a rather soft metal, while cobalt is harder and nickel much harder. The physical properties of the metals are, however, greatly affected by even small amounts of alloying or impurity elements. Steels can be made, for example, which are harder than nickel. Indeed, a great variety of steels are manufactured in which properties such as hardness, tensile strength, elasticity, magnetic properties, etc., are adjusted to suit the user's needs.

CHEMICAL PROPERTIES AND COMPOUNDS

The placing of the three elements, iron, cobalt, and nickel, and the six elements below them into one group of the periodic table and numbering this group VIII is a somewhat artificial procedure introduced by Mendeleef. The similarities of the elements in group VIII are no greater than those of other adjacent transition elements, and only two of the nine, ruthenium and osmium, attain the group oxidation number in any compound. Long usage has, however, firmly established this convention, and, in the absence of any much more suitable alternative, it will be continued.

The common oxidation states of iron are $+2$ and $+3$. In the $+2$ state both the simple cation and complex aggregates are known, with the ionic tendency somewhat predominant. In the tervalent state both ionic and covalent compounds are also formed, except that here the covalent state is more important. For cobalt the trends noticed in iron are carried to further extreme: the $+2$ state is displayed almost exclusively in ionic compounds, while the $+3$ oxidation state is confined almost completely to complex compounds. In fact, trivalent cobalt forms one of the largest groups of complexes among all the elements. In nickel the $+3$ state has become quite unstable, and in the vast majority of compounds the element exhibits oxidation number $+2$. In this valency the compounds of nickel are distributed among ionic and covalent about like those of divalent iron.

There are other less common oxidation states for all three of these elements, and research continues to extend our knowledge of these well-known elements. Iron reaches the highest oxidation state, $+6$, in potassium ferrate(VI), K_2FeO_4. Further oxidation numbers are: Fe, 0, 1, and 4; Co, 1 and 4; Ni, 0, 1, 3, and 4. It can be seen then that the stability of the upper oxidation states falls off from iron to nickel; a similar trend is observed among the platinum metals (see Chapter 25). As is true of all groups of transition metals, the higher oxidation states are less stable among the elements of the first long period. Also, while iron, cobalt, and nickel in many compounds behave as simple cations, the heavier elements of group VIII rarely if ever occur as simple ions, a gradation already noted among the transition groups.

Chemical Reactions of the Elements

Iron is the most active of these three elements, the Fe-Fe^{++} couple having a standard electrode potential in acid solution of 0.44v, while those of Co-Co^{++} and Ni-Ni^{++} are 0.28v and 0.25v, respectively. These values show that the three metals are more active than tin and lead, yet less active than zinc and manganese. The reactivity of the triad of elements towards various chemical reagents varies greatly with the state of subdivision of the metal. Most active nonmetals react with the bulk metals slowly, but the same reactions may proceed violently if the metals are powdered. Furthermore, the metals, especially iron, can exhibit passivity after exposure to strong oxidizing agents, such as fuming nitric acid, when they are protected by an adherent coating of oxide.

None of the three metals react with pure water at room temperature; nor do they react with alkaline solutions. Dilute solutions of nonoxidizing acids dissolve all three, iron rapidly, cobalt slowly, and nickel very slowly:

$$Me + 2H^+ \rightarrow Me^{++} + \overline{H_2}$$

Cobalt and nickel are dissolved by oxidizing acids to form $+2$ cations, but iron goes to the trivalent state:

$$3Co + 8HNO_3 \rightarrow 3Co(NO_3)_2 + 2\overline{NO} + 4H_2O$$
$$Fe + 4HNO_3 \rightarrow Fe(NO_3)_3 + \overline{NO} + 2H_2O$$

Bars of the metals do not react appreciably with dry oxygen at room temperature. At elevated temperatures oxide formation proceeds most rapidly in the case of iron and most slowly for nickel. Even at red heat, however, massive iron does not oxidize rapidly in air, a property necessary for the operation of steel mills. When finely divided enough, the metals may be pyrophoric. The slow oxidation of iron by moist air is a process of considerable economic importance. In it the iron is first converted to iron(II) by the water, and carbonic acid formed from dissolved carbon dioxide, a reaction called corrosion. This reaction is faster for impure iron in which electrolytic cells may be set up: strains also act as local centers of activity. Then the iron(II) is oxidized by oxygen to hydrated iron(III) oxide, which scales off as rust. The constant exposure of fresh surface by rusting results in continued destructive reaction. It is prevented by covering the surface with a protective coating, such as tin, zinc (galvanizing), paint, grease, etc. Keeping the iron dry, or free of oxygen, or in basic solution also prevents its corrosion.

The halogens do not react appreciably with the metals at room temperature, but at only slightly elevated temperature (about 200°) chlorine attacks iron rapidly, cobalt and nickel slowly. The varied behavior of the iron-group metals towards the active nonmetals is understood by considering that a fresh surface of any of the three reacts very rapidly with any active nonmetal. A thin layer of compound is formed on the surface of the metal; if, and only if, it is removed from the surface, further reaction can take place. In the above case chlorine attacks iron to give iron(III) chloride, but cobalt(II) and nickel(II) chloride for the others. Iron(III) chloride is easily volatile at 200°, but cobalt(II) chloride and nickel(II) chloride are not. Of course, this behavior raises a problem in the preparation of a substance like nickel(II) chloride from the elements. Even with finely divided nickel, small particles of unreacted metal are apt to be occluded by nickel chloride, and the product has to be ground up and chlorinated several times for complete reaction to take place. Of the three metals nickel is the most resistant to attack by nonmetals: it is often used to construct reaction vessels in which processes involving elemental fluorine are carried out.

Iron and cobalt absorb only small quantities of hydrogen, but nickel is able to absorb as much as 4 cc of H_2 per cc of metal. Nickel thereby acts as a good hydrogenation catalyst in many organic reactions.

Oxides and Hydroxides

Iron, cobalt, and nickel exhibit oxidation numbers of $+2$ and $+3$ in oxides or hydroxides, the higher number being the more stable for iron and the lower for nickel. The monoxides are formed when the metals react with oxygen under certain conditions, but they are better prepared by the decomposition of salts, such as the oxalate:

$$FeC_2O_4 \overset{\Delta}{\to} FeO + \overline{CO} + \overline{CO_2}$$

The black iron(II) oxide does not actually exist as a stoichiometric compound. Below $575°$ it is unstable with respect to disproportionation into iron and Fe_3O_4, although it exists in a metastable condition at room temperature. Even then it is always deficient in iron, so that the composition may be typically $Fe_{0.9}O$. It very readily takes up more oxygen; when made by the careful pyrolysis of the oxalate, it may be pyrophoric. On the other hand, cobalt(II) and nickel(II) oxides, both of which are green, are easily obtained and kept pure. The three monoxides all nominally have the sodium chloride structure, indicating that they are essentially ionic compounds.

The hydrous oxides of divalent iron, cobalt, and nickel are insoluble in water, so that they come down as gelatinous precipitates when alkali (not ammonia which forms complexes) is added to a solution of the Me^{II} salts. They all take up more oxygen, the iron(II) so easily that the white hydrous oxide is not seen unless oxygen is rigidly excluded. Hydrous cobalt(II) oxide, which is usually pink, and hydrous nickel(II) oxide, green, also go to darker-colored higher oxides in the presence of oxygen, although more slowly than iron. Air alone will take iron to the $+3$ state; strong oxidizing agents, such as hypochlorite, will take cobalt and nickel to compounds approaching the composition $Co_2O_3 \cdot H_2O$ and $Ni_2O_3 \cdot H_2O$. Upon dehydration, only the iron retains all of its oxygen, so that the only sesquioxide of these metals is Fe_2O_3. The red-brown iron(III) oxide is the most stable oxide of iron and is obtained when most iron compounds are ignited in a free supply of air. The common gravimetric determination of iron consists of oxidation to the trivalent state, precipitation of hydrous iron(III) oxide by ammonia, and ignition to the sesquioxide.

In the +2 oxidation state, the three metal oxides are strong but insoluble bases. They react with acids to form a variety of salts. Only iron in the +3 state reacts simply with acids to form salts; the higher hydrated oxides of cobalt and nickel usually lose oxygen and go to the divalent state. Iron(III) oxide is essentially a basic oxide, not amphoteric in the sense that aluminum oxide is. A number of compounds called "ferrites" are known, but they are best regarded as mixed oxides rather than salts with iron in a discrete anion. The best known are a series of general formula $Me^{II}Fe_2O_4$, made by coprecipitation of salt solutions with alkali and ignition or simply by heating the appropriate quantities of oxides together. They have structures related to that of the mineral spinel, $MgAl_2O_4$, in which the metal ions occupy tetrahedral and octahedral holes between close packed oxide ions. The divalent metal ion may be Zn, Cd, Cu, Mg, Ni, Co, Mn, and even Fe^{II} itself—that is, any dipositive ion with a radius of about 0.6 to 1.0Å. With the iron(II) ion, the black magnetite, Fe_3O_4, is formed. It is a ferromagnetic compound, one of the earliest known magnetic substances, described and named by the ancient Greeks. The iron spinels have been much studied because of their interesting magnetic properties.

Cobalt also forms a mixed oxide, Co_3O_4, made by careful heating of the hydrated sesquioxide. It also has the spinel structure and is ferromagnetic. On strong heating in air cobalt(II,III) oxide loses more oxygen and goes to the monoxide; compare iron(II,III) oxide, which goes to the sesquioxide. A definite mixed oxide does not seem to be stable for nickel.

While iron(VI) oxide does not exist, salts of it do. As is usual, the element in the higher oxidation state is acid and thereby prepared in and stabilized by the presence of excess base. Thus, potassium ferrate(VI) is made by oxidizing hydrous iron(III) oxide with hypochlorite in concentrated alkali:

$$3NaClO + Fe_2O_3 \cdot xH_2O + 4KOH \rightarrow$$
$$2K_2FeO_4 + 3NaCl + (2 + x)H_2O$$

The dark red K_2FeO_4 is very soluble in water, with which it reacts to release oxygen. It is more stable in strongly basic solution, but even then it is a powerful oxidizing agent. The ferrate(VI) ion resembles the sulfate ion in structure, as shown by the fact that barium ferrate(VI) is isomorphous with barium sulfate.

Sulfides

The sulfides of Fe^{II}, Co^{II}, and Ni^{II} do not precipitate from a dilute acid solution of hydrogen sulfide, but the black sulfides, MeS, are precipitated by ammonium sulfide; recall also from qualitative analysis that FeS precipitates when sulfide and iron(III) react in neutral solution. The fresh precipitates are easily soluble in dilute acids, releasing hydrogen sulfide, but cobalt and nickel sulfides age to forms which are soluble only in strongly oxidizing acids with the separation of sulfur:

$$NiS + 4HNO_3 \rightarrow Ni(NO_3)_2 + 2\overline{NO_2} + \underline{S} + 2H_2O$$

The monosulfides can also be made by direct synthesis. Then they have different colors from the precipitated variety; iron(II) sulfide is usually brown, but when quite pure it is colorless.

Another important sulfide is iron pyrites, FeS_2, which occurs as a natural mineral and is used as a source of both iron and sulfur. The synthetic cobalt compound, CoS_2, is also known. These disulfides have been shown to have the NaCl structure with Me and S_2 groups in the Na and Cl positions. Thus, there is a S—S bond and the metal ion is in the divalent state. The sulfides are properly named as analogs of the peroxides: thus, FeS_2, iron(II) persulfide. Chemically FeS_2 and CoS_2 are quite inert. They burn when heated in air.

Halides

All of the possible dihalides of iron, cobalt, and nickel have been prepared, but only the trifluoride, trichloride, and possibly the tribromide of iron and the trifluoride of cobalt are known: nickel does not form a trifluoride. The better ability of the first member of the triad to form stable compounds in the $+3$ oxidation state is well demonstrated by this behavior toward the halogens.

The fluorides are only slightly soluble in water, except for cobalt(III) fluoride which reacts rapidly, whereas all of the other halides are very soluble salts. Dilute solutions of iron(II), cobalt(II), and nickel(II) are colorless, pink, and green, respectively; and the highly hydrated salt crystals of (1) Fe^{II} are all white or nearly so, (2) those of Co^{II} are pink or red, and (3) those of Ni^{II} are green, regardless of the anion. The anhydrous halides of Co^{II} and Ni^{II} exhibit different colors, however. For example, pink cobalt(II) chloride 6-hydrate crystals turn to blue anhydrous cobalt(II) chloride on gentle heating. Anhydrous nickel(II) chloride and bromide are both yellow, in contrast to the green 6-hydrates.

+2 Halides

All twelve possibilities of combination between iron, cobalt, and nickel with the halogens to give +2 halides are known. The difluorides—white, pink, and green, respectively—are quite distinct from the chloride, bromide, and iodide. The latter are very soluble in water and quite hygroscopic in the anhydrous state. The anhydrous fluorides crystallize with the rutile (TiO_2) structure with 6:3 coordination, typical of ionic compounds, whereas the other anhydrous halides crystallize in the cadmium chloride structure, a layered arrangement.

Several synthetic methods are available for the preparation of the family of dihalides. Direct synthesis is possible except in those cases where a trihalide is formed; that is, iron and cobalt plus fluorine and iron plus chlorine. Iron(II) chloride can be made from iron by the action of dry hydrogen chloride gas. The hydrated halides are easily obtained from solution of metal or oxide in hydrohalic acid, followed by crystallization:

$$Me + 2HX \rightarrow MeX_2 + \overline{H_2}$$
$$MeO + 2HX \rightarrow MeX_2 + H_2O$$

It is difficult to generalize concerning the course of dehydration of the hydrates. In the case of cobalt(II) chloride 6-hydrate it is possible to carry the dehydration to completion by gentle heating:

$$CoCl_2 \cdot 6H_2O \xrightarrow{\Delta} CoCl_2 + 6\overline{H_2O}$$

On cooling, the blue salt absorbs water from the atmosphere, reverting to the pink hydrate. In other cases, however, thermal dehydration results in partial hydrolysis unless a stream of dry hydrogen halide gas is used. Considerable variation in affinity for water of hydration can be shown from measurements of the pressure of water in equilibrium with the hydrated salts; for example, $CoCl_2 \cdot 2H_2O$, $p_{H_2O} = 85$ mm at $100°$; $FeCl_2 \cdot 2H_2O$ $p_{H_2O} = 48$ mm at $100°$. Of course the last water of hydration is held even more firmly, and the anhydrous halides are good dehydrating agents at room temperature.

It is of interest to compare the color of the anhydrous halides with that of the hydrate obtained by crystallization at room temperature:

FeF_2	white	CoF_2	pink	NiF_2	green
$FeF_2 \cdot 4H_2O$	white	$CoF_2 \cdot 4H_2O$	pink	$NiF_2 \cdot 4H_2O$	green
$FeCl_2$	white	$CoCl_2$	blue	$NiCl_2$	yellow
$FeCl_2 \cdot 4H_2O$	pale green	$CoCl_2 \cdot 6H_2O$	pink	$NiCl_2 \cdot 6H_2O$	green
$FeBr_2$	yellow	$CoBr_2$	green	$NiBr_2$	yellow
$FeBr_2 \cdot 6H_2O$	pale green	$CoBr_2 \cdot 6H_2O$	pink	$NiBr_2 \cdot 6H_2O$	green
FeI_2	almost black	CoI_2	black	NiI_2	black
$FeI_2 \cdot 4H_2O$	pale green	$CoI_2 \cdot 6H_2O$	red	$NiI_2 \cdot 6H_2O$	green

The dihalides also absorb ammonia at room temperature:

$$MeX_2 + 6NH_3 \rightarrow Me(NH_3)_6X_2$$

The behavior of the hexammines toward water varies. Hexamminecobalt(II) halides are soluble in water, but dissolved oxygen oxidizes the Co^{II} to Co^{III}. Hexamminenickel(II) halides dissolve in water without change and can be crystallized out again. Hexammineiron(II) halides decompose in water, solvent molecules displacing the coordinated ammonia molecules as ligands. The released ammonia then precipitates hydrous iron(II) oxide, which gradually turns brown because it is oxidized to hydrous iron(III) oxide:

$$Fe(NH_3)_6Cl_2 \rightarrow Fe(NH_3)_6^{++} + 2Cl^-$$
$$Fe(NH_3)_6^{++} + xH_2O \rightarrow Fe(H_2O)_x^{++} + 6NH_3$$
$$Fe(H_2O)_x^{++} + 2NH_3 \rightarrow \underline{FeO \cdot xH_2O} + 2NH_4^+$$
$$4FeO \cdot xH_2O + O_2 \rightarrow \underline{2Fe_2O_3 \cdot xH_2O}$$

In addition to forming ammine complexes, iron, cobalt, and nickel form halocomplex ions in the $+2$ state. Thus, while a dilute solution of cobalt(II) chloride is pink, typically the color of the $Co(H_2O)_6^{++}$ ion, the addition of a large excess of Cl^- ion to such a solution turns the color to blue, indicating that the Cl^- ions have displaced the water molecules in the coordination sphere of the cobalt ion. Crystalline halocomplexes of all three metals have been isolated, such as Rb_2NiCl_4 and K_2CoBr_4.

$+3$ Halides

Four trihalides of the iron group are known: FeF_3, $FeCl_3$, $FeBr_3$, and CoF_3, all made by direct synthesis. Hydrated iron(III) fluorides, chlorides, and bromides are also known.

Cobalt trifluoride is a brown solid that loses fluorine easily at 200 to 300° and reacts with water to liberate oxygen:

$$2CoF_3 \xrightarrow{\Delta} 2CoF_2 + \overline{F_2}$$
$$4Co^{+++} + 2H_2O \rightarrow 4Co^{++} + 4H^+ + \overline{O_2}$$

Iron trifluoride is a grayish white solid, only slightly soluble in water, but soluble in fluoride-containing solutions, probably to form the hexafluoroferrate(III) complex ion. Iron(III) chloride, on the other hand, is quite hygroscopic. The dark green, almost black solid is the most volatile halide of the triad, subliming at about 300°. In the vapor state it exhibits a molecular weight of about 325, indicating that the solid vaporizes to the molecular species Fe_2Cl_6. Cryoscopic measurements in inert solvents show that iron(III) chloride dissolves in nonpolar solvents as the dimer also. In polar solvents, such as ether, it is monomeric, probably forming a monomer-solvent addition compound. It is very soluble in water, in which it ionizes. The 6-hydrate crystallizes when the solution is concentrated, and the anhydrous compound cannot be recovered by simple dehydration. The solid does not consist of Fe_2Cl_6 molecules, but of an infinite array of iron and chlorine atoms in which each iron has six chlorine nearest neighbors instead of the four in the dimeric molecule. The behavior of $FeCl_3$ is summarized as follows:

$$FeCl_6 \text{ (vapor)}$$

$$\uparrow \Delta$$

$$FeCl_3 \cdot solvent \xleftarrow[\text{solvents}]{\text{polar}} FeCl_3 \text{ (solid)} \xrightarrow[\text{solvents}]{\text{non-polar}} Fe_2Cl_6 \cdot solvent$$

$$\downarrow H_2O$$

$$Fe(H_2O)_x^{+++} + 3Cl^-$$

Like most other polyvalent halides, iron(III) chloride absorbs gaseous ammonia to form a complex ammine:

$$FeCl_3 + 6NH_3 \rightarrow Fe(NH_3)_6Cl_3$$

As for the hydrate, the hexammineiron(III) chloride cannot be converted back to the simple chloride by thermal means, because it undergoes ammonolysis upon heating.

In addition to the simple halides, there are several halo complexes of trivalent iron and cobalt. Iron forms many complexes (or compounds formally written as complexes) with fluorine and chlorine alone as the ligand, such as K_3FeF_6 and $KFeCl_4$, but the bromides do not exist. Cobalt(III), on the other hand, while forming a large number of complexes in which both halide and another group, especially ammonia, are attached to the same central ion, seems to give only one pure halo complex, K_3CoF_6.

When the chlorides of iron, cobalt, and nickel mixed with potassium chloride are heated in fluorine, some remarkable compounds result. Cobalt and nickel form fluoro complexes in the +4 oxidation state, while iron does not go beyond the trivalent:

$$FeCl_3 + 3KCl + 3F_2 \xrightarrow{\Delta} K_3FeF_6 + 3Cl_2$$
$$2CoCl_2 + 6KCl + 7F_2 \xrightarrow{\Delta} 2K_3CoF_7 + 5Cl_2$$
$$NiCl_2 + 2KCl + 3F_2 \xrightarrow{\Delta} K_2NiF_6 + 2Cl_2$$

The power of fluorine to bring out high oxidation states is again illustrated by these reactions.

Oxysalts

Among the most important compounds of divalent iron, cobalt, and nickel are the hydrated sulfates. When the metals or suitable compounds such as iron(II) sulfide or nickel carbonate are dissolved in dilute sulfuric acid and the solution concentrated, the 7-hydrates are usually isolated: $FeSO_4 \cdot 7H_2O$, light green; $CoSO_4 \cdot 7H_2O$ red; $NiSO_4 \cdot 7H_2O$, green. The 7-hydrates, commonly called vitriols, are all soluble to the extent of about 30 to 40 $g/100gH_2O$ at room temperature. Other hydrated sulfates can also be made. For example, crystallization from aqueous solutions containing iron(II) sulfate gives the 7-hydrate below 56°, the 4-hydrate between 56 and 65°, and the 1-hydrate between 65 and 90°. In addition, mixed sulfates of Fe^{II}, Co^{II}, and Ni^{II} are formed, of which the best known is the light green Mohr's salt, iron(II) ammonium sulfate, $(NH_4)_2Fe(SO_4)_2 \cdot 12H_2O$.

The nitrates of divalent iron, cobalt, and nickel are comparable to the sulfates. In the preparation of iron(II) nitrate, however, care has to be exercised to avoid oxidation. With cold dilute nitric acid, $Fe(NO_3)_2$ can be made, but the best way is to react the sulfate with lead nitrate, when the insoluble lead sulfate is formed and filtered off and the iron(II) nitrate 6-hydrate then crystallized:

$$FeSO_4 + Pb(NO_3)_2 \rightarrow Fe(NO_3)_2 + \underline{PbSO_4}$$

The perchlorates of Fe^{II}, Co^{II}, and Ni^{II} are also highly hydrated and soluble in water. Among the insoluble salts of the divalent metals, made by precipitation under various conditions, are the oxalates, carbonates, and phosphates.

As has been discussed above, Co^{III} and Ni^{III} hydrated ions are unstable, both oxidizing water. It is possible to stabilize the $+3$ oxidation state of cobalt by forming crystalline solids, so that a few cobalt(III) salts can be made. The most common is the blue sulfate, $Co_2(SO_4)_3 \cdot 18H_2O$, made by the electrolytic oxidation of the divalent sulfate dissolved in cold 40 per cent sulfuric acid. Alums, such as $NH_4Co(SO_4)_2 \cdot 12H_2O$, can also be made. These sulfates are stable when dry, but decompose on solution in water.

The $+3$ state is much more stable for the hydrated Fe^{III} ion, and many iron(III) salts are known. The hydrated sulfate is again one of the most important compounds; several hydrates can be crystallized from solution, of which the 9-hydrate is usually found in chemical stockrooms. If the compound is completely dehydrated by careful heating, the resulting white $Fe_2(SO_4)_3$ then dissolves so slowly in water as to appear to be insoluble. The same behavior is exhibited by anhydrous chromium(III) sulfate and chromium(III) chloride, which are soluble but do not dissolve in water. Alums of iron(III) are also known.

An insoluble iron(III) salt is the phosphate, formed as a hydrated white precipitate from solutions of iron(III) ions and sodium phosphate. Not many salts of weak acids can be made, however, because of the weakness of $Fe_2O_3 \cdot xH_2O$ as a base. For example, the carbonate cannot be made, because when sodium carbonate is added to a solution of a Fe^{III} salt, the hydrous oxide precipitates. Nickel forms no trivalent salts.

Complexes and the Variation in Relative Stability of Oxidation States

It has been observed that iron(II) and iron(III) seem to be about equally common states. Actually, the environmental conditions affect the relative stability of the two oxidation states. Dilute solutions of iron(II) chloride are oxidized rather rapidly by bubbling air through the solution:

$$4Fe^{++} + O_2 + 4H^+ \rightarrow 4Fe^{+++} + 2H_2O$$

On the other hand, bubbling air through solutions of iron(II) containing sulfate ion for many hours is without appreciable effect. The above facts mean either (1) that the iron(II) ions in the two cases do not exist as identical species or (2) that the mechanism of oxidation is different in the two solutions. It is considered likely that (1) is the explanation and that in chloride solution the iron-containing solute species is $Fe(H_2O)_x^{++}$ while in sulfate solution the sulfate ions replace some of the water in the coordination sphere of the iron, rendering it more stable and less susceptible to oxidation.

Iron forms many complexes in both the +2 and +3 oxidation states, with the tendency in the latter generally being the greater. When excess potassium cyanide is added to an iron(II) sulfate solution, the hexacyanoferrate(II) ion is formed and the yellow potassium salt can be crystallized. It is one of the most stable complexes of iron(II). Upon oxidation by hydrogen peroxide in acid solution, hexacyanoferrate(III) results, a complex not readily formed from the constituent ions. Again the effect of environment on the stability of oxidation states is illustrated, because the hexacyanoferrate(III) ion oxidizes hydrogen peroxide in basic solution and goes to the hexacyanoferrate(II):

$$Fe(CN)_6^{----} \underset{H_2O_2,OH^-}{\overset{H_2O_2,H^+}{\rightleftharpoons}} Fe(CN)_6^{---}$$

A large number of salts containing hexacyanoferrate(II) and hexacyanoferrate(III) are known, many of them brilliantly colored and used as dyes. Further series of cyano complexes are formed when one or more different groups, such as nitrite or water, replace a cyanide in the coordination sphere of the iron. A few other Fe^{II} and many other Fe^{III} complexes are known, of which some of the ammine and halogen compounds have been mentioned above.

Cobalt is a prime example of an element where one oxidation state, the +2, is stable in simple salts and a second, the +3, in complexes. We have seen that Co^{III} ion oxidizes water to liberate oxygen. Conversely, cobalt(II) complexes reduce water to liberate hydrogen. Thus, when cyanide is added to a cobalt(II) salt in the presence of air, hexacyanocobaltate(III) results, and if air is excluded, the hexacyanocobaltate(II) ion reacts with the water:

$$2Co(CN)_6^{----} + 2H_2O \rightarrow Co(CN)_6^{---} + \overline{H_2} + OH^-$$

Cobalt(III) forms a great variety of complexes, over 2000 of which are known. In all of them the central Co^{III} has a coordination number of 6. The most common are the ammines, nitrites, and cyanides. The reason for the large number is that different groups can be attached to the cobalt in different ways. The idea of a complex as we know it today, composed of a central ion with various molecules or ions attached to it in a regular structure, was introduced by the Swiss chemist A. Werner at the end of the last century. Werner's brilliant theories brought great light into the bewildering variety of compounds known at that time; this type of compound is still sometimes called a "Werner complex." The bonds that cobalt(III) forms to its 6 ligands, arranged at the 6 apices of an octahedron, are strong covalent bonds, so that the variety attainable is similar to that in organic chemistry, greater in fact than for a single carbon atom. Thus, in the ammine series, the ammonia molecules may be progressively replaced by other groups:

$$[Co(NH_3)_6]Cl_3{}^*$$
$$[Co(NH_3)_5Cl]Cl_2$$
$$[Co(NH_3)_4Cl_2]Cl$$
$$[Co(NH_3)_3Cl_3]$$
$$K[Co(NH_3)_2(NO_2)_4]$$
$$K_2[Co(NH_3)(NO_2)_5]$$
$$K_3[Co(NO_2)_6]$$

In addition, several different arrangements corresponding to the same empirical formula are often possible, a phenomenon called "isomerism" which is discussed in the next chapter.

Many of the cobalt(III) complexes are prepared from cobalt(II) salts by oxidation in the presence of the complexing agent. Thus, drawing air through a solution of cobalt(II) nitrate, ammonium carbonate, and ammonia gives carbonatopentamminecobalt(III) nitrate:

$$4Co(NO_3)_2 + 4(NH_4)_2CO_3 + 16NH_3 + O_2 \rightarrow$$
$$4[Co(NH_3)_5CO_3]NO_3 + 4NH_4NO_3 + 2H_2O$$

Many other derivatives can be made from this salt by reaction with acids:

$$[Co(NH_3)_5CO_3]NO_3 + 2HNO_3 + NaNO_2 \rightarrow$$
$$[Co(NH_3)_5NO_2](NO_3)_2 + \overline{CO_2} + NaNO_3 + H_2O$$

In contrast to iron and cobalt, nickel does not readily assume the $+3$ oxidation state even in complexes. Thus, the number of nickel complexes is limited, comparable to those of iron(II). Another respect in which nickel is different is that it usually attaches to itself 4 ligands. This can be rationalized from the electronic point of view by observing that $CoX_6{}^{+++}$ and $NiX_4{}^{++}$ both have the E.A.N. (see page 173) of krypton, 36. Thus, with cyanide the nickel(II) ion forms the yellow tetracyanonickelate(II):

$$Ni^{++} + 4CN^- \rightarrow Ni(CN)_4{}^{--}$$

A characteristic complex compound, used in both the qualitative and quantitative analysis of nickel, is the insoluble red dimethylglyoxime:

* The square brackets enclose the complex ion.

$$Ni^{++} + 2 \quad \begin{matrix} CH_3-C=N-OH \\ | \\ CH_3-C=N-OH \end{matrix} \quad + 2OH^- \rightarrow$$

$$\begin{matrix} & & OHO & & \\ & & / \quad \backslash & & \\ CH_3-C=N & & N=C-CH_3 \\ | & \backslash \quad / & | \\ & Ni & & + 2H_2O \\ | & / \quad \backslash & | \\ CH_3-C=N & & N=C-CH_3 \\ & \backslash \quad / & & \\ & OHO & & \end{matrix}$$

Nickel does sometimes achieve a coordination number of 6; in, for instance, the deep blue hexamminenickel(II) ion, occasionally mistaken for the tetramminecopper(II) ion in qualitative analysis. Many analytical separations are based on the differences between the complex ion chemistry of the elements to be separated. It was seen that Fe^{+++}, Fe^{++}, Co^{++}, and Ni^{++} compounds absorb ammonia to form ammines, but that only those of cobalt and nickel are stable in water. A separation of the aqueous ions is based on this difference. The addition of aqueous ammonia to solutions of these four ions precipitates hydrous oxides of iron while forming soluble ammine complex cations with the other two.

By the use of proper coordinating ligands it is possible to observe metals in otherwise unobtainable oxidation states. For example, potassium tetracyanonickelate(II) is reduced by zinc, sodium amalgam, or tin(II) chloride to a Ni^I compound, potassium tricyanonickelate(I), $K_2Ni(CN)_3$. With the stronger reducing agent of alkali metals in liquid ammonia, Ni^0 can be obtained in potassium tetracyanonickelate(0), $K_4Ni(CN)_4$. Both of these lower-valence cyano complexes of nickel are strong reducing agents, but their mere existence is remarkable for a transition metal.

USES

The manifold uses of iron and steel are apparent to everyone in an industrial society. A great variety of steels are produced to fill many needs. Prices of iron and steel vary according to their cost of manufacture; for the common varieties the prices are expressed in dollars (order of 100) per ton. For cobalt and nickel, on the other hand, the prices are of the order of magnitude of dollars per pound; in 1958 about two dollars per pound for cobalt and 75 cents per pound for nickel (compare the heavier metals of Group VIII, which sell for dollars per gram). Hence these scarcer metals find only specialty uses compared to iron, mainly being employed as alloying agents. Cobalt is principally used in an alloy called stellite (an old trade name) with iron or chromium, suited to making cutting tools, surgical instruments, cutlery, etc. The principal alloys of nickel are stainless steel—typically, 70 per cent iron, 20 per cent chromium, and 10 per cent nickel—and Monel metal—a tough corrosion resistant metal composed of about 60 per cent Ni, 35 per cent Cu, and 5 per cent Fe. Because it can be highly polished and does not rust, nickel is used to plate other metals, especially iron. It does corrode slowly in city air containing acids, however, so that steel parts, such as automobile bumpers, etc., are now chromium plated on top of the nickel plate (which is on top of a copper plate). The use of nickel as a hydrogenation catalyst has been mentioned.

SUGGESTIONS FOR FURTHER READING

W. M. Latimer and J. H. Hildebrand, *Reference Book of Inorganic Chemistry*, 3rd ed., Macmillan, New York, 1951, Chapter XIX.

N. V. Sidgwick, *The Chemical Elements and Their Compounds*, Oxford, London, 1950, pp. 1316–1453.

M. E. Weeks, *Discovery of the Elements*, 6th ed., Journal of Chemical Education, Easton, Pa., 1956, Chapters 1 and 5.

STUDY QUESTIONS

1. Before Moseley's determination of atomic numbers, chemists had already placed cobalt directly after iron in the periodic table on the basis of chemical properties even though the order of atomic weights is Fe, Ni, Co. Justify this placement on the basis of chemical properties alone.

2. What happens in the following cases?

    (a) Fe + hot, dil HNO_3

    (b) $K_4Co(CN)_6$ + H_2O

    (c) $Co_2(SO_4)_3 \cdot 18H_2O$ + H_2O

    (d) $NiCl_2$ + NH_3 (aqueous)

(e) $K_2FeO_4 + H_2SO_4$

(f) $Fe + I_2$

3. By means of equations and a few words about conditions, show how to carry out the following conversions:

(a) Make $K_3Co(CN)_6$ from Co.

(b) Make $FeCl_3$ from hematite.

(c) Make Fe_3O_4 from Fe.

(d) Make CoF_3 from $CoCl_2 \cdot 6H_2O$.

(e) Make $K_4Ni(CN)_4$ from Ni.

Chapter 25   **The**
Platinum
Metals

OCCURRENCE AND HISTORY

Four of the six platinum metals were discovered and named by
two English chemists working with Central and South American
ores. Platinum was used in limited amounts by man for many
centuries, but it was first recognized as a metallic element and
described by the Spaniard Ulloa and the Englishman Brownrigg in
about 1750. It takes its name from platina, a Spanish word meaning
silver plate. Fifty years later the Englishman Wollaston separated
chemically salts of two more elements from platinum ores, igniting
them to the metals. He named them palladium after the recently
discovered asteroid Pallas and rhodium for the rose color of its
salts. At the same time Tennant, another Englishman, isolated
two more elements from the black residue left when crude platinum
metal was dissolved in aqua regia. These residues had been known
earlier, but it was thought that they were graphite (such as is
obtained when steel is dissolved in acid). Tennant showed that they
were new metals which he named iridium, after the varied color
of its salts (Latin, *iridis*, rainbow), and osmium for the vile smell
of its textroxide (Greek, *osme*, smell). The sixth member of the
family, ruthenium, was discovered by the Russian chemist, K. K.
Klaus, in 1850 while he was investigating the platinum residues
from the Russian mint. He named it after his native land.

The platinum metals are among the least abundant of the elements. No one of the six metals makes up more than 0.01 part per million of the earth's crust. Often the metals occur as alluvial deposits with gold. They also occur in the combined state as trace impurities in the sulfide ores of copper, nickel, and iron. Significant quantities of the metals are recovered from the processes used to refine copper and nickel.

Despite their scarcity, the platinum metals have been used by man for many centuries. Like gold, the native metals were obtained by the simple expedient of picking nuggets from streams. Almost always such nuggets are alloys of several of the platinum metals with or without other noble metals admixed in the alloy. The South American Indians recognized the desirable qualities of such alloys as materials for use in making jewelry and ornaments long before this hemisphere was discovered by the Europeans. The only other large deposits occur in the Ural region of Russia.

PREPARATION OF THE ELEMENTS

In former times practically all of the platinum metals were obtained from alluvial deposits. Currently about half of the annual production of the metals comes as the by-product of the purification of copper and nickel (see Chapters 5 and 24). Alloys of the metals are treated by a number of processes to yield the individual metals. The details of individual industrial processes are the confidential knowledge of the several firms which process these noble metals. However, several general methods of separation are well known. An intimate mixture of the metals with sodium chloride is chlorinated, giving soluble sodium chlorometallates:

$$2NaCl + Pt + 2Cl_2 = Na_2PtCl_6$$
$$3NaCl + Rh + 1.5Cl_2 = Na_3RhCl_6$$
$$2NaCl + Os + 2Cl_2 = Na_2OsCl_6$$

The complex compounds can be separated by taking advantage of differences in solubilities of several salts or, alternately, by taking advantage of the differences in thermal stabilities of the above products. All of the complex salts can be decomposed back into salt, chlorine, and metal, but the temperature necessary is not the same in each case.

Platinum and palladium are more easily soluble in aqua regia than are the other four metals. Thus a partial separation can be effected by digestion in this medium.

If the metals are converted to their anhydrous chlorides, a separation of rhodium can be obtained by virtue of the insolubility of rhodium(III) chloride in dilute mineral acids.

Osmium can be separated from the other four by heating the finely divided metal in oxygen, the volatile tetroxide subliming:

$$Os + 2O_2 = \overline{OsO_4}$$

Manifestly no serious problems are encountered in the preparation of the pure individual metals, once pure salts have been obtained. Strong ignition of any compound of any of the six metals yields the metal. After all, the metals are the most noble of all elements.

PHYSICAL PROPERTIES OF THE ELEMENTS

All six metals are high melting (see Table I), the lowest, palladium, melting at 1555°C. Osmium and iridium are the most dense elements, greater than 22 grams per cc. Within each triad—Ru, Rh, Pd, and Os, Ir, Pt—hardness decreases with increasing atomic number and ductility increases in the same order. Ruthenium and osmium are relatively hard and quite brittle, while palladium and platinum are much less hard and quite ductile. Platinum is hardened by alloying with iridium.

While the noble metals exhibit metallic conductivity, they are not excellent conductors of electricity. For example, patents have been issued for the use of several of the platinum metals as filaments for incandescent lamps, indicative of resistivity similar to that of tungsten.

CHEMICAL PROPERTIES AND COMPOUNDS

The state of our knowledge of the chemistry of the platinum metals is inadequate when compared with other families of elements. Nevertheless, certain general properties stand out clearly.

As might be expected in light of the groups immediately preceding Group VIII, stable higher oxidation states are exhibited by the elements of the second and third triads. In the preceding chapter we saw that it is possible to prepare compounds in which iron exhibits an oxidation number of $+6$; but the state is quite unstable. In contrast ruthenium and osmium form compounds in which the elements exhibit oxidation numbers of $+8$, and the compounds are fairly stable. The known oxidation states exhibited by the platinum metals are listed below, those of marginal stability being enclosed in parentheses and the most common underlined.

Ru 8, 7, 6, 5, 4, $\underline{3}$, 2   Rh 4, $\underline{3}$, 2, (1)   Pd 4, (3), $\underline{2}$

Os 8, 6, $\underline{4}$, 3, 2   Ir 6, 4, $\underline{3}$, 2, (1)   Pt (6), $\underline{4}$, (3), $\underline{2}$

As is true with iron, cobalt, and nickel, a fairly regular decrease in maximum oxidation state is observed within both triads.

These metals seldom, if ever, form simple ions. Not only do iron, cobalt, and nickel form a great variety of coordination compounds, but they also form many simple hydrated salts. In contrast, while the platinum metals exhibit at least as great tendencies to form coordination compounds, few simple salts have been prepared.

The six platinum metals are truly noble. Consequently, all compounds of the metals are decomposed by strong ignition, leaving the metals.

Chemical Reactions of the Elements

The platinum metals are extraordinarily inert towards all chemical reagents. For example, bulk Ru, Os, Ir, and Rh are unattached by aqua regia in the absence of oxygen. Palladium and platinum are dissolved slowly by digestion in aqua regia:

$$Pt + 2HCl + 2Cl_2 \rightarrow H_2PtCl_6$$
$$Pd + 2HCl + 2Cl_2 \rightarrow H_2PdCl_6$$

Strong oxidizing acids attack all of the metals if they are very finely powdered.

In comparison with other metals, these noble metals are very stable toward oxygen attack. However, most of them do react with oxygen at high temperatures, when finely divided, albeit slowly:

$$\text{Os} + 2\text{O}_2 \xrightarrow[\Delta]{} \text{OsO}_4 \text{ yellow}$$

$$\text{Ru} + \text{O}_2 \xrightarrow[\Delta]{} \text{RuO}_2 \text{ black}$$

$$\text{Rh} + \text{O}_2 \xrightarrow[\Delta]{} \text{Rh}_2\text{O}_3 \text{ grey}$$

$$\text{Ir} + \text{O}_2 \xrightarrow[\Delta]{} \text{IrO}_2 \text{ black}$$

$$2\text{Pd} + \text{O}_2 \xrightarrow[\Delta]{} 2\text{PdO} \text{ black}$$

$$\text{Pt} + \text{O}_2 \xrightarrow[\Delta]{} \text{no reaction}$$

On the other hand, it is said that palladium can be melted in air, eliminating dissolved oxygen upon crystallization (see the discussion of silver in Chapter 5).

It almost need not be said that pure water does not react with any of the metals under any conditions tried thus far. Ordinary aqueous acids and alkalies are likewise without effect. All of the elements are attacked by fused caustic in the presence of an oxidizing agent, KClO_3, KNO_3, or even air in the case of ruthenium and platinum. Never fuse strong alkali in platinum ware!

$$2\text{KOH} + \text{Ru} + 3\text{KNO}_3 \xrightarrow[\Delta]{} \text{K}_2\text{RuO}_4 + \text{H}_2\text{O} + 3\text{KNO}_2$$

$$2\text{KOH} + \text{Pt} + \text{O}_2 \xrightarrow[\Delta]{} \text{K}_2\text{PtO}_3 + \text{H}_2\text{O}$$

Only the finely powdered metals are reactive toward the other nonmetals. Rh, Ir, Pd, and Pt react with sulfur to form monosulfides, whereas Ru and Os form RuS_2 and OsS_2 (both pyrite lattice). The halogens react with the powdered metals, fluorine most vigorously and iodine least so:

$$\left.\begin{array}{l} \text{Os} \\ \text{Ru} \\ \text{Rh} \\ \text{Ir} \\ \text{Pd} \\ \text{Pt} \end{array}\right\} + \text{F}_2 \xrightarrow[\Delta]{} \begin{array}{l} \text{OsF}_6 \text{ yellow} \\ \text{RuF}_5 \text{ green} \\ \text{RhF}_3 \text{ red} \\ \text{IrF}_6 \text{ yellow} \\ \text{PdF}_3 \text{ black} \\ \text{PtF}_4 \text{ yellow or red} \end{array}$$

$$\left.\begin{array}{l} \text{Os} \\ \text{Ru} \\ \text{Rh} \\ \text{Ir} \\ \text{Pd} \\ \text{Pt} \end{array}\right\} + \text{Cl}_2 \xrightarrow[\Delta]{} \begin{array}{l} \text{OsCl}_3 \text{ brown and OsCl}_4 \text{ black} \\ \text{RuCl}_3 \text{ black} \\ \text{RhCl}_3 \text{ red} \\ \text{IrCl}_3 \text{ green} \\ \text{PdCl}_2 \text{ red} \\ \text{PtCl}_4 \text{ red-brown} \end{array}$$

Reactions with bromine and iodine are very slow and less well understood. Apparently nitrogen reacts with none of the Pt metals. Ruthenium, osmium, and rhodium do not absorb hydrogen in the bulk form. On the other hand, palladium in any form can absorb as much as 1000 times its own volume of hydrogen, all of which can be removed by heating the hydride in a good vacuum. Platinum and iridium absorb lesser quantities than palladium. In the powdered form, palladium, platinum, iridium, and rhodium are excellent absorbers of hydrogen. In no case can it be said that a well-defined stoichiometric hydride exists.

Oxides and Oxysalts

Ruthenium and osmium form tetroxides. The latter can be prepared by direct synthesis, but the former cannot. Ruthenium tetroxide is made by the oxidation of a ruthenate ion solution with a stream of chlorine gas:

$$K_2RuO_4 + Cl_2 \rightarrow \overline{RuO_4} + 2KCl$$

They are both low-melting solids which can be distilled or sublimed at reduced pressure. Both are rather powerful oxidizing agents, liberating chlorine from hydrochloric acid. OsO_4 is much the more stable of the two unusual compounds. It can be distilled at atmospheric pressure, boiling at 130°, whereas RuO_4 decomposes spontaneously prior to reaching its normal boiling point.

A number of oxides of the six metals have been prepared—some by direct synthesis, others by precipitation from solution. In general, they are not important compounds, since in most cases they do not react with either bases or acids to produce simple salts. OsO_2 is a typical example. It is a black solid, unaffected by alkali, dissolving in hydrochloric acid:

$$OsO_2 + 6HCl = H_2OsCl_6 + 2H_2O$$

One other example will suffice, $PtO_2 \cdot 2H_2O$. A yellow insoluble solid, it is soluble in either base or mineral acid, but it cannot be said to be amphoteric, any more than is SnO_2, since the solution process yields complex anions in both cases:

$$2KOH + PtO_2 \cdot 2H_2O = K_2Pt(OH)_6$$
$$6HCl + PtO_2 \cdot 2H_2O = H_2PtCl_6 + 4H_2O$$

Sulfides

Acid solutions of each of the six elements in the most common oxidation states give sulfide precipitates with hydrogen sulfide, but the composition of the precipitates is not certain in all cases.

Common States of Ruthenium and Osmium

The most important valence state for ruthenium is $+3$, although a number of complex $+2$ and $+4$ salts have been prepared. Ruthenium trihalides react with ammonia to form hexammine salts which are very stable complex ions:

$$RuX_3 + 6NH_3 \rightarrow Ru(NH_3)_6^{+++}\ 3X^-$$

The hexammineruthenium(III) ion is unaffected by dilute hydrochloric acid, and many salts of the yellow cation can therefore be prepared with ease. Complex chlororuthenate(III) anions are known also, as well as the intermediate possibilities, such as $[Ru(NH_3)_4Br_2]^+$, etc. Complex cations seem to be more numerous and more stable.

In contrast the $+4$ state is the most common for osmium. Furthermore, complex anions outnumber complex cations. No hexammineosmium(IV) salt is known, whereas salts of the hexahaloosmate(IV) anions are relatively common.

Common States of Rhodium and Iridium

The $+3$ state is the most common for both rhodium and iridium. Both elements appear to be about equally willing to form cationic and anionic complexes in this state. Coordination number of 6 is almost universal for the considerable number of complexes that have been prepared. The variety of complex formation is perhaps best illustrated by citing one series of haloammine iridium complexes:

$Ir(NH_3)_6^{+++}\ 3Cl^-$	colorless
$Ir(NH_3)_5Cl^{++}\ 2Cl^-$	red
$Ir(NH_3)_4Cl_2^+\ Cl^-$	yellow
$Ir(NH_3)_3Cl_3$	yellow or orange
$2K^+Ir(NH_3)Cl_5^{--}$	yellow
$3K^+IrCl_6^{---}$	green

The neutral trichlorotriammine complex is quite insoluble in water and, indeed, very difficult to decompose by any aqueous reagent. The charged complex ions are all stable enough to be carried through ordinary metathetical reactions in water. In general, the cationic ammine complexes of most transition metals form soluble salts with most common anionic radicals—not so soluble, though, that the salts cannot be crystallized.

Common States of Palladium and Platinum

Compounds of Pd(II) are most common for that element; Pt(II) and Pt(IV) compounds are both very abundant. Pt(II) and Pd(II) chemistries are very similar. As with the other four elements of the family, coordination compounds are the most important. Here, however, coordination number 4 is more common than is coordination number 6. $PdCl_2$ reacts with ammonia to produce white $Pd(NH_3)_4Cl_2$ which ionizes as a 2–1 electrolyte, $Pd(NH_3)_4^{++}$ $2Cl^-$. The compound can be converted to the hydroxide, $Pd(NH_3)_4^{++}$ $2OH^-$, which is sufficiently stable and strong as a base to precipitate hydrous oxides. Also easily prepared are neutral haloammine complexes, such as $Pd(NH_3)_2Cl_2$. Anionic halopalladate(II) compounds are known.

Pt(IV) coordination compounds follow the same pattern seen above. In general coordination of 6 is observed. Hexammines, exemplified by $Pt(NH_3)_6^{++++}$ $4Cl^-$, and hexahalometallates, exemplified by $2K^+PtCl_6^{--}$, are typical of the complexes formed by Pt(IV).

ISOMERISM IN COORDINATION COMPOUNDS

Isomers are different chemical substances having the same empirical formula. Thus ammonium nitrate, NH_4NO_3, and hydroxylammonium nitrite, $NH_2OH_2NO_2$, are isomers. Isomerism manifests itself in diverse forms, some of which will be discussed in this section.

Coordination (Ionization) Isomerism

Red palladium dichloride can be converted into potassium tetrachloropalladate(II) by reaction with aqueous potassium chloride:

$$PdCl_2 + 2KCl \rightarrow K_2PdCl_4$$

The salt is yellow and quite soluble in water. When ammonia is added to a solution of the $PdCl_4^{--}$ ion, dichlorodiamminepalladium(II) is formed. $PdCl_2(NH_3)_2$ exists in at least three isomeric forms, only one of which is made by the foregoing procedure. One isomer is an electrolyte with the structure $Pd(NH_3)_4^{++} PdCl_4^{--}$, whereas the other two are nonelectrolytes with the structure $(H_3N)_2PdCl_2$—that is, two chlorine atoms and two ammonia molecules bound to each Pd. Another more often used example of ionization isomerism is the pair $[Co(NH_3)_5Br]^{++}SO_4^{--}$, $[Co(NH_3)_5-SO_4]^+Br^-$. Another possible type of ionization isomer of $Pd(NH_3)_2-Cl_2$ which might be postulated is $Pd(NH_3)_3Cl^+PdNH_3Cl_3^-$. Such an isomer has not been prepared.

GEOMETRICAL ISOMERISM (STEREOISOMERISM)

Geometrical isomers are two or more compounds having the same number and kind of ligands bound to a given central atom, but having the several ligand-atom bonds oriented differently with respect to each other. Two simple geometric figures might be suspected for coordination 4 complexes; i.e., complexes in which four ligands are bound to one central atom. The planar square and tetrahedron are shown in Figure 25.1. For complexes of the type

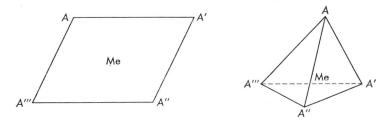

Fig. 25.1.   C. N. 4 complexes.

MA_2B_2, such as $Pd(NH_3)_2Cl_2$, it is seen that no geometrical isomers are possible for the tetrahedral configuration, since A', A'', and A''' are all equivalent in position with respect to A and the central atom. In the planar configuration, however, A'' occupies a position different from A' and A''' (which are equivalent) with respect to A and the central atom. A'' is said to be trans (across) to A, while A' and A''' are said to be cis (near) to A. The two structures of

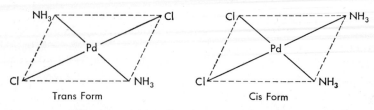

Fig. 25.2. Geometrical isomers of $Pd(NH_3)_2Cl_2$.

$Pd(NH_3)_2Cl_2$, shown in Figure 25.2, account for the two nonelectrolyte isomers mentioned above. The fact that cis-trans isomerism is observed for a coordination 4 complex is chemical proof that it has a planar square structure.

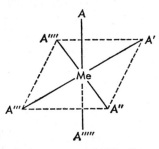

Fig. 25.3. Octrahedral coordination of central metal ion.

The geometry of coordination 6 compounds is almost always that of a regular or slightly distorted octahedron (see Figure 25.3). Note that A', A'', A''', and A'''' are all equivalent positions with respect to A, all cis positions; A''''', on the other hand, is a distinct position and said to be trans to A. Three different types of octahedral complexes should be considered:

Example	Type	Example
$Pt(NH_3)_6^{++++}4Cl^-$	MA_6	$2K^+PtCl_6^{--}$
$Pt(NH_3)_5Cl^{+++}3Cl^-$	MA_5B	$K^+PtCl_5(NH_3)^-$
$Pt(NH_3)_4Cl_2^{++}2Cl^-$	MA_4B_2	$Pt(NH_3)_2Cl_4$
$Pt(NH_3)_3Cl_3^+Cl^-$	MA_3B_3	$Pt(NH_3)_3Cl_3^+Cl^-$

For the MA_6 and MA_5B type only one isomer is possible, since all $6A$ positions are equivalent with respect to the central atom. Two isomers, cis and trans, are possible for the MA_4B_2 type.

Both forms are known for $Pt(NH_3)_2Cl_4$ (Fig. 25.4), and, similarly, for the MA_3B_3 (Fig. 25.5). Such isomers have not been observed in the case of Pt(IV), but they are known for other elements. The isomerism expected for a given structure is not always exhibited for each compound of that structure. Nor are the ionization isomer

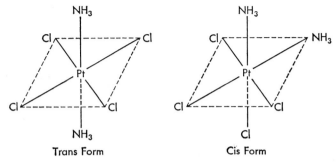

Fig. 25.4.   Geometrical isomers of $Pt(NH_3)_2Cl_4$.

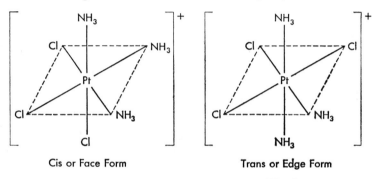

Fig. 25.5.   Geometrical isomers of $Pt(NH_3)_3Cl_3$.

possibilities always realized. For example, $Pt(NH_3)_2Cl_4$ might exist as:

$$Pt(NH_3)_6^{++++} \ 4Pt(NH_3)Cl_5^-$$
$$Pt(NH_3)_6^{++++} \ 2PtCl_6^{--}$$
$$[PtCl(NH_3)_5^{+++}]_2 \ [PtCl_6^{--}]_3$$
$$PtCl(NH_3)_5^{+++} \ 3Pt(NH_3)Cl_5^- \qquad \text{etc.}$$

No ionization isomerization has been observed at all for this compound.

Inert Complexes

The colorless solution of $Ir(NH_3)_6^{+++} \ 3Cl^-$ is remarkably stable toward reagents which might be expected to substitute other ligands for the NH_3 molecules coordinated to the Ir(III). Thus, the hexammineiridium(III) ion persists in strong hydrochloric acid solution as well as in pure water solution. The hexachloroiridate(III) ion might be expected to form in the first case, while aquation might be expected in the latter.

$$Ir(NH_3)_6^{+++} + 6Cl^- \rightarrow IrCl_6^{---} + 6NH_3$$
$$Ir(NH_3)_6^{+++} + 6OH_2 \rightarrow Ir(OH_2)_6^{+++} + 6NH_3$$

In the case of the analogous $Fe(NH_3)_6Cl_3$ compound, aquation proceeds instantaneously upon addition of the solid to water. The free ammonia then causes the iron to precipitate as the hydrous oxide.

$$Fe(NH_3)_6^{+++} + 6H_2O \rightarrow Fe(OH_2)_6^{+++} + 6NH_3$$
$$2Fe(OH_2)_6^{+++} + 6NH_3 \rightarrow \underline{Fe_2O_3 \cdot xH_2O} + 6NH_4^+$$

The persistence of $Ir(NH_3)_6^{+++}$ under conditions which result in chemical change for other analogous species is explained by the slow rate at which substitution reactions take place. The mechanism of substitution reactions is the subject of more advanced books, yet this much can be said: *The aquation (or other ligand substitution reaction) of complex ions must proceed step by step.* The probability of six water molecules simultaneously replacing six ammonia ligands around a given ion is vanishingly small. Thus, even though the intermediate cannot always be isolated, the conversion of an ion such as $Ir(NH_3)_6^{+++}$ into $IrCl_6^{---}$ must take place in a step-by-step procedure. One of the steps in the process, probably the first, must be so slow as to give the impression that the $Ir(NH_3)_6^{+++}$ ion is more stable than the $IrCl_6^{---}$ ion. However, the reverse conversion is equally slow. Apparently, in this case the relative stability of the two ions is of little consequence once either has been formed. Such complex ions are said to be inert, in contrast with those which undergo rapid substitution reactions. The latter are said to be labile. While most of the complex ions encountered in ordinary qualitative analysis are labile (indeed, that is why they are encountered there), it must not be concluded that the overwhelming majority of complex ions are likewise labile. As a matter of fact, most of the inert complexes are found among the less common transition elements or among some of the more common transition metals in less common oxidation states. Two notable exceptions should be made. Cr(III) coordination compounds are relatively inert (see Chapter 21).

Some Fe(III) complexes are inert. Thus, while $Fe(NH_3)_6^{+++}$ is labile, the more common $Fe(CN)_6^{---}$ ion is inert. Of course, great variation in rate of substitution is observed even among inert complexes.

Optical Isomerism

Cis and trans isomers of dichlorotetramminecobalt(III) chloride exist. If, as was first noted in Chapter 5, two ethylenediamine molecules replace the four ammonia molecules dichlorobis(ethylenediamine)cobalt(III) chloride is made. The cis isomer of the latter compound exists in two forms, called optical isomers, because the plane of polarization of plane polarized light is rotated upon passage through solutions of the isomers. The d-(dextrorotatory) isomer rotates the plane of polarization to the right (clockwise). The l-(laevorotatory) isomer rotates the plane of polarization to the left.

Optical isomerism of tetrahedral molecules is treated in organic chemistry, but it should not be supposed that the phenomenon is so

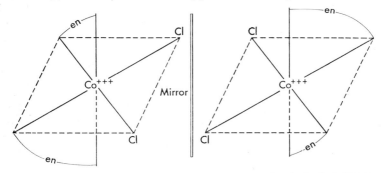

Fig. 25.6.   Optical isomers of cis-dichlorobis(ethylenediamine)cobalt(III) ion.

limited. In general, a structure which cannot be superimposed upon its mirror image is the optical antimer of its mirror image (Fig. 25.6); the structure is asymmetric and exists in d- and l-forms, commonly known as enantiomorphs.

USES

The world production of total platinum metals for the year 1950 was estimated at about 500,000 ounces, of which about 10 per cent was reclaimed metal. Most of the uses employ the metals themselves, for containers, electrical contacts, jewelry, catalysts, spinnerets, etc. Platinum and palladium catalysts are preferred in the synthetic ammonia industry (see Chapter 15). The extrusion of synthetic fibers and glass fibers through spinnerets containing as many as 1000 holes per square inch is a growing use.

OsO_4 has been used in the synthesis of cortisone, although alternate synthesis routes are known.

Much platinum ware is used in the chemical laboratory.

SUGGESTIONS FOR FURTHER READING

N. V. Sidgwick, *The Chemical Elements and Their Compounds*, Oxford, London, 1950, Vol. II, pp. 1454–1629.

H. Taube, "Rates and Mechanisms of Substitution in Inorganic Complexes in Solution," *Chemical Reviews*, Vol. 50, pp. 69–126 (1952).

STUDY QUESTIONS

1. What happens in the cases below?
   (a) $Os + O_2$ (heat)
   (b) Ir + aqua regia
   (c) Pt + aqua regia
   (d) $PtCl_4^{--} + NH_3 \cdot aq$
   (e) $Os + S$ (heat)

2. By means of equations and a few words about conditions, show how to carry out the following conversions:
   (a) Make K_2PtCl_6 from a natural platinum source.
   (b) Make RuO_4 from Ru.
   (c) Make K_3RhBr_6 from Rh.
   (d) Make $PtCl_4$ from Pt.
   (e) Make PdI_2 from Pd.

Appendix A

Balancing Equations

INTRODUCTION

The writing of balanced equations to stand for chemical reactions is the shorthand of chemistry. In the chemical equation are included the ideas of the atomic-molecular theory and stoichiometry, which form the basis of our modern concept of matter. Thus, this important topic, introduced in any beginning course in chemistry, is reviewed in this Appendix because of its fundamental significance.

Chemical equations can be divided into two broad categories, those for oxidation-reduction reactions in which some elements change oxidation number and those for all other reactions. For both of these categories, two types of equations may be written:

(1) molecular, in which the complete formulas of all reactants and products are written down

(2) ionic, in which only the formulas of participating ions are written down.

(Of course, molecular and insoluble substances are still represented by molecular formulas.) Examples of the two types, both expressing the reaction between silver nitrate and sodium chloride in aqueous solution, are:

(1) molecular $AgNO_3 + NaCl \rightarrow \underline{AgCl} + NaNO_3$

(2) ionic $Ag^+ + Cl^- \quad \rightarrow \underline{AgCl}$

Both types have their advantages and disadvantages. The molecular type is especially useful in the laboratory, where one has to weigh out specific reactants and does not deal with, say, a mole of silver ions. Ionic equations, on the other hand, focus attention on the reacting species and generalize the results of specific reactions. Thus, the above ionic equation expresses the fact that any soluble silver salt, the nitrate or perchlorate or sulfate, etc., reacts in solution with any soluble chloride, sodium or manganese, or hydrochloric acid, etc., to precipitate the insoluble silver chloride. They are especially useful in the ion-electron method of balancing oxidation-reduction reactions in aqueous solution, mentioned below. The latter is a great convenience for considering reactions from the point of view of oxidation-reduction electrode potentials.

THE METHOD AND AN EXAMPLE

Balancing equations for the so-called "metathetical" reactions is a special case of balancing redox equations, since the latter becomes the former when the oxidation-reduction part is balanced. Thus, we shall concentrate on redox reactions here, first considering a general oxidation number change method and then briefly the ion-electron method.

The process of writing a chemical equation may be divided into three parts:

(1) writing a skeletal equation with the formulas for the principal reactants and products
(2) balancing the electron-transfer (i.e., oxidation-reduction) part of the reaction
(3) balancing the equation metathetically (i.e., getting the same number of atoms of all kinds on both sides of the equation).

The process is best illustrated by a specific example. Writing a chemical equation usually begins with a verbal statement, either complete or to be completed by the student. Then chemical knowledge must be brought to bear to translate the verbal statement to formulas in part (1); for example, "Write a balanced equation for the reaction between manganese(II) nitrate and lead dioxide in a hot solution of sulfuric and nitric acids." We proceed in steps.

Step 1. Our chemical knowledge tells us that the strong oxidizing agent lead dioxide will take manganese(II) to manganese(VII) in acid solution while itself being reduced to lead(II). Thus, we translate:

$$PbO_2 + Mn(NO_3)_2 \rightarrow Pb^{++} + Mn^{VII}$$

Still relying on our knowledge of chemistry, we next write down the correct formulas for the species in which each element appears. Since the reactants are given, we look at the products. Manganese(VII) does not exist as such, but in oxygen-containing media it appears as the permanganate ion, MnO_4^-. Lead(II) can appear as the ion in aqueous solution, but in this case, where sulfate ions are present, the product in which it will occur is the insoluble lead sulfate. Now we have completed step (1), by far the hardest part:

$$PbO_2 + Mn(NO_3)_2 + H_2SO_4 \rightarrow PbSO_4 + MnO_4^-$$

Step 2. Balance the changes in oxidation numbers:*

$$Pb^{++++} \rightarrow Pb^{++} \quad \text{decrease of 2}$$
$$Mn^{++} \quad \rightarrow Mn^{+7} \quad \text{increase of 5}$$

It takes then 5 leads to oxidize 2 manganeses, $5 \times 2 = 2 \times 5$:

$$5Pb^{++++} + 2Mn^{++} \quad\quad\quad \rightarrow 5Pb^{++} + 2Mn^{+7}$$
or $\quad 5PbO_2 + 2Mn(NO_3)_2 + H_2SO_4 \rightarrow 5PbSO_4 + 2MnO_4^-$

Step 3. We bookkeep the atoms. Since five sulfate ions are needed for the product lead sulfate, five sulfuric acid molecules are taken:

$$5PbO_2 + 2Mn(NO_3)_2 + 5H_2SO_4 \rightarrow 5PbSO_4 + 2MnO_4^-$$

Not counted yet on the right are the 4 nitrate ions of the manganese(II) nitrate and the 10 hydrogen ions of the sulfuric acid. We can combine 2 of the hydrogens with the permanganates to give $2HMnO_4$, and 4 of them with the nitrates to give $4HNO_3$, leaving 4 over. In a molecular equation such as is being written here, they will appear in a water species, $2H_2O$. Thus, our equation

* It is assumed that the student is familiar with the concept and application of oxidation number. Briefly a few rules are: uncombined elements have oxidation number 0; oxygen usually has -2 except in peroxides (-1) and superoxides ($-\frac{1}{2}$); and hydrogen $+1$ except in metal hydrides, where it is -1.

has become:

$$5PbO_2 + 2Mn(NO_3)_2 + 5H_2SO_4 \rightarrow$$
$$5PbSO_4 + 2HMnO_4 + 4HNO_3 + 2H_2O$$

As a check on whether the equation has been written properly, the number of each atom on both sides should be counted at this time. Especially interesting is the number of oxygen atoms, which was not used in balancing the equation metathetically (it could have been used; then the number of hydrogen atoms would have provided a critical check). In this census, time can be saved by counting unchanged radicals as such, although they can be broken into their constituent atoms if desired. Thus, to check the above equation:

Left-Hand Side	Right-Hand Side
5 Pb	5 Pb
10 O (in 5 PbO_2)	10 O (8 in 2 $HMnO_4$, 2 in 2 H_2O)
2 Mn	2 Mn
4 NO_3	4 NO_3
10 H	10 H
5 SO_4	5 SO_4

or

Left-Hand Side	Right-Hand Side
5 Pb	5 Pb
42 O	42 O
2 Mn	2 Mn
4 N	4 N
10 H	10 H
5 S	5 S

The equation is then in correctly balanced molecular form. If we had wanted an ionic equation, we would have written ionic species all along, following the same procedure as above. Thus, the steps would have been:

Step 1.

$$PbO_2 + Mn^{++} \rightarrow Pb^{++} + Mn^{VII}$$
$$PbO_2 + Mn^{++} + SO_4^{--} \rightarrow PbSO_4 + MnO_4^{-}$$

Step 2. As before, giving:

$$5PbO_2 + 2Mn^{++} + SO_4^{--} \rightarrow 5\underline{PbSO_4} + 2MnO_4^-$$

Step 3.

(a) $5\underline{PbO_2} + 2Mn^{++} + 5SO_4^{--} \rightarrow 5\underline{PbSO_4} + 2MnO_4^-$

(b) We wonder now what to do with the 10 oxygen atoms from the $5PbO_2$ on the left. We see that 8 of them appear in $2MnO_4^-$ on the right, leaving 2 over to appear as $2H_2O$, which requires the addition of $4H^+$ (since we are working in acid solution) on the left:

$$5PbO_2 + 2Mn^{++} + 5SO_4^{--} + 4H^+ \rightarrow 5\underline{PbSO_4} + 2MnO_4^- + 2H_2O$$

We check the equation by counting the atoms on both sides and, in addition, for ionic types the *charge* on both sides. Just as atoms can neither be created nor destroyed in chemical reactions, neither can charge. The atoms are correctly balanced, and for the charge we have:

Left-Hand Side	*Right-Hand Side*
$+2 \times 2 - 2 \times 5 + 1 \times 4 = -2$	$-1 \times 2 = -2$

DISCUSSION

In the above equation, the $PbSO_4$ and PbO_2 species were underlined to indicate that they are insoluble species. An arrow pointing down after the formula, $PbSO_4\downarrow$, is sometimes used for the same purpose. Gaseous species can be analogously indicated by overscoring the formula or using an arrow pointing up: $\overline{CO_2}$ or $CO_2\uparrow$. Often these symbols are used on the left side of the equation as well to indicate the state of the reactants, as for PbO_2 above.

There are many pitfalls in writing equations and only by practice can one become adept at the shorthand of chemistry. Here are a few *don'ts*.

(1) Don't mix ionic and molecular equations. Use one or the other.

(2) Don't add something to the left side of an equation that is not there in the reaction simply to get the equation to balance.

(3) Don't add something to the right side of the equation that will obviously react with some other species in the equation. A simple example is: do not write OH^- on the right if the reaction is being carried out in acid solution; write H_2O instead, and put another H^+ on the left.

(4) Having determined the coefficients necessary to balance the oxidation-reduction part of the equation, don't change the numbers unless some of a reactant is oxidized or reduced and some of the same reactant is consumed in a metathetical way.

Among the most frequently manipulated atoms in the metathetical part of the equation are hydrogen and oxygen, because they are the basis of the most common solvent, water, and the acids and bases therein. Therefore it is useful to systematize the ways of getting (sources) and ways of getting rid of (sinks) these elements when changes of oxidation number are not involved. The table below lists these ways; it need not be memorized since it is quite simple and easily figured out.

	Acid Solution	Basic Solution
Source of H^+	Write H^+ on left	Write H_2O on left, OH^- on right
Sink for H^+	Write H^+ on right	Write OH^- on left, H_2O on right
Source of O^{--}	Write H_2O on left, $2H^+$ on right	Write $2OH^-$ on left, H_2O on right
Sink for O^{--}	Write $2H^+$ on left, H_2O on right	Write H_2O on left, $2OH^-$ on right

FURTHER EXAMPLES

As further illustration of the technique of balancing equations, we will work out a few more examples.

Example A

Write a balanced equation for the oxidation of chromium(III) by hydrogen peroxide in basic solution.

Step 1. In basic solution, Cr(III) will by virtue of its amphoteric nature appear as chromite, CrO_2^-. Hydrogen peroxide will oxidize it to Cr(VI), which in basic solution will be in the species chromate, CrO_4^{--}. The oxidizing agent is -1 oxygen in H_2O_2, which goes to -2 oxygen on the right. The hydrogen atoms will appear tied up in water, and since we do not yet know how the extra oxygen will appear, let us write it temporarily as O^{-2}:

$$CrO_2^- + H_2O_2 \rightarrow CrO_4^{--} + O^{--} + H_2O$$

Step 2. $Cr^{+++} \rightarrow Cr^{+6}$ increase of 3
            $O^- \rightarrow O^{--}$ decrease of 1

Since the oxygens come in pairs in H_2O_2, we must double the above changes in oxidation numbers, then take 2 chromium and 6 (3 pairs) of oxygen:

$$2CrO_2^- + 3H_2O_2 \rightarrow 2CrO_4^{--} + 3O^{--} + 3H_2O$$

Step 3. Since the chromium has gained 2 oxygen atoms per Cr in the reaction, 4 oxygens must be found for the chromium. Three of the oxygens are already present as the reduction product of the hydrogen peroxide, and the fourth can come from two OH^-. Thus, the equation becomes:

$$2CrO_2^- + 3H_2O_2 + 2OH^- \rightarrow 2CrO_4^{--} + 4H_2O$$

That it is a balanced equation is seen by checking the atoms and the *charge* on both sides.

Example B

An alkaline solution of potassium manganate disproportionates to manganese dioxide and potassium permanganate when the solution is saturated with carbon dioxide. Write a balanced equation for the reaction.

Step 1. $K_2MnO_4 + \overline{CO_2} \rightarrow \underline{MnO_2} + KMnO_4$
Step 2. $Mn^{+6} \rightarrow Mn^{+4}$ decrease of 2
            $Mn^{+6} \rightarrow Mn^{+7}$ increase of 1
            $2 \times 1 = 1 \times 2$
            $3K_2MnO_4 + \overline{CO_2} \rightarrow \underline{MnO_2} + 2KMnO_4$

Step 3. Now a closer examination of the reaction is necessary. What is happening? The solution was alkaline to begin with. When

CO_2 reacts with alkali, first CO_3^{--} is formed, and with excess CO_2, HCO_3^-. In other words, no CO_3^{--} can exist in a solution that is saturated with CO_2. In this equation there are now 6 K on the left and only 2 K on the right. The other 4 K must form a salt with some acid radical; they will appear as $KHCO_3$:

$$3K_2MnO_4 + \overline{CO_2} \to \underline{MnO_2} + 2KMnO_4 + 4KHCO_3$$

Now there are 4 H on the right, and none on the left. The only sources of H among the reactants are KOH and H_2O. It would be folly to add KOH to the left, since difficulty has already been encountered in balancing the potassium. Trying then water on the left, inspection soon shows that $2H_2O$ are needed with $4CO_2$ to make the $4KHCO_3$:

$$3K_2MnO_4 + 4\overline{CO_2} + 2H_2O \to \underline{MnO_2} + 2KMnO_4 + 4KHCO_3$$

If we wished to write an ionic equation, we could easily convert the above by leaving out the nonparticipating potassium ions:

$$3MnO_4^{--} + 4\overline{CO_2} + 2H_2O \to \underline{MnO_2} + 2MnO_4^- + 4HCO_3^-$$

Example C

Write a balanced equation for the oxidation of arsenical pyrites by nitric acid.

Step 1. The elements of arsenical pyrites, FeAsS, will be carried by nitric acid to Fe^{+3}, As^{+5}, which will appear in acid solution as H_3AsO_4, and S^{+6} as H_2SO_4. The nitric acid will be reduced to nitrogen(II) oxide, NO:

$$FeAsS + HNO_3 \to Fe(NO_3)_3 + H_3AsO_4 + H_2SO_4 + \overline{NO}$$

Step 2. The assignment of oxidation numbers in many cases is an arbitrary and flexible undertaking, well illustrated by the present case of arsenical pyrites. It does not matter what numbers are assigned so long as the algebraic sum of the oxidation numbers is equal to the net charge on the species, in this case zero. Let us assign Fe = +2, As and S = −1 each. Then for the oxidation-reduction part of the equation:

$$\left.\begin{array}{lll} Fe^{++} \rightarrow Fe^{+++} & \text{increase of 1} \\ As^{-} \rightarrow As^{+5} & \text{increase of 6} \\ S^{-} \rightarrow S^{+6} & \text{increase of 7} \end{array}\right\} \quad \text{total increase of 14}$$

$$N^{+5} \rightarrow N^{++} \quad \text{decrease of 3}$$

$$3 \times 14 = 14 \times 3, \text{ and, therefore,}$$

$$3FeAsS + 14HNO_3 \rightarrow 3Fe(NO_3)_3 + 3H_3AsO_4 + 3H_2SO_4 + 14\overline{NO}$$

The same result would have been obtained if we had assumed three other numbers with sum zero for the initial oxidation numbers of Fe, As, and S; for example, assign, say, Fe $= +3$, As $= -3$, and S $= 0$. Then:

$$\left.\begin{array}{lll} Fe^{+++} \rightarrow Fe^{+++} & \text{no change} \\ As^{---} \rightarrow As^{+5} & \text{increase of 8} \\ S^{0} \rightarrow S^{+6} & \text{increase of 6} \end{array}\right\} \quad \text{total increase of 14}$$

Step 3. Balancing the equation metathetically, we see that there are 9 nitrate radicals on the right, and 9 more HNO$_3$'s are therefore needed on the left:

$$3FeAsS + 23HNO_3 \rightarrow 3Fe(NO_3)_3 + 3H_3AsO_4 + 3H_2SO_4 + 14\overline{NO}$$

Now all the atoms are balanced except the hydrogen and oxygen. Adding them up shows that there are 8 H and 4 O more on the left than on the right. The addition of 4 H$_2$O on the right remedies this imbalance:

$$3FeAsS + 23NHO_3 \rightarrow$$
$$3Fe(NO_3)_3 + 3H_3AsO_4 + 3H_2SO_4 + 14\overline{NO} + 4H_2O$$

THE ION-ELECTRON METHOD

In the ion-electron method of balancing oxidation-reduction reactions, the above steps are applied separately to both the oxidizing agent and the reducing agent in ionic equations. Numbers of electrons corresponding to the changes in oxidation number are added to the resulting half-reactions to make their charges balance. Then the two half-reactions are multiplied by suitable numbers to make the electrons disappear. At the same time, the coefficients of each species are reduced to a minimum. By way of illustration, let us balance the first equation of this Appendix by the ion-electron method.

Step 1. We write the half-reactions with the proper species:

Oxidizing agent (gains electrons, decreases in positive oxidation number, gets reduced):

$$\underline{PbO_2} \rightarrow Pb^{++}$$
$$\text{or } \underline{PbO_2} + SO_4^{--} \rightarrow \underline{PbSO_4}$$

Reducing agent (loses electrons, increases in positive oxidation number, gets oxidized):

$$Mn^{++} \rightarrow MnO_4^{-}$$

Step 2. We balance the change in oxidation number with electrons added to one side or the other:

Lead(IV) gains 2 electrons in going to lead(II):

$$\underline{PbO_2} + SO_4^{--} + 2e^{-} \rightarrow \underline{PbSO_4}$$

Manganese(II) loses 5 electrons in going to manganese(VII):

$$Mn^{++} \rightarrow MnO_4^{-} + 5e^{-}$$

Step 3. Balance the half-reactions metathetically:

In acid solution, the oxygens of the PbO_2 are used up by reacting them with H^+ to form water:

$$\underline{PbO_2} + SO_4^{--} + 4H^+ + 2e^{-} \rightarrow \underline{PbSO_4} + 2H_2O$$

4 oxygens for the manganese come from 4 H_2O:

$$Mn^{++} + 4H_2O \rightarrow MnO_4^{-} + 8H^+ + 5e^{-}$$

At this point the half-reactions have been written, and it is beneficial to check each one separately to see that the atoms and the *charges* are balanced (each electron, e⁻, counts as −1 in charge, nothing in mass).

Step 4. The last step is to multiply the equations by numbers to make the electrons cancel out, and add, reducing the coefficients of other species as required:

$$\underline{PbO_2} + SO_4^{--} + 4H^+ + 2e^{-} \rightarrow \underline{PbSO_4} + 2H_2O \qquad \times 5$$
$$\underline{Mn^{++} + 4H_2O \rightarrow MnO_4^{-} + 8H^+ + 5e^{-}} \qquad \times 2$$
$$5\underline{PbO_2} + 5SO_4^{--} + 4H^+ + 2Mn^{++} \rightarrow 5\underline{PbSO_4} + 2H_2O + 2MnO_4^{-}$$

SUGGESTIONS FOR FURTHER READING

Any textbook of Freshman Chemistry

STUDY QUESTIONS

1. Write balanced equations to show what happens when:
   (a) NO_3^- is reduced to NH_3 by aluminum in boiling NaOH solution.
   (b) $Co(H_2O)_4^{++}$ is converted to $Co(NH_3)_6^{+++}$ when treated with an ammoniacal solution saturated with oxygen.
   (c) Mn^{++} is oxidized and precipitated as MnO_2 when treated with alkaline hydrogen peroxide.
   (d) Sodium stannite is oxidized to sodium stannate by air in basic solution.
   (e) Lead azide is hit with a hammer.
   (f) PbO_2 is prepared from $Pb(C_2H_3O_2)_2$ by oxidation with $Ca(ClO)_2$ in basic solution.
   (g) H_2O_2 oxidizes NO_2^- in basic solution.

2. Balance the equation for the oxidation of arsenical pyrites by nitric acid (Example C of the text) using at least two separate sets of oxidation numbers for Fe, As, and S different from those in the text.

Nomenclature
of
Inorganic
Compounds

INTRODUCTION

Certainly one of the most important aids to the understanding and development of chemistry as a science is a system of comprehensible and unequivocal names for the great number of compounds formed between the elements. The most desirable situation, of course, would be to have a logical set of rules universally accepted and used by which compounds, old and new, might be named. Chemical nomenclature, though, being an endeavor of human beings, has not achieved this ideal state. Progress has been made, however, and in this Appendix a brief account is given of the latest methods of naming inorganic compounds.

It was recognized early that organic chemistry would degenerate into chaos if its nomenclature was not systematized. The Geneva System of Nomenclature, constantly but logically revised and extended since its inception, resulted in 1892 from a meeting of organic chemists. The situation did not become acute so soon in inorganic chemistry, and the first *international* rules for the nomenclature of inorganic compounds were not laid down until 1940, with the issue of the Report of the Committee of the International Union of Chemistry for the Reform of Inorganic Chemical Nomenclature. We describe here this *systematic* nomenclature, as originally set

410

forth and modified over the years, with the hope that it will enjoy wider and wider usage by all chemists as they recognize its virtues. For the names of the chemical elements, also dictated by the Committee on Inorganic Nomenclature of the International Union of Chemistry, the reader is referred to the list in Table 1.1 of Chapter 1.

BINARY COMPOUNDS AND COMPOUNDS NAMED LIKE BINARY COMPOUNDS

Binary compounds consist of two elements. They are named by giving the name of the more electropositive element first followed by the name of the other element with its last part replaced by the suffix "-ide." Examples are:

$BaCl_2$	barium chloride
Mg_3N_2	magnesium nitride
NiO	nickel oxide
$ZnTe$	zinc telluride
BF_3	boron fluoride

Many binary compounds composed of two nonmetals exist. In these cases, the following order of electronegativity is adopted for nomenclatural purposes: B, Si, C, Sb, As, P, N, H, Te, Se, S, I, Br, Cl, O, F. Examples are:

$SeBr_4$	selenium bromide
NF_3	nitrogen fluoride

A class of compounds of more than two elements are named like binary compounds. These compounds are those in which an anionic radical acts as the less electropositive element in a binary compound. An abbreviated list of such anionic radicals follows:

OH^-	hydroxide
O_2H^-	hydrogenperoxide
SH^-	hydrogensulfide
N_3^-	azide
NH_2^-	amide
NH^{--}	imide
CN^-	cyanide
CN_2^{--}	cyanamide

Examples are:

$Ba(O_2H)_2$	barium hydrogenperoxide
AgN_3	silver azide
$CaCN_2$	calcium cyanamide
KNH_2	potassium amide

Binary compounds containing hydrogen also follow the rule:

HCl	hydrogen chloride
NaH	sodium hydride

There are, however, several binary compounds of hydrogen that are given trivial names. These names are so widely used that they are retained within the structure of systematic nomenclature. Examples are:

NH_3	ammonia
N_2H_4	hydrazine
PH_3	phosphine
AsH_3	arsine
SbH_3	stibine
SiH_4	silane
GeH_4	germane
CH_4	methane
SnH_4	stannane

Binary compounds of hydrogen that act as acids in water solution are named "hydro- · · · -ic" acids when dissolved in water. Examples are:

H_2S	hydrosulfuric acid
HBr	hydrobromic acid
HCN	hydrocyanic acid

When more than one compound is formed between a set of elements, it is necessary to indicate the proportions of the constituents. This can be done in either of two ways:

(1) by indicating the oxidation state of an element of variable valency

(2) by indicating the subscripts in the formula by means of prefixes in the name

The first is called the Stock system, after the German chemist whose method has been adopted; it is usually preferred for compounds of the metals where the oxidation state is clear-cut. The second is called the stoichiometric system; it is used especially for nonpolar compounds or in cases where the valency is uncertain.

In the Stock system the oxidation state is indicated by Roman numerals in parentheses immediately (without a space) following the name of the elements to which they refer. Examples are:

$TiBr_4$ titanium(IV) bromide
$TiBr_3$ titanium(III) bromide
$TiBr_2$ titanium(II) bromide

In the stoichiometric system Greek numerical prefixes are used, "mono-" generally being omitted in unequivocal cases. Examples are:

NO nitrogen oxide
NO_2 nitrogen dioxide
N_2O_4 dinitrogen tetroxide
$Ni(CO)_4$ nickel tetracarbonyl

It is seen from the above that the use of "-ous" and "-ic" endings is *not* recommended. Thus,

ferrous compounds become iron(II) compounds
ferric compounds become iron(III) compounds
stannous salts become tin(II) salts
stannic compounds become tin(IV) compounds, etc.

The advantages of the new system are readily apparent, especially to the student; he immediately knows that thallium(I) chloride is TlCl while he might not know the formula for thallous chloride.

OXYGEN ACIDS

The well-established rules for naming oxygen acids have been retained in the systematic nomenclature. Thus, the terms "per- · · · -ic," "-ic," "-ous," and "hypo- · · · -ous" are still used to indicate the oxidation state of the acid-forming element, except in more complicated cases where the Stock system is clearer.

The "-ic" acid is normally the acid in which the acid-forming element exhibits its maximum oxidation state. Examples are:

HNO_3 nitric acid
H_2SO_4 sulfuric acid
H_3BO_3 boric acid
H_2SnO_3 stannic acid

The only exceptions appear in group VII, where the "per- · · · -ic" acid is that in which the acid-forming element exhibits its maximum oxidation state. Examples are:

$HMnO_4$ permanganic acid
$HClO_4$ perchloric acid
$HTcO_4$ pertechnic acid

There is no fixed relationship between the "per- · · · -ic" acid of an element and its "-ic" acid, the way there is a definite difference in oxidation number between the "-ic" and the "-ous" and the "hypo- · · · -ous" acids. In the case of the halogens there are in fact two differences in oxidation state between the "per- · · · -ic" and "-ic" acids, but there is only *one* in the group VIIA elements.

Another set of compounds formerly called "per- · · · -ic" acids is that containing the —O—O— linkage. They are derived from hydrogen peroxide, and they are now named to indicate that relationship without confusion about the oxidation state of the central element. These acids are called "peroxy- · · · -ic" acids and no longer simply "per- · · · -ic" acids. Examples are:

$H_2S_2O_8$ peroxydisulfuric acid
H_2TiO_4 peroxytitanic acid
H_2UO_5 peroxyuranic acid

Usually the "-ous" acid is one in which the oxidation state of the element is *two* less than that of the "-ic" acid. Examples are:

H_3PO_4	phosphoric acid	P^5
H_3PO_3	phosphorous acid	P^3
H_2SeO_4	selenic acid	Se^6
H_2SeO_3	selenious acid	Se^4
$HClO_3$	chloric acid	Cl^5
$HClO_2$	chlorous acid	Cl^3
H_2TcO_4	technic acid	Tc^6
H_2TcO_3	technous acid	Tc^4

The "hypo- $\cdots$ -ous" acid generally contains the acid-forming element in an oxidation state *two* lower than that of the "-ous" acid. Examples are:

$HClO_2$	chlorous acid	Cl^3
$HClO$	hypochlorous acid	Cl^1
H_3PO_3	phosphorous acid	P^3
H_3PO_2	hypophosphorous acid	P^1

In a few cases elements form acids intermediate between the "-ic" and "-ous" acids. It has become customary to name them "hypo- $\cdots$ -ic" acids. Examples are:

$H_4B_2O_4$	hypoboric acid
$H_4P_2O_6$	hypophosphoric acid

Sulfur acids are so numerous that a complete listing is given:

H_2SO_2	sulfoxylic acid
$H_2S_2O_4$	dithionous acid
H_2SO_3	sulfurous acid
$H_2S_2O_2$	thiosulfurous acid
$H_2S_2O_5$	pyrosulfurous acid
H_2SO_4	sulfuric acid
$H_2S_2O_3$	thiosulfuric acid
$H_2S_2O_7$	pyrosulfuric acid
H_2SO_5	peroxymonosulfuric acid
$H_2S_2O_6$	dithionic acid
$H_2S_nO_6$	polythionic acids
$H_2S_2O_8$	peroxydisulfuric acid

The degree of hydroxylation of an acid is indicated with the prefixes "holo-," "ortho-," "pyro-," and "meta-." "Holo-" is used to denote the highest possible hydroxylated acid (whether or not it is known). "Ortho-" is used to denote the highest hydroxylated acid known (as either free acid, salts or esters of the acid). "Pyro-" acids are generally two "ortho-" acids minus one molecule of water. "Meta-" acids are generally one "ortho-" acid minus one molecule of water. Examples are:

H_5PO_5 holophosphoric acid
H_3PO_4 orthophosphoric acid
$H_4P_2O_7$ pyrophosphoric acid
HPO_3 metaphosphoric acid

In many cases the "ortho-" acid and the "holo-" acid are one and the same. In such cases the "ortho-" prefix is used. Examples are:

H_4SiO_4 orthosilicic acid
H_3AsO_3 orthoarsenious acid

SUBSTITUTED OXYGEN ACIDS

Many acids (or salts) are known where the oxygen has been partially or completely replaced by another element. These acids are named as though they were oxygen acids with the addition of a prefix to indicate the substitution. Examples are:

Na_3AsO_4 trisodium arsenate
Na_3AsO_3S trisodium monothioarsenate*
$Na_3AsO_2S_2$ trisodium dithioarsenate
Na_3AsS_4 trisodium tetrathioarsenate

H_2SO_4 sulfuric acid
$H_2S_2O_3$ monothiosulfuric* acid

H_2SiO_3 silicic acid
H_2SiF_6 hexafluorosilicic acid†

HBO_2 metaboric acid
HBF_4 tetrafluoroboric acid†

K_2CrO_4 potassium chromate
$KCrO_3Cl$ potassium chlorochromate
K_2PtO_3 potassium platinate
K_2PtCl_6 potassium hexachloroplatinate(IV)†

* The "mono-" prefix is best used here because no prefix has been used to mean complete substitution.
† See also the last section, on coordination compounds.

ACID HALIDES

Acid halides form an extensive list of ternary compounds with their own system of nomenclature. The rule is to replace the end of the acid-forming element by the suffix "-yl" and name the halide. Examples are:

CrO_2Cl_2	chromyl chloride
MoO_2Cl_2	molybdenyl chloride
SO_2F_2	sulfuryl fluoride
$POCl_3$	phosphoryl chloride
$VOCl_3$	vanadyl chloride
NO_2Cl	nitryl chloride

The system is similar to that used by the organic chemists. An organic acid halide is a compound in which the

$$-C\overset{\displaystyle O}{\underset{\displaystyle OH}{\Big\backslash}}$$

group has been changed to

$$-C\overset{\displaystyle O}{\underset{\displaystyle X}{\Big\backslash}}$$

In the same way each of the examples above can be thought to arise from the replacement of an —OH by —X:

$$\overset{O}{\underset{O}{\diagdown\!\!\diagup}}N{-}OH \leftrightarrow \overset{O}{\underset{O}{\diagdown\!\!\diagup}}N{-}Cl$$

The "-ic" ending of the acid is then changed to "-yl," as above:

HNO_3	nitric acid
NO_2Cl	nitryl chloride
H_2MoO_4	molybdic acid
MoO_2Cl_2	molybdenyl chloride (the "-en-" is put back in for euphony)

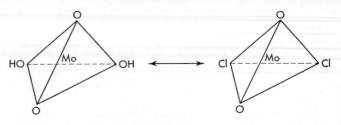

In some cases the well established name of an acid halide does not fit into the system, but where usage is almost universal, the name is retained without objection. Examples are:

$SOCl_2$ thionyl chloride
$NOCl$ nitrosyl chloride

Extension of the systematic names to more recently discovered acid halides is straightforward. Examples are:

MnO_3F permanganyl fluoride
ClO_2F chloryl fluoride
$S_2O_5Cl_2$ pyrosulfuryl chloride

It is unfortunate that the compound $ZrOCl_2 \cdot 8H_2O$ has been called zirconyl chloride 8-hydrate. The other "-yl" compounds are volatile molecular compounds, but this zirconium compound cannot be dehydrated to simple $ZrOCl_2$ and the structure of the hydrate does not consist of $ZrOCl_2$ units. It is better called zirconium oxychloride 8-hydrate (see below).

SALTS

Salts and esters of oxygen acids are named in a manner similar to the system for naming binary compounds. The more electropositive constituent is named first and is followed by the name of the acid, changing "-ic" endings to "-ate" and "-ous" endings to "-ite." Examples are:

$KClO_4$ potassium perchlorate
$Ba(H_2PO_2)_2$ barium hypophosphite
$K_2S_2O_8$ potassium peroxydisulfate
$(CH_3)_2SO_4$ dimethyl sulfate
$(C_2H_5O)_4Ti$ tetraethyl titanate

With salts containing two or more cationic species, the more electropositive is named first. With compounds containing two or more electronegative species, the most electronegative is named last. Examples are:

$CsAl(SO_4)_2$ cesium aluminum sulfate
$CaCO_3 \cdot MgCO_3$ calcium magnesium carbonate
PbClF   lead chloride fluoride
BiOCl   bismuth oxychloride

Acid salts are preferably named by indicating the protons by the word "hydrogen." The terms "primary," "secondary," "tertiary," etc. for an acid that has the first, second, third, etc. hydrogens replaced are also acceptable. The older prefix "bi-" to denote hydrogen should no longer be used. Examples are:

$NaHCO_3$ sodium hydrogen carbonate
            (*not* sodium bicarbonate)
KHS   potassium hydrogen sulfide
$FeHPO_4$ iron(II) hydrogen phosphate
KH_2PO_4 potassium dihydrogen phosphate
            or primary potassium phosphate

A number of metals form compounds that appear to be salts of oxyacids which are themselves unknown. For example, solutions of tin(II) in strongly basic aqueous solution contain anions composed of tin and oxygen (and very probably hydrogen too). Such anions have been called stannites and have been written in a variety of ways, because the kinds of anionic species vary with the conditions. Nonetheless, it is certain that discrete oxyanions of tin exist. The "-ite" ending is used to indicate the oxidation state of the metal. It is considered better to name such metallates by the Stock system, which for anions always uses the "-ate" ending followed by the oxidation state in parentheses. Examples are:

$Na_2Sn(OH)_4$ or Na_2SnO_2 sodium stannate(II)
$Na_2Sn(OH)_6$ or Na_2SnO_3 sodium stannate(IV)

The formulas for the solid compounds $NaNbO_3$ and $MgTiO_3$ make the compounds appear to possess oxyanions also. They are sometimes called sodium niobate and magnesium titanate. In fact, however, the structures do not contain the discrete units NbO_3^- and TiO_3^{--}. The solid oxides do not dissolve in water to give simple oxymetal anions. Consequently, it is recommended that such compounds be named as mixed oxides: sodium niobium trioxide (perovskite) and magnesium titanium trioxide (ilmenite). The words in parentheses indicate the crystal structures of the mixed oxides.

There are several radicals consisting of a basic molecule that has added one or more protons that behave as cationic species in salt formation, such as NH_4^+, $NH_2OH_2^+$, etc. These radicals are named by using the suffix "-onium." Examples are:

PH_4I phosphonium iodide
NH_4Br ammonium bromide
NH_2OH_2Cl hydroxylammonium chloride

HYDRATES AND OTHER ADDITION COMPOUNDS

Many salts come out of solution with solvent molecules built into their lattices. These and additional compounds formed in other ways are written with the formulas of the constituents separated by a dot, as in $BaCl_2 \cdot 2H_2O$. When the added molecule is H_2O, NH_3, or H_2O_2 they are named hydrates, ammoniates, or peroxyhydrates. The number of added molecules is indicated by an Arabic number; a Greek prefix is allowed but not preferred. Examples are:

$BaCl_2 \cdot 2H_2O$ barium chloride 2-hydrate
$CuSO_4 \cdot 4NH_3$ copper(II) sulfate 4-ammoniate
$NaOOH \cdot H_2O_2$ sodium hydrogen peroxide 1-peroxyhydrate

In many cases the added molecules may be complexed onto a metal ion, and if the structure is known, it can be indicated in the formula and the name:

$Cu(H_2O)_4SO_4 \cdot H_2O$ tetraaquocopper(II) sulfate 1-hydrate
                               (see below for the naming of complex ions)

For other added molecules it is recommended that the formula be used, as in $AlCl_3 \cdot H_2S$.

COMPOUNDS OF SILICON AND GERMANIUM

Increasing numbers of molecular compounds of silicon, germanium, and many of the borderline metals have been made in recent years. For their nomenclature, the style of organic chemistry is used, and they are named as substitution products of the parent hydrides. Examples are:

SiH_4	silane
$SiHCl_3$	trichlorosilane
Ge_2H_6	digermane
$(C_2H_5)_3GeGe(C_2H_5)_3$	hexaethyldigermane

ISOPOLY AND HETEROPOLY ACIDS AND THEIR SALTS

Several methods have been used to name isopoly and heteropoly acids and their salts. We give here some of them in the hope that some day one system will be defined and universally used.

Isopoly acids (that is, those formed from the condensation of two or more molecules of one and the same acid by the elimination of water) strictly include "pyro-" and "meta-" acids, discussed above, as special cases. We have to deal here, however, with elements which carry this behavior further and further to higher and higher polymers, behavior especially noted for boric, silicic, molybdic, tungstic, and vanadic acids. Since these isopoly acids have the acid-forming element in its highest oxidation state, the acids are "-ic" acids and the salts "-ates." We shall consider three methods of naming isopoly acids and their salts. They are:

(1) As for other compounds, the composition as expressed by the simplest empirical formula is named by Greek numerical prefixes. For numbers above 10, Arabic numbers are easier. For example, $Na_2B_4O_7 \cdot 10H_2O$, disodium tetraborate 10-hydrate.

(2) The composition is given by listing the various subscripts in the simplest empirical formula, including that of the oxygen, by Arabic numbers in parentheses after the name. For example, $Na_2B_4O_7 \cdot 10H_2O$, sodium borate (2:4:7) 10-hydrate.

(3) The formula (for salts) is resolved into the simplest form which expresses the composition in terms of base anhydride and

acid anhydride. Then the ratio base anhydride:acid anhydride is shown in the middle of the name by Arabic numbers in parentheses. For example, $Na_2B_4O_7 \cdot 10H_2O \equiv Na_2O \cdot 2B_2O_3 \cdot 10H_2O$, sodium (1:2) borate 10-hydrate.

The number of hydrogen atoms in the free acids and in acid salts is always indicated, when possible. (It may not be possible, if the structure is not known, to differentiate between acid hydrogens and the hydrogens of water molecules of hydration.) Examples of isopoly acids and their salts are shown in the accompanying table.

Simplest Empirical Formula	Name Formed by Greek Prefixes	Name Formed by Listing Subscripts	Resolved Formula	Name Formed by Base Anhydride: Acid Anhydride Ratio	Other Customary Name
Na_3BO_3	Trisodium (mono)borate	Sodium borate (3:1:3)	$3Na_2O \cdot B_2O_3$	Sodium (3:1) borate	Sodium orthoborate
$Na_4B_2O_5$	Tetrasodium diborate	Sodium borate (4:2:5)	$2Na_2O \cdot B_2O_3$	Sodium (2:1) borate	Sodium pyroborate
$NaBO_2$	Monosodium (mono)borate	Sodium borate (1:1:2)	$Na_2O \cdot B_2O_3$	Sodium (1:1) borate	Sodium metaborate
$Na_2B_4O_7$	Disodium tetraborate	Sodium borate (2:4:7)	$Na_2O \cdot 2B_2O_3$	Sodium (1:2) borate	
NaB_3O_5	Monosodium triborate	Sodium borate (1:3:5)	$Na_2O \cdot 3B_2O_3$	Sodium (1:3) borate	
$Na_2B_8O_{13}$	Disodium octaborate	Sodium borate (2:8:13)	$Na_2O \cdot 4B_2O_3$	Sodium (1:4) borate	
NaB_5O_8	Monosodium pentaborate	Sodium borate (1:5:8)	$Na_2O \cdot 5B_2O_3$	Sodium (1:5) borate	
$Na_2B_{12}O_{19}$	Disodium 12-borate	Sodium borate (2:12:19)	$Na_2O \cdot 6B_2O_3$	Sodium (1:6) borate	
$H_2W_4O_{13} \cdot 7H_2O$	Dihydrogen tetratungstic acid 7-hydrate	Hydrogen tungstate (2:4:13) 7-hydrate			

Heteropoly acids in the widest sense are acids formed by the copolymerization of "oxy-" anions of two or more different acid-forming elements. In the limited sense considered here, they are condensed oxygen acids containing many (generally six, nine, or twelve) atoms of one acid-forming element, almost always molybdenum or tungsten, joined by oxygen bridges to a small number (usually one) of atoms of a second acid-forming element, which may come from a variety of elements, such as phosphorus, arsenic, silicon, boron, titanium, etc. The second element has been shown by x-ray crystallography to be a central atom attached by the oxygen bridges to the other acid-forming element. The heteropoly acids are, therefore, named in a manner similar to that used for coordination compounds, discussed below. The formula is resolved as follows:

(1) for the heteropoly acids into (a) the *acid* of the central structure-determining element, (b) the *oxide* of the multiple acid-forming element, and (c) water

(2) for salts of the heteropoly acids into (a) the *salt* of the central structure-determining element, (b) the *oxide* of the multiple acid-forming element, and (c) water.

Further resolution of (a) in the second case is made if necessary. Then the name is formed by indicating the numbers of the two acid-forming elements by means of Greek numerical prefixes up to 10 and Arabic numbers beyond. The suffix "-o" is added to the stem of the ligand acid-forming element and the central element is named last, in the acids with the suffix "-ic" and in the salts with the suffix "-ate," thereby showing that the compound is a coordination compound. Examples are:

$H_3PO_4 \cdot 12WO_3 \cdot 29H_2O$	12-tungstophosphoric acid 29-hydrate
$Na_3PO_4 \cdot 12MoO_3$	Sodium 12-molybdophosphate
$2Na_5PO_5 \cdot 17WO_3$	Sodium 17-tungstodiphosphate
$Na_6TeO_6 \cdot 6MoO_3$	Sodium hexamolybdotellurate

COORDINATION COMPOUNDS

Coordination compounds, because of their complexity, require several rules for their naming. The original system of Werner, modified only by the use of the Stock system for indicating the oxidation state of the central atom, is the accepted one. The following general rules apply:

(1) The compounds are named as usual, cation first and anion second.

(2) The names of the groups attached to the central atom, with Greek prefixes to indicate their number, are prefixed to the name of the central atom. When the coordinating group is a large, com-

plicated radical, the simple Greek prefixes "bi-," "tri-," and "tetra-" are replaced by "bis-," "tris-," and "tetrakis-" and the name of the coordinating group is enclosed in parentheses.

(3) When more than one species is attached to a single central atom, they are named in the following order: first, negatively charged species; then, those with no charge; last, positively charged species. In writing the formula of the complex species, the sequence in which the symbols are written is the reverse of that in which they are named. Thus, the central atom is written first, positive species second, neutral species next, and negative species last. When any possibility of ambiguity exists, square brackets are put around the complex entity.

(4) The suffix "-o" indicates a negatively charged coordinating group, as in $C_2O_4^{--}$, "oxalato-." No suffix is attached to neutral coordinating groups. The suffix "-ium" is used for positive groups (very few are known). There are two exceptions to this rule, where long established usage has been retained; they are:

$$H_2O = \text{"aquo-"} \quad \text{and} \quad NH_3 = \text{"ammine"}$$

(5) The oxidation state of the central atom is indicated by a Roman numeral in parentheses immediately following the name of the central atom, without a space between them. If the complex is neutral or a cation, no suffix is attached to the name of the central atom; if an anion, the "-ate" suffix is always used. Sometimes in the anions, the Latin name of the metal is used for euphony.

Examples are:

$K_3Fe(CN)_6$	potassium hexacyanoferrate(III)
$K_4Fe(CN)_6$	potassium hexacyanoferrate(II)
$Cu(NH_3)_4SO_4$	tetramminecopper(II) sulfate
$K_3Cr(C_2O_4)_3$	potassium trioxalatochromate(III)
$Cr(H_2O)_6Cl_3$	hexaquochromium(III) chloride
Cu_2HgI_4	copper(I) tetraiodomercurate(II)
H_2PtCl_6	hexachloroplatinic(IV) acid
$[Cr(H_2O)_4Cl_2]Cl \cdot 2H_2O$	dichlorotetraaquochromium(III)- chloride 2-hydrate

$[Co(NH_3)_4CO_3]NO_3 \cdot 1/2H_2O$ carbonatotetramminecobalt(III)-nitrate 1/2-hydrate

$Ni(PCl_3)_4$ tetrakis(trichlorophosphine)-nickel(0)

$\{Cu[C_2H_4(NH_2)_2]_2\}Cl_2$ bis(ethylenediamine)copper(II)-
or $Cu(en)_2Cl_2$ chloride

An extensive list of worked examples of systematically named compounds, both complex and simple, can be found in the Formula Index of any volume (except Volume I) of *Inorganic Syntheses*—the later the volume, the more extensive the index, since it is cumulative.

SUGGESTIONS FOR FURTHER READING

W. P. Jorissen, H. Bassett, A. Damiens, F. Fichter, and H. Rémy, "Rules for Naming Inorganic Compounds. Report of the Committee of the International Union of Chemistry for the Reform of Inorganic Chemical Nomenclature, 1940," *Journal of the American Chemical Society*, Vol. 63, p. 889 (1941). Reprints can be obtained for 20 cents each from *Chemical Abstracts*, The Ohio State University, Columbus 10, Ohio.

J. D. Scott, *Inorganic Syntheses*, Vol. II, p. 257 (1946).

STUDY QUESTIONS

1. Give systematic names for the following compounds:

$HgCl_2$	$K_2Zr(C_2O_4)_3$	KAu
$NaNH_4HPO_4 \cdot 4H_2O$	$EuCl_2$	NaH_2BO_3
$CaSO_4 \cdot \frac{1}{2}H_2O$	Na_2SnO_2	H_2S_2
$KAg(CN)_2$	$Be(ClO_4)_2$	KI_3
$Zn(NH_3)_4SO_4 \cdot 2H_2O$	$H_4Sb_2O_7$	SeO_2
Li_3N	K_2SnI_6	$Sr(AlO_2)_2$
LiN_3	$Tm_2(SO_4)_3$	$FrAt$
K_2WO_4	$Na_2B_4O_7 \cdot 10H_2O$	Fe_3O_4
$NaNO_2$	AgF_2	Pb_3O_4
$[Cr(H_2O)_5Br]Br_2 \cdot 2H_2O$	$KSbO_3$	$KOOH$
SiH_4	P_4O_{10}	$GeHBr_2Cl$
$H_2WO_4 \cdot H_2O$	$Na_2Mo_4O_{13}$	$(NH_4)_6MoO_6 \cdot 6MoO_3$

2. Write the formulas for the following compounds:

Potassium hexacyanomanganate(II)
Rubidium pyrosulfate
Hydroxylammonium chloride
Aluminum nitride
Sodium thioantimonate
Thionyl bromide
Nitrosyl chloride
Hexahydrogen tetraphosphoric acid
Magnesium perchlorate
Cesium chromium alum
Sodium sulfide 9-hydrate
Hexamminechromium(III) chloride

Lead(II) azide
Trichlorosilane
Strontium hydride
Zinc phosphide
Stibine
Hydrazine
Chlorous acid
Disodium trisilicate
Dinitrogen tetroxide
Potassium peroxydisulfate
Potassium manganate
12-molybdotitanic acid

Index

Michael Jennings
U. of North Carolina